1961

This book may be kept

FAREWELL TO
VALLEY FORGE

Farewell to
VALLEY FORGE

BY DAVID TAYLOR

J. B. LIPPINCOTT COMPANY

Philadelphia and New York

To those Officers who, because
they were unfaltering in their
devotion to Washington, were
damned by Conway's Cabal

CONTENTS

FAREWELL TO
VALLEY FORGE

1 THE MEETING

The tongue is the enemy of the neck.——ARAB PROVERB

Captain Kimball, Continental Army, slowed his horse to a walk and turned off the dusty highway into the cobbled High Street of Port Chatham. A group of happy, mud-splashed children were sailing their toy boats in the refuse gutter that ran down the center of the street, and a fastidiously dressed merchant, his silk stockings and black breeches shiny new, gave the laughing children a wide berth as he hurried past. Halfway up the street a servant wench, with her sleeves rolled up to her plump elbows, was kneeling on the front steps of an oyster-shell-plastered house, scouring the pink marble threshold with handfuls of fine river sand.

As his horse clumped over the uneven stones the Captain kept an eye on the darting children. He nodded and smiled to the comely wench, and saw the disapproving face peering down from behind the frilled curtains of an upstairs window—but his mind was elsewhere. He was reminding himself that he was no longer Captain Kimball. He was plain Jonathan Kimball, in civilian dress, and the price of forgetting it would be a gallows party.

Mentally he rechecked his clothes, his papers and the few articles in his saddlebags. He was worrying unnecessarily, he told himself for the hundredth time. There could be nothing to betray him, not with the scrutiny General Stirling and Alex Hamilton had given him before they let him set out from Valley Forge. Just the same he couldn't shake the feeling of apprehension that being out of uniform brought. That one thing alone made him a spy, and he didn't enjoy the sensation.

A certain amount of his feeling was a mixture of resentment and pride. He was proud of the Rebel uniform he had worn for two years. This was the first day he had been out of it and he felt uncomfortable. And though this scheme he was embarked on required that he dress as a civilian, he was resentful at being taken for a Tory, even by a Tory.

This resentment of his toward anyone able to carry a musket, yet not in the Rebel Army, was something he had to be on guard against. For two days Stirling had pounded away at him, telling him he must not curl his lips back in a snarl when the English were mentioned. The General had also cautioned him against his instinctive drawing himself up to his full six feet when anyone made a slighting remark about Washington. Nor could he knit his brows together in a black scowl every time he saw civilians gorging themselves on a meal that would feed a company of Rebels.

A most distasteful venture this that he had agreed to undertake at Stirling's request. Six months back, had anyone suggested that he go to Philadelphia disguised as a servant to some wealthy family, he would have laughed scornfully and suggested they find someone more suited to the role of country loon. He grinned sheepishly and wondered which had swayed him the more: the Rebel need for intelligence from inside the Colonies' greatest city, or Stirling's persuasive tongue? Whichever it might be, he had agreed; and the next step was a meeting at the Silver Dolphin Inn with this Mistress Elizabeth Ladd whose home he was to invade in the guise of servant.

Also for the hundredth time, he tried to visualize this Mistress Ladd he was to meet. The General had said she was a beauty, but then Stirling had also persuaded him to undertake this abhorrent mission. Still, he cheered himself with the thought that the General's ideas on beauty were somewhat like his own, for Lady Stirling was the most beautiful woman he had ever met.

His horse, stumbling on a loose cobblestone, put an end to Jonathan's imagery. Best perhaps for the moment that he follow another of Stirling's warnings. "Wherever you go," the General had said over and over, "avoid useless speculation. It interferes with the working of the mind. Keep your eyes open and retain every detail of what you see. Keep your ears open and remember all you hear. Keep your mouth shut, for what you don't say may save your neck."

Certainly there was much to observe in this town he had heard of, but never seen. The houses on either side of the High Street were substantial and well proportioned. Their blue, and green, and white shutters were held back from the windows with decorative S-shaped catches that were snug against the walls instead of dangling loose like so many he had seen. Gleaming white flagpoles with weather pennants fluttering from their halyards stood in the front yards of the merchant captains.

A figure on the porch of the third house from the end of the street waved as Jonathan rode abreast the garden. Returning the salutation, the Rebel Captain saw that the townsman was an old seaman wearing a heavily gold-braided tricorne on top of his loose, white-powdered wig. Across his knees lay a telescoping spyglass, and scattered about his feet were all a sea captain's paraphernalia from sextant to dividers and parallel rulers. Jonathan's eyes rose quickly to the English Jack, with an emblazoned A in a faded gold field, whipping at the flagpole in front of the old man's house. Seeing Jonathan's look, the old sea dog raised his hand in a stiff salute. Gravely Jonathan saluted back. Here was one Royalist there was no need to fret over. He wasn't thinking about King George; he was dreaming of the days of Queen Anne.

High Street made a slight upward rise where the houses opened up to form the market square. Hardly enough of a rise to be called a hill, it was a vantage point from which the whole port could be seen at a glance, and Jonathan pursed his lips as he reined in his horse to look at it.

No need here to worry about being clad in civilian dress, he thought, sweeping the Delaware bank with eyes half closed against the sunlight. This bustling town was thronged with men, working, gossiping, idling as though no such thing as the war existed. Groups of sailors in ankle-length white canvas trousers, and wearing their distinctive red and white striped stocking caps, lounged about the tavern doors waiting for their ships to be loaded or unloaded. Sea captains, weather-beaten to a dull mahogany, and vying with the shipowners in the richness of their dress, stood in front of the warehouses talking tonnage and ballast and cargo. Interspersed in these groups were the merchants; portly gentlemen whose badge of office was the frilled cravat and a gold-headed, ebony walking stick as long as a town crier's staff.

Wherever he looked Jonathan found color running riot. In the market square the women's bonnets with their tapes and streamers and ribbon bows outdid the rainbow in the variety of their hues. Here and there, a Quaker-dun habit, topped by a deep, shaded bonnet, showed conspicuously among the full, flowing dresses. Although it was not yet eleven o'clock, Jonathan marked more bare shoulders and uncovered bosoms than he could remember at any ball in his native Virginia.

All this display was the result of sudden wealth brought about by the relaxing of the British sea patrols in the southern waters. Five months of high living in Philadelphia had made the English generals lax, and not knowing the currents, their own sailors had failed to find the schools of fish, so the Redcoat quartermasters closed their eyes and willingly paid out King George's coin for the seafood their troops craved. Other things being scarce, the merchants spent their hard money on silver shoe buckles and gold snuffboxes, while their wives put the homespun in the bottom drawers and overdressed in foreign stuffs.

Twisting in his saddle, Jonathan looked down beyond the market square. Directly below him, curving round to the right and past the Silver Dolphin Inn, was a whole street of blacksmiths' shops. Smoke belched from their wide-mouthed chimneys each time a bellows rope was pulled, and children danced in and out the open doorways, shouting when the hammers clanged on the anvils, and running away screaming when the hissing sparks showered the smithy floor.

Between the blacksmiths' shops and the wharves that lined the Delaware's banks, ship chandleries bulged with stores. Everything, from anchors and oval water casks to whaling harpoons and spermaceti candles, was piled to the roof beams and spilling over onto the narrow plank sidewalk spiked to adzed logs laid on the ground.

Spurring his horse down the slope toward the Silver Dolphin, Jonathan remembered Stirling's admonition and tried to ungrip his tight lips. It was true that he'd been warned and told what to expect, but expecting it didn't lessen his anger and dismay at seeing it. Any rebel officer who had ever led a foraging party, or tried to buy goods with Continental paper, or, indeed, had moved about the Colonies at all, knew that the Tory-minded and neutral-minded outnumbered the Rebels by two to one. He knew it all right, but it had never been more than a vague knowledge till now. When the Rebel Army was nigh to a town, the Tories kept within doors, and the Patriots had opportunity to express their Rebel leanings. The situation was reversed when the Continental Army moved on or was driven back; then for the Tories came out of hiding and took their revenge on the hapless Patriots.

A town in the hands of the Tories was what he was seeing as he rode along. It was hard to believe that, only seventeen miles to the north, the main body of the Rebel Army was dressed in rags and lived off scraps. Every road leading to the Valley Forge showed the scars of the pillaging, burning and murdering Redcoat patrols that scourged the countryside night after night. There was no hamlet between Philadelphia and the Rebel encampment but had its smoke-blackened houses and barns, wrecked grist mills, and hanging trees.

But Port Chatham showed no such signs of wanton destruction, Jonathan thought grimly as he passed the market stalls and shops loaded with foodstuffs. Here was prosperity with no thought of thrift; trade and trade and trade and the devil take the hindmost. From the slipways at the east end of town to the fishers' cottages on the west, it was make the coin while there were thirty thousand English soldiers in Philadelphia to spend it. He tried to stifle his anger as he wheeled his horse into the stable yard at the Silver Dolphin. Why be enraged at Port Chatham? It was no different from a hundred other towns. As he saw the hostler leave the stables and come toward him, he made an effort to quiet himself by remembering that Rebels couldn't be in two places at once; they couldn't be in Port Chatham and the Delaware Light Horse, too.

Swinging his leg over the saddle he dropped to the ground, gave the reins to the hostler, and slipping his arm through the sling of his saddlebags hoisted them off the horse's back. Throwing the sling over his shoulder, he walked across the stable yard to the Silver Dolphin. The inn door was open, and the potboy ran forward and relieved Jonathan of the saddlebags when he stepped into the taproom.

Showing no interest whatever, the innkeeper watched Jonathan stalk through the taproom to the main hallway. With the lofty disdain of a man whose business had grown faster than he had, mine host cocked his bald pate to one side and, without any visible movement of his lips, mumbled, "Yes, sir?"

"A chamber till sundown, landlord?" Jonathan asked casually. "I expect to meet a young lady here."

There was a moment's silence. The innkeeper's face unfroze, and the potboy's stifled laugh broke out in a high-pitched squeak.

"Your pardon, sir." Mine host bowed. "But such requests are usually for a chamber for the night, and never with such honesty."

Jonathan grinned down at him. "I have never seen the young lady. She is riding up from Virginia, and I am meeting her at the behest of a very close friend."

"If I have your word, sir, that you will leave before sunset—"

"You have it, landlord," Jonathan interrupted. "I expect to leave much before sunset."

The innkeeper jerked his thumb upward as he spoke to the potboy. "Take the gentleman to the southeast chamber."

"The lady's name is Mistress Ladd." Jonathan turned to follow the boy. "Mine is Jonathan Kimball," he said over his shoulder, and walked up the staircase after his guide.

Taking the upper hallway to the left, the potboy led the way to a bright corner chamber at the front of the inn. He deposited Jonathan's saddlebags on a bench in front of the fireplace, and waved an invitation for Jonathan to examine the room. The Captain's quick glance took in a big, many-mullioned window, bow topped, and with green bottle-glass lights filling the upper half of the sash. A smaller window, no more than a foot square, and head-high, was set in the same wall as the fireplace, and looked out along the highway that dropped into the southwest on its way to Dover and the Southern Colonies.

Jonathan nodded approval and dropped an English shilling on the red and white cover of the four-poster.

"You will be gone before sunset?" the boy asked anxiously.

"Certain-sure," Jonathan said. "What's your worry?"

For answer, the lad picked up the shilling and tapped it with his forefinger. "A certain English colonel will be wanting this room tonight. He pays well."

"Tempting Providence, isn't he," Jonathan feigned indifference, "venturing so far from Philadelphia?"

"Naw." The boy stuffed the shilling in his breeches pocket. "He's out here every second night. Who's to stop him?—not the Rebels."

Jonathan shrugged his shoulders. "I don't know." He sat on the edge of the bed. "I'm strange to these parts myself as you doubtless know from my speech. But I'd thought Philadelphia was fifteen miles to the east of you, and Valley Forge not much more to the north."

"So they are, and 'tis said that the English have thirty thousand soldiers in Philadelphia, and the Rebels between fifteen and twenty thousand at the Valley Forge and about—but neither do any raiding on Port Chatham."

"Oh! Why is that?" Smothering a yawn, Jonathan hoped his voice held more politeness than interest.

"I can't rightly say," the lad admitted, moving toward the door. "I only know what I hear. They do say that Washington has his orders to leave us be—and that the English have like orders s'long as we keep no arms in the town."

"I'd not heard that." Jonathan stretched lazily on the four-poster. "But a good arrangement I'd say."

"It hasn't allus been like that." The boy pointed toward the river. "Port Chatham had its raids—English and Rebel—more'n once we've gone a day or two without victuals. Five month back we never had enough to eat."

"Things are different now, eh?"

"Yes, sir, they are." The boy's answer was defiant. "We sent our quota of militiamen—and what happened?"

"I don't know." Jonathan fished another shilling from his pocket and spun it toward the boy. "Tell me."

The lad pocketed the shilling and stuck out his jaw. "When the Redcoats attacked us we had no men—no guns—no nothing. Did the Rebel Army come to help us? No, sir!"

"Might be they were too far away," Jonathan said quietly, fighting down the urge to take the young whelp and wallop his backside.

"That weren't our concern. We sent out men and the Rebels should have defended us." He wiped his nose with his forefinger. "Our Committee of Safety told the Congress so, too."

"What did the Congress do?"

"Nothing. So now we deal with the English, same as the Nantucket whalers do. We get permits from the English that lets us go fishing and trading."

Before Jonathan could say anything, the potboy came close to him. The lad's earnestness would have been comical at any other time, or on any other matter, but he was a tragic echo of the grown folks about him and he mouthed their lying, taproom talk like a well-learned lesson.

"I'll tell you somewhat that most like you don't know. You being from different parts as you said yourself. The Congress knows we get permits from the English. They don't say yes—but they don't say no. Do ye know why?"

"No?" Jonathan half closed his eyes to hide the anger in them.

"Because Ben Franklin told them to leave us be. Ben told them that if they didn't want the fishing and whaling and boatbuilding to die out—then the Congress better issue permits like the English do." He pointed out the window again. "This is a town that builds ships and gear for fishing and the like. The English have so many ships out there that a fishing smack would be blowed out of the water afore she reached the mouth of the Delaware—if she didn't have a permit."

"I understand."

"And some more to think on," the boy said insolently as he walked to the door, "you can't buy gear for ships without good English coin, and you can't get that without you sell to the English. The Congress knows it, and so does George Washington, for they do say he has more whale-oil lamps and spermaceti candles at Mount Vernon than anyone else in the Colonies."

The door closed on the potboy and Jonathan slowly unclenched his fingers. Perhaps this stupid boy hadn't noticed his anger, but Jonathan Kimball was going to need better control of his Rebel sentiments when he reached Philadelphia and had to listen to more of the same Tory talk. He pushed himself up from the bed and walked to the big window that looked out over the town. There was nothing new in the talk he'd just heard. It was the stock argument of those who objected to being counted as Tories but who wouldn't give up their trade with England. Some of these seafaring men seemed to reckon themselves a class apart. Their perpetual plaint was that they couldn't replace their stocks without the King's coin, but neither could a farmer or miller or cobbler for the matter of that.

Thinking back on what the potboy had said, Jonathan was furious that a lad so young—he could be no more than fourteen—should be growing up with such an evil picture of the war in his mind. It was true that Massachusetts had issued permits of a sort to some whaling masters, but it was just as true that the Congress had labelled the Nantucket whale hunters traitors for selling their oil to the English. And, of course, no number of denials would ever stop the lies that Franklin approved the permits, or that Washington was under such orders.

Nor was there any real substance to the belief that the Congress wanted to keep the shipbuilding and whaling and fishing from dying out. The truth was that in the opinions of Generals Stirling and Glover, the Congress was shortsighted in not encouraging these trades in the far south where the English couldn't spare ships to maintain a blockade. Jonathan wondered if the young potboy had ever heard of General Glover and his Marblehead fishermen. They were the finest soldiers in the Rebel Army. They had made the escape from Long Island possible, and they had made the crossing of the Delaware and victory at Trent's Town a reality; they were all shipowners and shipmasters who had lost everything to the English rather than trade with them.

No, Jonathan reflected sadly, these plausible reasonings were no more than excuses put forward by those who had no understanding of liberty, or, if they did, weren't willing to fight for it. Perhaps if they had seen what he had seen, Norfolk burned to the ground, house by house, when red hot cannon shot didn't do it quickly enough, they might change their minds. Maybe, too, had they watched Patrick Henry at the head of a hundred and fifty armed farmers defy the great Lord Dunmore—and defeat him—they'd change their minds about the English might, and getting permits to use the seas, and carrying "protective" papers signed by General Howe.

A flash of red put a sudden end to Jonathan's thoughts and pulled him back to the present. He dug his shoulder into the right-hand corner of the window and squinted along the pike that led to Philadelphia. Abruptly he drew back and moved behind the curtain. He hadn't been mistaken. A patrol of Lobsterbacks, a big patrol, English Dragoons by the looks of them, was riding into town. "Devil take it," he muttered, and jumped to the smaller window. It would be the worst kind of luck to have Mistress Ladd come asking for him, with the tavern hall filled with Redcoat officers.

The southern highway was deserted he saw, and sighed with relief. Surely Mistress Ladd would have sense enough not to ride on in if she saw Redcoats. And surely, he tried to reassure himself, she'd not ask for him in front of anybody. He swung around on his heel and went back to the big window. No one was paying the slightest heed to the Lobsterbacks clumping along the road that paralleled the river. Down by the fisher cottages, the barefooted women, their skirts pulled up between their legs and tucked into their waist-bands, looked up briefly and went on about their chore of mending the nets.

Again Jonathan turned and looked out the small window. Still no sign of Mistress Ladd. There was no call to worry, he told himself. This Mistress Ladd must know that by her very act of meeting him here she was helping a spy. She was coming in response to a letter Lord Stirling had sent ten days ago by the Virginia post, so she knew something about the proposed venture. And, since Stirling's letter had been handed to the post rider after he had left the Red Lion Inn on the South Colonies Pike, there was no chance that it had been intercepted by the English.

There wasn't much to the plan at the moment, Jonathan thought, and went back to watching the Lobsterbacks through the large window. Certainly not enough to get exercised over, but still enough to assure hanging for him and the girl should one slightest whisper of it reach the English. When General Stirling had first suggested the plan he had warned

that its very simplicity concealed its many dangers. Jonathan was reminded of that now, as he watched a Redcoat colonel slide from his saddle
and walk into the Silver Dolphin.

The General had warned him again this morning, and told him that
if he had the slightest hesitation about going on with the scheme, or if
Mistress Ladd had any fears in the matter—then he was to return alone
to Valley Forge and send Mistress Ladd and her servant on their way to
Philadelphia. Stirling had explained to him that in an effort to carry on
her father's shipping business the girl had been visiting her uncle in Virginia, and that she had in her possession a piece of paper worth its weight
in gold to the Rebels: a pass signed by Sir William Howe permitting her
to "make the journey and return accompanied by one male servant." When
she re-entered Philadelphia, Jonathan would be her male servant. Once
inside the garrisoned city he would gather what information he could, assess its worth, and smuggle the results to Stirling at Valley Forge.

Shouted orders from a Dragoon subaltern brought the patrol into
formation and, with a clattering of sabres against stirrups, the troop
wheeled about and started back for Philadelphia. The Dragoon Colonel,
wiping the back of his hand across his mouth, now marched out of the
Silver Dolphin, swung himself into his saddle and cantered after his command. In a few minutes a cloud of dust on the road that followed the river
was all that could be seen of the Redcoat patrol.

Jonathan walked to the small window. There was still no sign of Mistress Ladd and her servant on the southern highway. He rubbed his thumb
over his chin. Stirling was counting on their arrival before darkness set in,
for the General had arranged a council with Von Steuben and Wayne.
Wayne, who had been absent from the camp, scouring the countryside,
might have fresh intelligence, and Stirling wanted his two spies to have
the benefit of every scrap of information; but, also, Jonathan knew, Stirling
hoped to have Mistress Ladd and himself on their way to Philadelphia before midnight.

It was going to be a ticklish business, that meeting. Stirling hadn't
said so in so many words, but Jonathan knew that the General wanted him
and Mistress Ladd out of Valley Forge and on their way before General
Lee returned to the encampment. Stirling said little about the matter, and
he was guarded in his comments, but the truth was, and Jonathan knew it,
Stirling did not want Lee to know anything about the Philadelphia affair.
For himself as well, Jonathan would just as soon not have Lee know about
it.

He was about to turn away from the window again when he saw two
figures on horseback emerge from behind the trees that hid the bend in the
road. One was a woman all right. Even at this distance the voluminous
skirts and a fluttering cape couldn't hide her slim figure, and she rode

with a straight back and head held high. Her servant rode a good horse indifferently.

The closer she came the better she looked, Jonathan decided. He liked black-haired women and this Mistress Ladd's hair was like an ebony-black frame around an ivory oval—if indeed it was Mistress Ladd! She was talking to her servant, and, as she rode out of the tree-shaded stretch of the pike, he could see that her eyebrows were well arched above big eyes, and that she had a straight, definite nose. He was glad of that for he had a positive dislike for tilted or too-dainty noses; probably because his own was large and with a prominent bridge.

Drawing back from the window, he saw his reflection in the glass. He was behaving like a damned fool about this girl he didn't know. He was here to meet her strictly in the line of military duty, not to ogle at her like a schoolboy because she was somewhat of a contrast to the harpies and camp wenches who haunted Valley Forge. Just the same, he grinned at himself, if he had to play servant to a woman he'd as lief she was pretty.

In spite of his self-advice, he felt a quiver of excitement when she turned off the highway and rode up to the Silver Dolphin. Three long strides took him to the big window and he satisfied himself at close range that she was lovelier than he had thought, and that little doubt remained but that she was Mistress Ladd. He watched her rein in her horse by the stirrup-high stone in front of the inn door. A neat and expensively shod foot slid from the stirrup to the mounting stone, and in a swirl of petticoats she was out of the saddle and being helped down by the Boniface whose smiles of welcome reached halfway across his bald pate.

In the midst of much bowing and scraping she disappeared and Jonathan could hear the rumbling voice of the innkeeper and the cracked and changing voice of the potboy welcoming her all the way across the hall to the bottom of the staircase. Walking around the foot of the bed, Jonathan went to the door and opened it. Between the turned balusters of the stair rail, he could see upturned faces watching Mistress Ladd's progress up the stairs. In a moment she sailed into view, skirts held clear of her toes by a pair of firm, gloved hands.

She smiled, showing a sparkling line of small white teeth between curving lips, and dropped her skirt as Jonathan bowed slightly and held out his hand. She said nothing as she gave him a firm handclasp, and waited until they were in the chamber and the door closed.

"You are Lord Stirling's friend, Captain Kimball?"

"Your obedient servant, mistress." Jonathan waved to the ladderback chair by the bed, inviting her to sit. "The General asked me to convey his compliments."

"Thank you, Captain." Seated, she took off her bonnet, laid it on the bed, and fluffed her hair with a vigorous shake of her head. "I dislike bonnets, but the roads are ankle-deep in dust."

"They are, indeed, Mistress Ladd." He walked to the window, looked out, and turned to face her again. "Are we quite wise in speaking names so freely?"

Throwing her head back she laughed merrily. "Here—in this inn?" She pulled off her gloves and, shaking them by the fingers, dropped them beside her bonnet. "Mine host and his lackeys neither ask nor care who we are or what we say; so long as we pay with coin and not paper."

"I'd gathered as much."

She turned and waved her hand at the four walls. "I've lodged in this tavern more than once, Captain and I tell you General Washington and General Howe could sup together here and cause no raised eyebrows."

Jonathan laughed and moved back, to face her. "Then shall we discuss the—ah—matter?"

"Is there aught to discuss?" She looked up surprised.

"You mean you've made up your mind?"

She raised one shapely shoulder and its companion eyebrow as she answered what seemed to her to be an unnecessary question. "Lord Stirling did that. He asked that you be allowed to play servant in our house so that he could get accurate intelligence from a military man." Her voice dropped. "Were my father free to answer he would say yes, but, as you doubtless know, he was imprisoned by the English in the Walnut Street Prison."

"I know." Jonathan nodded understandingly.

"My brothers are in a like fix—prisoners aboard their own ships—but they would say yes. And my mother would wipe Lord Stirling's boots if he asked her to."

"Aye, mistress. These things I doubt not. But willingness to carry out a plan is not the same as being assured of success, and we must be assured of success. There is little merit in having you, your family, and me, all dangling at the end of English hemp ropes if we gather no intelligence for the Rebel Army."

Slowly she crossed one knee over the other and looked up in Jonathan's face. "Tally your fears, Captain, one by one."

"Is there any doubt but what your pass will get me into Philadelphia?"

"None," she answered crisply. "The sentries who will examine it have no knowledge as to whether my servant be tall or short—black or white."

Jonathan clasped his hands behind his back and paced the floor. "But in Philadelphia, 'twill be known I am not the same servant."

"Lord Stirling provided for that." Her answer came quickly. "He suggested that I obtain a letter from my uncle's medico that my servant

—the one I left Philadelphia with—was taken with the smallpox. I have the letter."

"I knew the General had suggested it." Jonathan continued his pacing. "Will I be able to move freely in the city?"

She smiled ironically. "There are supposed to be nigh to thirty-five thousand people in Philadelphia. The English can't know them all by night. In the daytime, you can go marketing with me—"

"That might cause comment."

"In Philadelphia? Mercy no, Captain!" She doubled up with mirth. "Any morning you'll see the most staid and proper Quaker women doing their marketing with strings of men servants marching behind them, and every man of them with a market basket on each arm. Any housewife who has a man servant takes him on her marketing. Philadelphia women don't carry baskets if they have a man to do it for them."

"What about night?"

"Curfew of a sort, but slackly enforced if you're not out overly late." Uncrossing her knees she leaned forward eagerly. "The English officers do a lot of talking. They seem to have no fear of telling what is afoot, and many of them visit our house—almost every day it seems."

Jonathan felt a sudden chill. It was as though the whole room had turned cold in an instant. He had felt it once before, at Brandywine, looking into the muzzle of an English musket for a second of eternity before the serpentine fell. The feeling of foreboding, like the premonition that cautions one when utter darkness hides a pitfall, froze him where he stood. He stared unseeing at the turkey carpet before the fireplace. This girl was wholly unaware of the dangers they faced. She was agreeing to help simply because patriotism dictated that she should; without any understanding of the hazards involved. Every sense told him that she wasn't of a nature to be facile or adept in conspiracies and devious dealings, that her very self-assurance would trap her at a crucial moment. But how could he explain his feelings to Stirling? And what could he point to as proof? How could he convince anyone that he himself wasn't afraid to go on with the venture? There was but one answer to all the questions and he was wasting time thinking about them. The thing had to be done. He couldn't bring himself to blast all Stirling's hopes, no matter how he felt about the girl.

The silence had been acute and uncomfortably long. Besides, he could feel that those black eyes with their dancing flecks of gold were staring at his back curiously, wondering. He turned abruptly. "One more thing, Mistress Elizabeth, what of the servant you brought with you, where is he—and is he to be trusted?"

"With my life, Captain. He is in the taproom, and once we are on our way he will return to Virginia. You need have no fears on that score. No one at my uncle's will betray us."

"Then when you are rested, and we are assured that there are no Redcoat patrols abroad, we'll make for Lord Stirling's headquarters at Valley Forge. It's a long, hard ride over a rough road." He smiled as he finished, hoping that the anxiety he felt didn't show in his face.

2   LOYALTIES

There is treachery, O Ahaziah.——II KINGS

Kneeling on the flagstoned porch at the rear of General Varnum's quarters, Lord Stirling thrust his hand down the muzzle of a four-pound cannon and ran his fingers over the scored and pitted bore. Pushing his arm out and in like a swab, he felt for the pits that were dangerously deep, and when his thumb caught in a groove that didn't run all the way out to the muzzle, he stood up and shook his head at the gunners who had trundled the piece down from Knox's artillery park on the far side of the parade ground.

"Not safe, lads." He held his thumb and forefinger apart to show the groove was half an inch deep. "Given a full charge, this one would kill more Rebels than Redcoats."

"What about grapeshot, sir?" the artillery sergeant asked hopefully. "The trunnions and caps are sound, and the wheels and axles are better than many."

"We will trade the wheels and axles for the poor ones on some other piece." Stirling examined the studs that projected from the barrel, and the heavy iron straps clamped over them holding the barrel in the carriage. "As you say, Sergeant, the trunnions and caps are still firm."

"If we make a trade, sir, we end up with one good piece and a lump of iron."

"Instead of two doubtful pieces?"

"Yes, sir."

"I think not." The General signed to the sergeant to feel the groove in the gun barrel. "We'll smooth down the jagged edges of the scores so that they won't snag the shot and blow up the barrel. Then we'll have the lads up at the forge shrink bands around the weak parts to strengthen them, and we will have a piece that will take a four-pound ball with a light charge of powder. As it is, we have too many guns that will only take grape."

"We'll roll her over to the forge at once, sir." Saluting, the sergeant

[23]

and the gun crew trundled the cannon off the flagstones and onto the camp road that ran westward to the old iron forge that gave the valley its name.

September the year before, when the British mercenaries under Von Knyphausen had fired the forge, they had failed in their attempt to demolish it, and Stirling's artificers sweated and fumed in the ruins, trying to recondition Knox's dilapidated cannon. The big undershot water wheel that once drove the trip hammer was a pile of charred boards, and the massive shaft, burned through and upended, had plunged deep into the silted creek bed below the dam. The fire had not destroyed the heavy sets and dies. These oblong blocks of iron, hollowed into half-spheres to shape cannon balls, had been found in the heaped wreckage of the bloomery. Scraped and cleaned, they were back in use, forming much-needed shot for the Rebel cannon. To Stirling's everlasting surprise, the small wheel that worked the wheezy bellows had escaped the holocaust, and though the bellows were patched with scraps of leather from boots that would no longer hang together, they pumped enough air to keep the forge working.

Behind him, Stirling heard the droning voices of "Mad" Anthony Wayne and the other officers of the court-martial being held in General Varnum's quarters. Two spies were being tried, and it brought forcibly to his mind the worrisome fact that young Kimball and Mistress Ladd should have arrived several hours before. Unless they arrived within mere minutes, there would be little use to look for them before morning. Once darkness fell, no one but a local lad, born and bred within sight and sound of the Schuylkill, could find his way among the network of roads and paths that veined the countryside like an autumn leaf. Besides this, the whole slope, from Valley Forge east and south, was infested with English patrols as soon as darkness fell.

Kimball's tardiness must be due to caution, Stirling reassured himself as he walked over from Varnum's quarters to the edge of the parade ground. The Captain had been in actions enough so that he was not likely to run afoul of, or be caught by, any English patrol. And the lad would doubtless take more than extra precautions since he was out of uniform and engaged in the risky business of escorting Mistress Ladd to the encampment.

But, even as he watched Drillmaster Von Steuben putting the lads through their paces, the fear that gnawed at him would not be thrust aside. Everything else in this Godforsaken camp had gone awry; why not this? How he hated the Valley of the Forge and everything concerning it. Physical beauty it might have when the trees were filled with green, and the rushes whispered along the banks of the Valley Creek, and the frogs croaked in the dams above the ruined forge—but even then it was the beauty of a graveyard. To him, it would always be a graveyard, for more than three thousand of the staunchest soldiers the Rebel Army had ever enlisted lay buried in unmarked graves along the roadsides and on the edges of the encampment, or between the rows and rows of hideous log huts.

Watching the burly but agile Von Steuben showing the troops how to "guard—point—thrust" with the bayonet lightened his humor somewhat, and Stirling had to admit that the training and discipline the Baron had maintained were among the gains made out of the winter's quartering in the miserable hellhole. Von Steuben had been good for the Rebel Army, and in more ways than one. He understood cavalry, and for hours on end he would explain its proper use to the younger officers. With his broad shoulders thrown back, and the blue veins on his bull neck standing out like welts, he would take to the parade ground—as he was now—bellowing orders and instructions in a voice that only Henry Knox could equal for volume.

When the Baron's patience—or English—failed him, he would swear in thick German and brittle French, and when that produced no better results from his fumbling recruits, he called on the nearest officer to do his swearing for him.

Even now, as Stirling watched him, the Baron was warming up to something. Throwing the musket and bayonet to one Rebel, he tore off his coat and flung it to the ground. His tricorne followed the coat in a spinning arc, and pushing his wig down firmly with his left hand he reached again for the musket with his right. Feet well apart, he braced himself and lowered the bayonet menacingly. Holding the musket butt tightly against his hip he took one step forward. On the next step he bent both knees and inclined the bayonet tip upward. Then with a roar he lunged forward as though face to face with a combatant, thrust the musket before him at arm's length, stopped suddenly, and, balancing on one foot, gruesomely pushed the imaginary victim off the end of the bayonet with his upraised foot. He drew himself up to his full height and pointing to the ground he screamed, "Kill—or be killed!"

As Stirling turned away to return to Varnum's quarters, the Baron was walking backward across the parade ground waving his arms like a drum major beating time, while a thousand Rebels pointed and lunged and yelled in imitation of the inimitable Drillmaster. In spite of his irascible manner and strict enforcement of discipline, the Baron was worshipped by the men. He had never led any of them in action, but every man knew that when the time came Von Steuben could be counted on to lead them as an officer should.

Stepping onto the flagstones behind Varnum's, Stirling could hear Wayne, who was President of this particular court-martial, telling the prisoners that each officer on the court would render his own verdict without consultation with the others. Waving to the four sentries who were doing duty as prisoner-escorts to be at their ease, the General sat down on the steps that went down from Varnum's quarters to the small springhouse. The little stone building with the stream of water flowing through it was an ironic reminder that there never had been surplus food to store in a springhouse.

Resting his arms on his knees, Stirling's eyes travelled along the range of hills that started with Mount Joy in the west, and ended at the Provost's guardhouse at the eastern tip of the camp. Mount Joy was ill-named. Its companion hill, Mount Misery, on the other side of the Valley Creek bore a name better fitted to his mood. The truth was, though he'd not admit it to Washington or any other officer, he was thoroughly digusted with the Valley Forge camp and well nigh everything connected with it. He was sick to death of the petty jealousies and backbiting and name-calling and duelling that no amount of disciplinary action could halt.

Almost every day he had the unpalatable duty of confirming or annulling sentences imposed by courts-martial before passing the papers on to General Washington for his approval. And almost every day he had to witness the degrading ceremony of "drumming out" officers—"mounted on a horse back foremost without a saddle, coat turned wrong side out, hands tied behind—the fifes to play and the drums to roll till he be out of the lines of the Army—never more to return." He shuddered. If not a "drumming out," then it was the whipping post outside the Provost guard. It was nicked and gouged by the lash, and sticky with the blood of those whose offenses were more than mere theft. Nights when he couldn't sleep, the prisoners' welted backs and the Provost General's voice would haunt him. "A soldier for striking a Lieutenant, one hundred lashes—a Sergeant for taking a Private's allowance of whiskey—a Corporal for getting drunk and threatening his Major—a camp wench for remaining in a hut all night, fifty lashes—"

The door at his back squeaked open, and Stirling rose to meet Mad Anthony as he walked out into the open. There was no need to ask either the verdict or the sentence, for the Pennsylvania General's haggard face was answer enough.

"They had papers. Positions and numbers of cannon. Notes on the size of the guard on Sullivan's bridge." Wayne hunched his shoulders. "All the officers rendered the same decision."

"I thought they would." Taking the sheaf of papers Wayne held out, Stirling tucked them inside his coat. "I'll look at them tonight and give them to General Washington tomorrow."

"I thought—" Wayne stopped.

"They've not arrived. I'll get word to the Baron and the others. Tomorrow night will have to serve—if they're not at my quarters when I get back. Will you ride there with me?"

Wayne nodded agreement, and stood aside as the guard marched the prisoners out through the narrow hallway that divided the two down-stairs rooms of Varnum's quarters. Both spies, one young and the other old, had their arms bound to their sides, and both were cowed and white-faced, where before the trial they had been arrogant and blustering.

"Both asked for shooting instead of hanging," Wayne said, walking toward his horse.

"As who doesn't when they're caught?" Stirling unteddered his mount from the rail at the end of the porch. "What did you say?"

"The same as always." Wayne slipped his foot into the stirrup and swung into the saddle. "I told them to try escaping. Any sentry would oblige by shooting them—in the back."

Stirling grunted as he hauled himself onto his horse. The thousand little red hot knives of his rheumatics stabbed between his shoulder blades, and he gritted his teeth till the spasm passed. Holding his breath in agony, he wished he'd paid more heed to Shippen's advice when the medico had told him that he'd never recover from the soaking and freezing that Christmas night when they'd crossed the Delaware to march on Trent's Town. Hard to tell, he mused, riding behind Wayne, which was worse: the winter of '76 along the iced banks of the Delaware, or this past winter in the Valley of the Forge. Trent's Town had provided victory, and that had raised their spirits. Valley Forge was the opposite, for it was the gall and wormwood that climaxed a long succession of ignominious defeats, and a graveyard of more than dead soldiers—it was a graveyard of ideals and reputations.

A roll on the orderly drums rattled through the hills as the two Generals came abreast the Ironmaster's Mansion. Riding side by side now, on the wider road, they wheeled right, parallel to the Valley Creek, and cantered along to General Washington's headquarters. In response to the drums, Caleb Gibbs, the commander of Washington's Life Guards, stood at the foot of the flagpole before the Commander-in-Chief's quarters, watching his men form a deep hollow square about the colors.

One by one the general officers whose duties permitted, gathered in the narrow space between the flagpole and the creek to witness the colors being lowered for the day. It was no such formal ceremony as the English observed at Retreat, nor was there any designated behavior for the as-sembled officers, but as Stirling looked about, he was reminded that most of these men had served with Washington in more defeats than victories—yet never once wavered in their loyalty:

John Glover, slight, but hard as the deck on any of the ships he had once owned, and a face as clean-cut and firm as though it were carved from his native Massachusetts marble. Alex Hamilton of the sensitive face and the burning eyes that could train a cannon better than Britain's best. Stubborn James Monroe, jaw thrust out, who would rather argue freedom than sleep. The Quaker general, Nathanael Greene, with his big blacksmith's hands, as gentle off the battlefield as they were capable on it. The young Frenchman La Fayette was missing, for he was sharing duty with John Sullivan on the opposite bank of the Schuylkill, guarding the log bridge that Sullivan's men had thrown across the river near the natural ford. Von Steuben, dressed again in coat and tricorne, galloped along the road, followed by Henry Knox, the Boston seller of books, who had turned his study of artillery to good account, and whose bravery was as familiar on the field as his booming voice.

The drums rolled again as the Commander-in-Chief, bareheaded, appeared in the headquarters doorway. The Life Guards snapped their muskets from their shoulders and lowered them to the Present. Major Caleb Gibbs, stepping smartly to the quick double taps on the drumheads, marched to the flagpole and grasped the lanyard. Stirling wondered what the others thought of when they took off their tricornes and watched the flag with its circle of thirteen stars floating down on the halyard.

For himself, the General thought of other officers who had not been loyal, who had traded honor for a promise of promotion, who had conspired with certain members of the Congress to remove Washington as Commander-in-Chief. Stirling closed his eyes for a moment, as though that would blot out the memory of the most distasteful duty he had ever performed—that ghastly night when he had told Washington that three of his generals had entered into a cabal against him—that Conway, Gates, and Mifflin were working hand in hand with some of the Congress to have Gates appointed Commander-in-Chief.

Opening his eyes, Stirling saw the furled colors carried into the Chief's headquarters. Looking up to the second story, he saw, as he knew he would, four women's faces framed in the small window of Mistress Washington's sewing chamber. He waved his tricorne, and Patsy Washington, Kitty Greene, Lucy Knox and his own beloved Sarah, took time to wave back before returning to their sewing, their darning and patching of threadbare Rebel uniforms.

With the last ceremony of the day completed, the general officers rode off to their own divisions. Wayne pulled his horse alongside Stirling's and, looking about to see that no one was within earshot, leaned from the saddle. "If they've not arrived by the time we reach your quarters, should we not send out a few patrols?"

They rode past the Ironmaster's Mansion and across Gulph Road before Stirling answered. "I don't think so, Anthony. I don't fear young Kimball's capture on the road as much as I fear the loss of time."

"After waiting this long to plant a spy in Philadelphia, one day can't make much difference." The Pennsylvanian spurred his horse impatiently. "We should have had spies there long ere now."

"We have. And we've had much intelligence from them." Stirling held up his left hand with the fingers spread. "But five of them have been caught—three hanged we know. The others seem to be suspected by the English, and can learn nothing of value. Things have changed since André has been made Howe's Chief of Intelligence."

"How do you know that?" Wayne was surprised.

Stirling grinned. "Because the woman who is honored by having André as her uninvited guest is one of our sources of information. She feels that she has been somewhat under suspicion ever since she warned us of the attack on Whitemarsh."

The roar of the water wheel and the clanging of metal in the Old Forge made conversation impossible as they rode past the rebuilt sluice-way. Stirling's artificers, dressed in nothing but their underwear, hammered red hot tires over the rims of loose-spoked artillery wheels, or risked fatal burns clamping dazzling white bands of iron on cannon muzzles, so that the metal, shrinking as it cooled, would give added strength to the weakened barrels when the guns were fired.

"Anthony?"

"Yes?" Wayne turned quickly at the peculiar quality in Stirling's voice.

"I have a confidence to share."

"It will be kept, William."

"I know it will," Stirling said quickly, then searched for the best way to explain a suspicion that had been too close to a certainty in his own mind for a year and a half. "You weren't here, Anthony, when Lee was welcomed back to camp—somewhat in the manner of the Prodigal Son—after the prisoner-exchange in which he was traded for that worthless English general, Prescott?"

"No. But I heard tell of quite a to-do," Wayne answered wryly. "I was down Wilmington way, persuading Tory farmers that it was better for their health, if not for their pockets, to sell for Continental paper in preference to seeking English gold in Philadelphia."

Stirling rubbed his hands back and forth over his horse's crest. "You know where he is now, of course?"

"I'd supposed he was at York, reporting to the Congress—"

"General Charles Lee," Stirling cut in harshly, "may be in York, but he is being wined and dined by the self-same, self-seeking toadies who gave their aid to Conway and their praise to Gates. Lee may return here tomorrow. And I want young Kimball and Mistress Ladd on their way to Philadelphia before Lee gets back, for 'tis my belief that Charles Lee is a traitor."

Wayne was about to guide his horse over the narrow covered bridge that crossed the Valley Creek, but, instead, he pulled the animal to a halt. "Do you know what you are saying, William?"

Stirling reined in, and they sat in their saddles, facing each other in the shadow of the roof that overhung the rails of the bridge. "I have believed that Lee was a traitor ever since he was captured by the English Dragoons at White's Tavern in December 'seventy-six."

"You've told your suspicions to Washington?"

"Indeed yes. It is a suspicion he does not share."

"Have you one bit of proof?" Wayne's voice was filled with disbelief.

"No proof, but my suspicions are shared by John Sullivan, and we have ample grounds." Leaning forward, Stirling spoke quickly and earnestly. "Lee is no coward, yet when he was captured he pleaded with the English to spare his life. It was play-acting, Anthony, for the benefit of witnesses. John Sullivan warned Lee that the English were close to his camp, but Lee ignored the warning and slept at White's Tavern—far outside the lines. I am persuaded his capture was planned."

"But, William—"

Stirling held up his hand. "Hear me out. You know that Major Wilkinson was Gates's aide and carried the famous—or infamous—letter that Conway wrote to Gates, to the effect that heaven has determined to save our country or a weak general would have ruined it?"

"Yes—the letter you exposed to Washington."

"Aye." Stirling gripped his saddle till his knuckles showed white. "But did you know, Anthony, that this same Wilkinson was Lee's aide when Lee was captured? That Wilkinson was carrying a letter from Lee to Gates couched in almost identical terms—that Washington was damnably deficient and that our councils had been weak to the last degree?"

"I did not." Wayne's voice was still doubtful. "How did you know?"

"I have seen the letter," Stirling said quietly.

Watching the Pennsylvanian's face, he realized again the difficulty of trying to explain the diabolical cleverness of the conspiracy against Washington. To him, the workings of the Cabal had always been clear. Conway and Mifflin, aided by various members of the Congress and the gifted Doctor Rush, had missed no opportunity to insinuate that Gates did not spend an inactive winter at the Valley Forge. Hot anger rose within him when he thought of the Congress wasting precious time investigating anonymous complaints about the Commander-in-Chief's timidity and indecisiveness. He had tried in vain to point out to Washington that the style of many of these anonymous letters bore a striking similarity to that of Conway's and Wilkinson's. But Washington would not listen, even to him. The Commander-in-Chief had no guile, no pettiness, no jealousy in him, and he could not be made to believe that his officers were unworthy.

To every protest and piece of proof, Washington made the same answer. He insisted that the generals had every right to their opinion, and that it was the duty of Congress to listen to every complaint made against the Commander-in-Chief.

"And now, Lee returns to lend his aid to the conspiracy." Stirling voiced his thoughts, hardly expecting an answer from Mad Anthony. "Do you wonder that I don't want Lee knowing that I have planted Kimball in Philadelphia?"

Wayne pushed his tricorne to the back of his head, rubbed his hand over his eye, and answered slowly, "Then I suggest that you swear everyone to secrecy—everyone who knows of your plan."

"I shall do that if we hold our council before Lee returns, but it will be of little value if Lee is in camp at the time. It would be too much to expect that he'd not find out."

"If you feel so strongly, William," Wayne slapped his saddle with the palm of his right hand, "why don't you have it out with the Commander-in-Chief? Surely, Washington will not place Lee in any position of trust if you speak your mind plainly."

"The Chief has no choice in such a matter. Not only is Lee Senior Major General—now that he has returned to our fold—but he is the darling of certain members of the Congress. Were Lee to suspect, for one moment, that Washington intended to withhold a command from him, he would again ride to York. Do you know what would happen then?"

"I can hazard a guess. Lee would return bearing written instructions from the Congress, to the effect that he is to be given any command he desires."

"Which could only embarrass Washington more than he is already. Therefore I can say nothing."

Both started their horses across the covered bridge that led to Stirling's quarters, and again there was no conversation as the clattering hooves echoed and boomed in the wooden tunnel. When they came out on the Yellow Springs Road, Stirling spoke again.

"I will have no peace of mind nor yet a good night's sleep once Lee returns and is once more a party to our military planning. I had hoped that 'Mad' Anthony would share my vigil."

Significantly, Wayne tapped the butt of the horse pistol stuck in his jack boot. "Since I share your suspicions I'll share your vigil, but I pray God we're both wrong."

"I knew you would," Stirling said simply.

"You have no fears on the score of Kimball getting into Philadelphia?" Wayne asked after a moment.

"No. Mistress Ladd has a pass for herself and one man servant. No, Anthony, the danger will come when he tries to find out what's afoot in the city. But he's a smart lad. He's seen danger afore, at Trent's Town and Princeton and Chadds Ford."

"Most likely you are right." Wayne nodded agreement. "Women whose husbands or brothers and the like are in the army have no choice but to travel with a man servant."

"When Mistress Martha and Lucy Knox leave here to return to Mount Vernon they'll have nobody but their coachman," Stirling pointed out.

"And Lady Sarah?"

"My wife, Anthony, is as independent as you. She'll ride to Basking-ridge alone in spite of all my pleading. She and my daughter Kitty are talking of—"

A shout outside Stirling's quarters cut the General short. A lank corporal came running down the road to meet them. Spurring their horses to a gallop, both could see that the corporal was waving a paper in his hand. There was no sound of any alarm, and no sign of the blue and white warning flag at the upstairs window of his quarters so far as Stirling could see, but the corporal was mightily worked up as he seized Stirling's bridle.

"Thought as how you ought to have this quick-like, sir." The corporal was breathy, his voice husky, as he thrust the paper into Stirling's out-stretched hand.

"Thank you, Corporal." Stirling's eyes narrowed and his lips pressed to whiteness as he spread the paper on his saddle and saw that it was a detail map of the entrenchments around the Rebel encampment. Silently he handed the map to Wayne.

"God A'mighty!" Wayne looked from General to corporal. "How did you come by this, lad?"

"Well, sir—" The corporal took off his battered tricorne, hung it on Stirling's spur, and scratched his head. "Well, sir, I was on picket duty behind your quarters. I'm corporal in charge of the Stone Chimney picket down on Gulph Road."

"Yes, yes." Wayne's obvious impatience hurried the corporal along.

"Well, sir. I saw three or four horsemen ride out of the woods—looked like they might ha' ridden down the trail from Fort Moore, and they turns their horses east as if they was headin' for Philadelphia. One of them looked like a body I'd seen afore—but I couldn't place him. Then it comes to me sudden-like—I seen him at General Stirling's quarters—right here, sir, yesterday."

"Here?" Stirling said blankly.

"Yes, sir, a big beefy man—with a pate as bald as an egg, except for a fringe of red hair that stands out like a brim on a hat."

"I never saw him in my life," the General said, astounded. "And you say you saw him here?"

"Yes, sir, nice-spoken gentleman he was, too." The corporal was reflective. "Said yesterday as how he was from the Congress—noseying about and making a report—was the way he said it."

"God A'mighty—what next!" Stirling exploded. "Not that I blame you, Corporal; we've had a spate of reporters to Congress in the past few weeks. Go on—go on!"

"Soon as I recognized him I knew no gentleman from the Congress would be heading Philadelphia way—"

"That's the God's truth," Wayne interjected. "No member I know will set foot in the bloody city till the last English sentry is miles at sea."

"Anyways, sir, I gives this beefy gentleman the order to halt. Shouted it I did, as loud as I could. The only heed he pays is to dig in with his spurs and follow the others down the road toward King of Prussia crossroads. Well, sir, I let him have it with my musket. 'Course the musket's no damn good so I misses him—just knocked his hat off. But he didn't stop for his hat, he kept riding. I ran down the road and picked up the hat. The paper—the map—was inside, sir, and I thought you should have it like I said, quick-like."

"Thank you, Corporal, you did the right thing." Stirling waved his dismissal.

"I'd a-liked to have blown his bloody head offen his neck I would, sir." The corporal saluted, retrieved his tricorne from Stirling's spur, and started away.

"You say you're at the Stone Chimney picket?" Wayne called after him.

"That's right, General."

"Report in at my quarters tonight after you are relieved—I'll see that you get a bite of fresh meat and a pot of ale if you've the tongue for it. What's your name, lad?"

"Hayes, sir."

The dust flew as the long-legged corporal ran down the road. Wayne handed the map back to Stirling and the tanned Pennsylvanian's face was white with a pent-up anger.

"This map was never drawn by anyone riding through the Valley on horseback."

"No," Stirling agreed. "Nor was it drawn by any stranger to the defenses. Look at it closely, Anthony. Is it like any other map you have seen of the camp?"

"It seems so to me, William. The inner and outer lines of defense, the Star Redoubt, Knox's cannon by the schoolhouse at the crossroads. And the redans and lunettes are marked accurately to my way of thinking."

"They are indeed. But look again, Anthony. Who marks his maps

[33]

with 'breastworks' instead of 'earthworks'? And who consistently draws a lunette in the form of a crescent instead of three angled lines as we do?"

"Lee does. But, William, most English officers call 'earthworks,' 'breastworks.' And Arnold's maps of Saratoga show the lunettes in the form of crescents."

"In truth they do." Stirling took the map from Wayne and pointed to a small cross, half a scale-mile from where they stood. "Do you know what that represents?"

Wayne looked closely, shook his head, and answered with a long-drawn-out no.

"It is a point on Mount Joy where we purpose to place a twenty-four-hour lookout. It is the best place in the encampment from which a day and night watch can be kept on Barren Hill and the hamlet of Plymouth Meeting."

"And why a watch on Barren Hill?"

"Because the Chief decided that the Marquis is to take twenty-two hundred men and establish a strong outpost there. It hasn't been announced yet, but La Fayette and Allan McLane of the Delaware Light Horse have been told to prepare for the move."

"How many besides Washington, you, the Marquis and McLane know that?" Wayne's voice betrayed his uneasiness, and the dread that he already knew what Stirling's answer would be.

"How many?" Stirling echoed the question. "Nat Greene, Alex Hamilton—" He drew a deep breath. "The Post for the twenty-four-hour lookout was decided on the day that Lee was in camp!"

3   AT THE RED LION

And so to bed.——Samuel Pepys

Elizabeth, hidden behind a row of spindly pines, sat on a fallen tree trunk holding the reins of the two horses while Jonathan pressed his face into a screen of sumac in an effort to get a clear view of the road. Four or five times now—she'd lost count—they'd gone through the same clambering out of the saddle and hiding in the thicket till this gangling Captain satisfied himself that a red bonnet or a green dress hanging on some washline wasn't a Redcoat or Hessian patrol.

Except for the slight rustle of the wind in the leaves, there wasn't a sound anywhere. In the last mile and a half they'd not seen a soul on the road, and, if it weren't for the nose-stinging smell of charred wood that still hung in the air, the blackened farmhouse on the other side of the rutted road might have been burned long ago.

She was irked at the waste of time. Her eyes were as good as this Jonathan Kimball's, and she'd seen nothing that resembled a Redcoat, much less a whole patrol of them. She was the more irked because he had growled at the time lost in stopping for a bite to eat back at the Red Lion. Hitching herself forward on the tree trunk, she rested her elbow on her knee, and her chin in her hand. Part of her resentment, and she had to admit it, was nothing but sheer dislike of climbing back into the hard saddle. She liked horseback riding, but not in three-day stretches, as this journeying up from Virginia had been.

Her waspish mood wasn't something that had come on her since meeting up with this Captain. It was an irritation that had been building ever since she left her uncle's plantation, and it was brought on by nothing else than the slowness of horse travel. Accustomed to making any longish journey in one of her father's ships, she missed the feel of the heaving deck under her feet, the sense of speeding before the wind; and she hated the dirt and dust and discomforts of jolting along a rough roadway, with dull brown earth for a horizon instead of the shimmering line of blue water.

She hadn't wanted to go to Virginia, but her uncle had sent word that two of her father's oldest and smallest ships had escaped from the English and were safe in southern waters. At her father's pleading, and her mother's insistence, she had made the journey and conveyed to her uncle the various plans her father had suggested for using the ships to aid the Rebel cause.

Worry about her mother, her father, and her two brothers did nothing to improve her mood, she had to admit. These stops on the road, because this overcautious Captain smelled Redcoats, would have made her laugh at any other time. But she'd been gone now for over two weeks with no word as to whether her mother's ailment was worse or better, or how her father fared in the fetid Walnut Street Prison.

Two or three times she'd opened her mouth to ask the Captain if he'd seen his Redcoats yet, and each time she'd bitten the question off for the sake of not provoking an argument. Much more of this sort of dallying on the road and they'd not reach Valley Forge tonight.

"See your Redcoats yet, Captain?" Her question was out before she could stop it.

"They're about," he answered without turning his head.

"I asked if you saw them."

At that he turned and moved back from the thicket. "I don't have to see them, mistress. I know the signs. There are five farmhouses within seeing distance, and not a wisp of smoke from any of them. There's not a beast of any description in any of the fields, and for the past twenty minutes I've heard neither a hoofbeat on the road nor the sound of a voice."

"And if we stay here much longer, we'll be in time for breakfast at General Stirling's tomorrow instead of supper tonight." She rose from the log, smoothed her dress over her knees, and stood waiting.

"You should have thought of that, Mistress Ladd, when we wasted two hours on a bite at the Red Lion." He pulled his timepiece from his pocket, looked at it, and put it back. "Or was it half an hour for a bite, and an hour and a half for you to pretty yourself?"

"We're wasting time now," she snapped angrily.

"Not as much time as we'd lose if we rode into a patrol of Lobsterbacks."

She stamped her foot. "That's all I've heard all afternoon. Lobsterbacks—patrols—Redcoats. I have a pass—or have you forgotten? And I never heard any of the English officers in Philadelphia speak of coming out here on patrols." She stopped abruptly as Jonathan held up his hand.

"But we're not on the road to Philadelphia, mistress, and until we are, your pass would be more likely to betray us than to help us." He spoke quickly, dashed back to the thicket and stood listening.

Bending her head she listened intently. The sound was distant, but there was no mistaking it for anything other than the throbbing beat of cavalry. Quickly she looped the horses' reins about a pine branch, and ran to join Jonathan at the tangled sumac. She had no need to ask where or what it was, and she felt her face and neck grow hot with confusion as she watched Dragoons and Rangers converging on the crossroads less than a mile away.

Feeling Jonathan touch her arm, she turned and followed his pointing finger. To the north, on a road she didn't even know was there, a troop of Hussars was riding in their direction. They looked for all the world like mounted skeletons in their black uniforms with silver braid stitched in rows across their chests. She shivered at her own comparison, and looked up at Jonathan's face.

"You, mistress, complained of hearing me speak of Redcoats. I, in turn, am somewhat tired of hearing about your pass." He jerked his thumb in the direction of the patrols to stress his point. "Do you think these patrols would glance at your pass, and wave you on your way—at right angles to Philadelphia and in the direction of Valley Forge?"

She shrugged her shoulders and tried to smile. "You were right, Captain, and I was wrong."

"I gain no pleasure from your being wrong, Mistress Ladd. But even were the English to accept your pass, and me as your servant, they'd see to it that we got back on the right road, or they'd bid us wait and escort us back to Philadelphia themselves. Our whole scheme fails if we do not get to Stirling for our instructions."

"And what do we do now? Stand here all night?" She tried hard not to sound critical, but he was a captain in the Rebel Army, wasn't he? He ought to make the decisions.

"I don't rightly know," he answered frankly. "I've been racking my mind to recall some road that we could turn west on—then strike north again. Trouble is—" he hesitated, "'twill be dark afore long. That cross-roads back there, where the Dragoons are trooping, is about six miles from General Stirling's quarters. Only other road I can think on takes off from Chadds Ford, runs through Paoli and on up to the Bull Tavern."

"And the Bull Tavern is where?"

"Two and a half mile west of the encampment." Shaking his head he frowned and pointed to the sun dipping behind the fields. "It's fifteen mile by the road I'm thinking of, and we'd never find our way over the Paoli road in the dark. It wanders through a patchwork of farms, and any one of the farm roads could lead us out in the middle of nowhere. We'd be lost for sure and have to sit in some ploughed field till daybreak to find out way out."

"'Tis no use to seek help from me." And this time Elizabeth made no effort to keep the edge out of her voice. "I've journeyed a'tween Virginia and Philadelphia enough times that I've lost tally—but on my father's ships, or on the Lower Road that follows the river. And I don't get lost," she finished acidly.

"Mistress, I'm far from lost. Were I journeying alone I'd strike off across the ploughed fields and ride all night. I'll remind you, lass, that I'm under orders, distasteful as they be, to escort you to the General's quarters —and 'tis no part of these orders to have you raped by English Dragoons—or me hanged afore I've completed my chore."

There was enough ire in his voice to make her snap her mouth shut in time to cut off another tart reply, and content herself by turning her back as he returned to his vigil at the thicket. Why in the name of the Continental Congress had Lord Stirling picked this ungainly bundle of contradictions to be her escort? For the life of her, she couldn't help contrasting his indecision and want of manners with the briskness and fault-less manners of the English officers she had to deal with in order to keep the family's shipping business alive.

She had no desire to deal with the English officers, but she had no choice. Her shipmaster father was more a hostage than a prisoner; and her brothers were in a like position. They were masters aboard their ships, but they had to sail wherever the English ordered them to. The ships had to carry what cargo the Redcoats wanted, and English officers were stationed aboard to see that it was done.

Under the circumstances, the English officers could have been very stiff and formal and domineering in their dealings with her. Instead, they had been polite and friendly, and seemed to be bent on making things as pleasant as possible for her in the occupied city. Certainly Lieutenants Smythe and Bygrove treated her as they would an older sister. She felt her ears grow noticeably pink when she thought of her most constant visitor, and she shot a half-guilty glance in the Rebel Captain's direction to see if he still had his face buried in the sumac.

Major Broadmoor was going to prove somewhat of a problem in this venture. The Major was a constant visitor, and most adept at finding excuses to call on her. He was extremely proper in everything he did and said, and the other officers accepted his visits as quite ordinary and in the line of his duty. She knew differently. Broadmoor was in love with her, and one eyelid-flutter too many would precipitate a proposal that she wouldn't know how to handle.

All her speculating came to a sudden stop as Kinball left the hedge and stepped to her side. The look on his face convinced her that they were in a serious plight, and honestly compelled her to admit that in spite of her twitting him about Redcoats, he had proved to be right. By way of answering her questioning look, he pointed through the sparse trees to a moving cloud of dust far across the fields.

"English cavalry on the Devon Road, too. The Redcoats are foraging far afield tonight, and in larger patrols than usual. Doubtless because Mad Anthony and General Lacey have choked off the supply lines to the city. God knows they've tried hard enough."

"How can you be certain-sure they're English?"

"You can't see the riders, can you?"

"No." She looked again before she answered.

"And that tokens the riders are on the other side—the northern side—of the dust cloud. Were they on this side you'd see them."

"So?"

"So they're riding north and east."

"But why English—could they not be Washington's men—riding back to Valley Forge?" She felt the first twinge of fear now, and she looked closely at his troubled face.

"No, Mistress Elizabeth. At the Valley Forge we send out no patrols in the day hours. We wait for dark afore we send the lads out. And we wait till dark afore we make it into the camp. That way—Tories and spies and the like—can hazard no shrewd accounting of our numbers."

"And all that portends what, Captain?"

"It portends, mistress, that we've no prospects of—bed or roof for the night. Should we escape one patrol we encounter another. Had we

[38]

made it past the Redcoats at the crossroads, we'd have been caught by that other patrol—right on the Valley Forge Road."

"And we're to spend the night with our backs propped against a pine tree?" She waved disdainfully at the circle of trees about them.

"No." He laughed at the dismay on her face. "'Bout a mile back on the Red Lion Road is Lenni Creek. Off the road apiece is an overhanging ledge of rock. It's well screened with brush, and sheltered somewhat. We'd be safe enough to light a fire. There's fresh water for laving and drinking—and at dawn—"

"Doubtless a pirate cave you played in as a child," she cut in scornfully.

"No, Mistress Ladd, 'tis where General Stirling dressed my wounds after Brandywine. The General and the Captain both owe their lives to that pirate cave." He bowed mockingly as he finished.

"I'm sorry—I didn't know—"

He brushed her words aside with a wave of his hand. "There's naught to be sorry over. Why should you be expected to know till I told you. In all truth, mistress," his voice brightened, "'tis a tolerably hideaway."

"If it's beside any creek I recall—then it is close to the Red Lion Inn?"

"It is," he agreed. "The Red Lion is but a mile beyond the creek."

"Since you've a mind to backtrack to the creek, why don't we journey one more mile, and bed in some comfort?"

He stared at her in surprise, and his answer was short. "You forget, mistress, we ate our last meal there."

"I don't forget it. I remember it well. A good meal—but I would have eaten more had I counted on it serving me till tomorrow."

"Then you've forgotten that mine host mistook us for man and wife. Were we to go back now—asking for separate chambers and trying to explain that we were not wed—" He shrugged his shoulders. "The fewer questions asked and the fewer answers to give at any tavern in these parts —the longer you stay out of English hands."

"But, Captain—"

"'Tis impossible," he answered gruffly. "Should we go back there and try to bargain with the host, we'd arouse his suspicions. And to save his own neck he'd report us to the closest Redcoat, and at the same time collect the five-pound reward."

"But he'd not report us if he thought we were man and wife?"

"He'd be suspicious, because we'd turned back."

"Not if we had a right smart tale to tell him."

"Now lookee, mistress—"

"You lookee, Captain! 'Tis your turn to listen—mine to prate." Shak-

[39]

ing a gloved finger under his nose, she threw her head back and stared him up and down with eyes that crackled fire.

"I'm no prude, nor yet a Philadelphia cozey. I'm still maiden and expect to be so for some little while. But if it be a matter of bedding down under your rock ledge—or sharing a bedchamber with you—then my mind's clear on it! We share the chamber—and my mother can be the first to hear of it for all that I'll be shent." Lowering her hand as she finished, she tucked her thumb into her skirtband and watched his face, trying to foretell his humor. She learned nothing from the slow smile that started with a quiver of his straight lips and ended with the right eyebrow arching higher than the left. Impatient, she was about to repeat her demand when he spoke slowly with a bite in every word.

"Mistress, we can share the bed, as well as the chamber—and you'll die a maid—it's that little interest to me." Finished, he walked to the horses and unwound the reins. "So now we'll concoct a tale for mine host of the Red Lion, and afore long we'll see how smart our tale is." Lifting the saddlebags from his mount's back, Jonathan slung them over his shoulder. "You, mistress, will ride my horse."

"For why?"

"Your horse has a lame shoulder muscle." He handed her his reins. "I'll walk back to the Red Lion. 'Tis a more likely tale," he explained, putting his hand under her foot and helping her into his saddle. "Women ruin horses—and yours pulled a muscle because you mishandled him when he shied at a white boulder—a couple of mile this side of the crossroads." He took her saddlebags and threw them on his own mount, then gripping her horse's bridle, he led the way out of the coppice and along the fast-darkening road.

Against the red glow that welded the low-lying clouds and the ascending folds of the upland hills into a shimmering golden line, the pale window lights of the Red Lion were scarcely visible. Vague twists of thin blue smoke rising from the fieldstone chimneys of a dozen houses were all that marked the nameless village which would have no existence were it not for the tavern that was just four hours' carriage ride from the busy ports of Chester and Chatham to the south.

Winter or summer, there was always hustle and bustle at the Sign of the Red Lion. The mornings were filled with guests departing for the ships that sailed with the afternoon tide, while after midday, new arrivals from as far away as York and Lancaster filled the courtyard with excited chatter about the ships they must board before the next morning tide was lost.

On a shelf at the left of the front door, a big black tôle lanthorn with a polished tin reflector threw a broad beam of white light into the stable yard, and it was the sudden jumping of the beam across the open space that showed Jonathan and Elizabeth they were closer to the Red Lion than they had thought.

"Remember, mistress, your horse shied at a white boulder."

"I'll remember I'm no horsewoman and be properly clumsy."

The windows of the scattered houses were ruddy with firelight, the twinkling of candles, and the uneven yellowish flickering of fat lamps. Seeing the fires, Elizabeth felt chill and hungry, and she threw a welcoming smile at the potboy who ran out from the tavern and took possession of the horses.

"That one has a lame right shoulder," Jonathan said as he lifted Elizabeth from the saddle, "But I venture he'll be able to bear a load after a night's rest."

"I reined him too sharply when he reared at a white boulder by the roadside." Elizabeth pressed an English shilling in the potboy's hand as she watched Jonathan take her saddlebags from his own mount.

"Leave the bags by the door, master, and I be takin' them to your chamber whiles you and your lady sup. And take no worries about the horse, sir. I'll rub the shoulder when I bars the stables for the night— oftner iffen I be able to."

"Do it, that's a good lad."

As Jonathan reached for the heavy wrought-iron handle of the tavern door it was thrown open and Host Calvit stood facing them in the candle-lighted passageway. His smile froze, then after a moment, dissolved into a look of genuine concern.

"What befell, sir?" He looked closely at Elizabeth. "Your lady, sir, she looks unwell—"

"Naught that was serious, landlord, the mistress' horse fell lame—not so ill but what a night's rest will work a cure." Jonathan closed the door behind him. "I've had a fairish walk; a meal—a room—if the house be not filled to the garret."

Elizabeth watched Calvit's face through the screen of her long lashes and decided that the landlord believed Jonathan's tale completely.

"Supper you shall have on the instant." Mine host slapped two horny hands together with a resounding crack that echoed in the narrow hall like a musket shot. "Two suppers, Hannah, for the ingle table," he shouted in a sharp voice that bounced from one white plastered wall to the other. Turning to the left, he opened the door to the eating room and led Elizabeth and Jonathan around the other tables filled with travellers making more noise with their eating, Elizabeth thought, than with their converse.

"I'll have you a chamber readied, mistress, while you sup. 'Tis the last in the house—and not used much—but one of the wenches will set a fire and that'll chase out the spring damp." His voice, as he spoke over his shoulder, was mild and quiet and in odd contrast with his bellowed order of the minute before. " 'Tis a cosy room—but it be cursed with slantwise ceilings and the bed be a mite short for a full-growed man. That be the only reason for leaving it out of use." He finished with a smile of apology and bowed her into the narrow space between the ingle seat and the wide three-boarded trestle table.

The hissing and popping of the logs in the fireplace at the end of the table sent a surge of warm blood coursing through her veins, and Elizabeth began to feel that the misadventure and delay had been greatly magnified in her own mind. She was loath to admit it, but so used had she become to the soft living of the Colonies' gayest city, she was actually afraid of spending a night in the open; not afraid of English Dragoons or footpads, but plain unwilling to suffer the discomfort.

So shocked was she at her own appraisal that she closed her eyes and turned her face from the fire. She had behaved like any one of the pampered Tory wenches of Philadelphia. She, a Patriot, with her father and mother life-long friends of Lord Stirling, and her brothers press-ganged aboard their own ships, had played the spoilt brat in front of a Rebel officer.

She was pulled out of her mood of self-scorn by the clatter of a pewter dish on the table, and she opened her eyes to find Kimball staring at her.

"Fatigued, lass?"

"Not so much fatigued as abashed at the manner of my behavior," she admitted honestly.

" 'Tis of no moment. Women are not built for such rude journeyings." He picked up a horn spoon, pointed to her dish and grinned. "You're like to feel better after you laddle some o' that venison stew inside."

Disjointed bits of conversation drifted over the high back of the ingle seat and Elizabeth found herself listening to talk of trade, of farming, of the comfort and speed of one vessel over another, of the new patterned Conestoga wagon that had the rear sprung like a carriage. Deaths, weddings, christenings and the sale or exchange of farms and taverns punctuated or interrupted the rising and falling stream of chatter, but never once did she hear war or Rebel or Tory or English. It was as if the ceaseless talk were a feverish effort to forget the war or, leastwise, pretend that it did not exist.

And yet it was no matter for surprise, she thought watching a dull-witted serving wench, uselessly prisoned and tortured by too-tight stays, waddling from table to table replenishing bread basket and stew platter. The talk was little different from what she heard daily in her home in the city. Even the English officers who called almost daily, rarely spoke of the war. Their talk was of letters from home, the cost of horses, whose bird was favorite that night at the cockpit, or—when they thought she was out of earshot—which of Philadelphia's ladies were open to persuasion and which would respond with a slap to the face.

Most of the travellers were finished with the meal and Host Calvit, making long-legged strides between his guests, carried a glowing coal to light the curved-stem, clay pipes of the menfolks. His good wife followed close at his heels, showing a wide expanse of well-favored bosom as she leaned over to decant thin red wine to the women who looked wedlocked —or should have been. Elizabeth smiled on Mistress Calvit as the wine frothed into the stubby wine glass. Drinking it, she kept a pleasant face, although the stuff tasted as though it had never been in a tun but had been made the day before in a not-too-clean iron kettle. Host Calvit, Elizabeth decided, ate well and knew good food, but his taste in wines was that of a barbarian.

As Elizabeth set down the glass, a thunderous clumping of hooves filled the courtyard. Mounted figures in red coats and blue breeches, blurring past the windows, surrounded the tavern before the travellers' chattering had died away. With the barest glance at the door, Calvit continued his pipe-lighting, but Mistress Calvit with her wine decanter backed into the shadows and slipped along the pine-panelled wall toward the kitchen.

Instead of opening, the door of the eating room exploded inward as though it had been blasted off its lock. A short, fat, gross British general with a red-fleshed neck as thick as his head, and pink saucer-shaped ears that looked as if they were ironed flat, strode in, followed by a tall handsome colonel in the gold facings of the Royal Grenadiers. With a contemptuous flash of his eyes the General swept the eating room at a glance and addressed Calvit without looking near him.

"All Loyalists—all Rebels—or half and half, landlord?"

Calvit raised his hands in mock surrender and bowed from the waist. "Your Lordship knows that to stay in trade—an innkeeper asks no awkward questions."

"You know me, sirrah?" The General favored the landlord with his glance.

"Of a surety, sire. I know General Grant, the Laird o' Ballachulish. Will your Lordship sup—or is his visit in the line of duty?"

"A rogue, eh, Monckton?" General Grant turned to the Grenadier Colonel. "But he has a civil, well-spoken tongue, and that should be remembered to his credit." He swept the room with a slow, penetrating stare that searched out all the corners.

At the mention of Monckton's name, Elizabeth shrank herself inside her clothes and drew back into the corner of the ingle bench. She saw that Jonathan had noted her movement, and she watched the Rebel Captain's hand move across the table to the candlestick. Slowly, without any perceptible movement, he slid the candleholder along the boards till the flickering light no longer reached her face. Out of the corner of her eye, she saw Grant's eyes pass from her to Jonathan to the table beyond, and finally to the landlord.

"The chambers are empty, Sir Boniface? All your patrons are here?" The Laird o' Ballachulish's rows of chins worked up and down over his stiff military collar.

"The chambers are empty, m'Lord, except for the wenches and pot-boy tending the fires and warming the sheets with the pans."

"I'll take your word for it, sirrah. None of your patrons looks like the quarry we seek, albeit the scalawags we search for have been seen in these parts. It will go ill with any of you—" He stopped and his eyes, too small and too close to his nose, circled the room again. "Ill indeed, if any of you harbors or gives hiding to the deserters I seek. Come, Monckton, we'll press our search elsewhere." Grant turned on his heel and walked to the doorway. "We will be back, landlord, if further searching avails us nothing. See to it that you take no more guests for the night," he threw over his shoulder as the Colonel closed the door behind him.

"They know you?" Jonathan whispered across the table.

"Not as yet." Elizabeth put her heels firmly on the floor and tried to stop the shaking of her knees before she said more. She'd not counted on any such thing as this. She'd never met Monckton, nor seen him for the matter of that. But Monckton might well have seen her, and there was the frightening possibility that he would in the future. Monckton had but recently been detailed to duty in Philadelphia—as Major Broadmoor's commanding officer.

"Colonel Monckton is the superior of one of the officers with whom I—I have to deal." Hoping that her hesitation had been marked as part of her upset at seeing the British officers so far from Philadelphia, she attacked the dish in front of her.

"Then he might recognize me, too." He kept his voice low but the tenor of it demanded an answer as he whispered, "Best tell me more so that I know what to do."

She followed his lead, and spoke without looking up. "Monckton is Major Broadmoor's superior, and Broadmoor comes to the house on various matters connected with my father's business. It is possible that some day Monckton may come with him."

"I saw no sign of recognition in his look," Jonathan said, more to himself than to Elizabeth. "What we have to worry about is that some time in the future, he might remember seeing us here." He paused and tapped the table with his finger. "What answer will you make if he asks you?"

"I don't know."

"Then I'll tell you. Smirk at him, and say that a gentleman doesn't ask such questions."

"Oh, but I—he would think—"

"Certainly he would." Jonathan leaned over the table toward her. "And, thank God, you can prove it. The Boniface and his wife, the potboy, the wenches would all save your pretty neck by swearing that you spent the night here as my wife." He grinned at her outraged look, and pushed her glass of wine close to her clenched fist. "Drink up, lass, look as if nothing were wrong, and make some pretense of enjoying the supper. The landlord is headed this way."

The noisy chatter that had stopped so abruptly was slow in building when the door closed on the Redcoat officers. The Tory-minded guests worked hard at showing their unconcern, only to be outdone by the over-played ease of the Patriots. Landlord Calvit fetching himself a new coal from the fire, winked at Jonathan and whispered, "Quite a figure is the Laird o' Ballachulish—they do say he can drink a cask of wine at a sitting—and never show it."

"He shows it." Jonathan didn't raise his voice. "One more sitting and he'll look like a vat himself."

"It profits me to know them all, and be civil to boot." Calvit reached over Jonathan's head and took a clay pipe from the array on the mantel-shelf. "I'll be civil to the devil himself to postpone the stretching of my neck."

"As who wouldn't." Jonathan laughed up at the innkeeper. "At the expense of a hanging a man can be very civil."

"Aye, master. By civil manners, a man can bide his time—till there's no longer need for civility." Calvit spoke softly between puffs on his pipe—gave Elizabeth a long look, and, carrying his hissing coal by the small brass tongs, went about the business of lighting the pipes that had gone out during the Redcoats' visit.

Having no wish, under the circumstances, to be the one to suggest going to their bedchamber, Jonathan leaned back in the ingle settle, stretched his legs under the table, and considered the common room.

Watching this perpetually nervous Rebel, Elizabeth had to admit that he seemed oblivious of everything but his scrutiny of the room. His face in repose was quite different from its usual haggard ruggedness, for the jaw was no longer aggressive; and his eyes, now without their hard glitter, were a deep gray. Even his aquiline nose had become less eagle-like in the soft light of the candles.

"An agreeable room," he said, knowing that she had been watching him, "somewhat different in design from the buildings where I was raised."

Elizabeth nodded, thinking of her uncle's white pillared plantation house with its fanlighted doorways, and wide, open hall with the flying staircase curving up to the balcony. "Virginia houses are different from anywhere else in the Colonies."

"Mine was different from anything in Virginia." He chuckled ruefully.

"Where is it?" Actually she asked the question more from politeness, than any desire to know.

"Place you never heard of, mistress." This time he laughed outright. "'Tis called Kimball, and lies up the James River a stout fifteen mile from Jamestown. 'Tis as badly situate and nigh to being in ruin as Jamestown itself. When my mother and father are done using it—I'll put the torch to it and that will be the end of Kimball on the James."

"But why?"

"Mistress, 'tis as monstrous and ugly a place as ever was builded." He leaned his elbows on the table and cupped his chin in his hands. "In plan and shape, it is somewhat like an English moat house, but in the stead of stone, 'tis builded of adzed logs chinked with ground oyster shell. The apartments are too large to heat and 'twould take an army of foresters, as it did when it was builded eighty-five years ago, to feed the yawning holes that we call fireplaces."

"And Kimball—town, village or what—was founded by your ancestors?" Elizabeth, holding the wine glass by the stem, twirled it unconsciously between her thumb and fingers.

"Neither town nor village, mistress. 'Twas more of a manor, with a big house sitting on the hill. The old hall was there in King Charles' time." He shrugged his shoulders. "We were proper Royalists then. The main hall with its table and benches—enough to seat a hundred—had Charles' portrait draped in black, above the mantelboard, whilst a crude picture of Cromwell with the hangman's rope about his neck lay on the floor under the table." He shook his head sadly. "'Tis still that way after more than a hundred years. My father lights one candle every night —in the center of the table—all because his father did it, and his father afore that."

A shuffling of feet interrupted him. Elizabeth, looking across the room, saw Calvit handing flaring tapers to his guests as he bid each one good rest. Jonathan jumped to his feet, came to the end of the table and offered his arm. Slowly she slid along the settle—in full realization that the time for making good her ill-tempered and ill-timed boast was upon her. Jonathan, guiding her between the tables, continued to talk as though this matter of their going to the bedchamber were a nightly affair.

The landlord stopped them at the door. "I'll lead you to your chamber. 'Tis reached by the back stairs." He beckoned them to follow him down the hall. "'Tis the old part of the house."

[46]

A knobless door in the panelling swung open at his touch, and the dancing flame of the taper showed a tight-fitting spiral of steps climbing up the dark closet. High above, a dull yellowish gleam showed that the staircase made a full turn and ended on the third floor.

"If Grant and his Grenadiers come back I'll have to bring them up should they remember you—and demand to see you." Calvit's voice was low and muffled. "Most times, when the bastards indulge in their midnight searches, they're content to look in the other chambers."

"What can they expect to find?" Elizabeth whispered. "They know you'd not be stupid enough to hide deserters."

"Madame, your opinion on that be as good as mine." As he answered, Calvit stepped down a short passageway, opened the bedchamber door, and stood aside to let them enter.

Jonathan walked to the fireplace and leaned his elbow against the mantelboard. "You risk your neck somewhat, landlord, judging us to be Patriot."

"No, young master, that I do not. And if by chance you land near the Old Forge, or hold any converse with Mad Anthony or Lord Stirling—well, tell them you slept in their room."

"You know them?" Elizabeth sat on the gaudily painted Dutch chest at the foot of the spool bed.

Calvit nodded. "Better than I know the Laird o' Ballachulish. You see, madame—" he turned to Elizabeth—"I was at Chadds Ford and I saw most of the wounded—"

"But how?" Jonathan burst out.

"Doctor Irvine of Carlisle sent word that he needed bandages and mosses and grain for poultices. The folks about the Red Lion tore up sheets and the like—and I took them to the battlefield. 'Twas that simple, you see. General George and others—like the Marquis de La Fayette, Stirling, Greene—know the inn. Mad Anthony has had many a dram here—even afore the Revolt."

"Then we were quite safe in returning here?" Elizabeth asked archly.

"No, madame. That you were not. Your tale of a lame horse was good—but not good enough if the Grenadiers make a true search. Iffen they question the villagers—or my wenches—they'll find that you left here about three o' the clock and they'll know that you ran afoul the Dragoons and that's why you turned back." He raised his hand as Jonathan was about to speak. "I've doctored the horse a mite, rubbed some liniment that burns like hell fire itself into the shoulder. He'll twitch and lash out if a body touches him. 'Twill at least lend credence to your tale if the English come back askin' more questions."

"You think we'd be better served to leave now—spend the night in the field and get away from these parts in the dawn?" Jonathan asked anxiously.

"Not now." Calvit was emphatic. "The English have patrols on every road—and these are no light patrols, as you saw. General Grant on one, General Leslie commands the detachment on the road up from Chatham, 'No-Flint' Grey is on his favorite road—Paoli."

"No-Flint?" Elizabeth was curious.

" 'Twas him as surprised Mad Anthony at Paoli. Took the flints away from his men so they'd fight with the bayonet—in silence. 'Tis a given name that will stick with Grey—as 'Mad' Anthony will stick to Wayne."

"Well—" Jonathan bent low to avoid the sloping ceiling as he went to the dormer—"we'd best rely on you, landlord, to tell us when to leave."

"I'll do that, lad." Calvit opened the door and stepped into the passage. "Best you be getting all the rest you can—and best that you doff your clothes—both of you. If the English come sudden-like and find you dressed—" He stopped, drew his hand across his throat suggestively, and eased the door shut.

"Does he think I'm in the way of bedding down with my clothes on?" Elizabeth untied the tapes of her cloak and dropped it across the back of the chest.

"I'll make no pretense of knowing his reason," Jonathan answered. "Might well be that he fears we'd stay dressed and try to make an escape if the English return. Then, by the other hand—" he turned and watched Elizabeth rise from the chest, go to the commode, and pour water from the ewer into the basin—"he might reckon that we're not man and wife and be embarrassed—"

"Then either whichway, his reckoning is amiss." Elizabeth dabbed at her face with a damp flannel smeared with soap. Sputtering between rubs with the flannel, she leaned forward and looked in the small lead-backed glass on the wall. "I've lived all my life with two outspoken brothers who paid no heed to their dress just because I was near by. I'm no wise put out of face because we're compelled to share the same bed-chamber."

"Most like our landlord was thinking of you," was Jonathan's mild rejoinder.

"Then he's a ninny." She wrung out the flannel and rinsed her face. "Either you've seen a lass undress afore or you haven't. Tomorrow you can say you have, and, for the favor, you can lift my saddlebags onto the Dutch chest."

Smothering a laugh, Jonathan crossed the room and lifted the saddle-bags. "Shall I open them, mistress, or will that merit no more favors?"

"As I recall it you said I could die a maid, it was that little interest to you. What favor do you seek?"

"I did but jest and that's the truth. I'm sorry my joke was a squib in the pan."

"You're forgiven," she said cheerily. "God's truth you're better company in jest than you are trying to win the war all by yourself."

"I'm afeared that holding our own, rather than winning the war, has been in the front of the minds of all of us at Valley Forge this past five months. There was neither time nor mood for jesting."

"We heard tell, of course, in Philadelphia." She untied the tapes at her waist, and her wide-skirted dress, falling about her feet, disclosed as slim a pair of ankles as ever Jonathan had seen.

"It was a frozen hell on earth. The lads were so beat—what with half of them without shoes—it took us all one day to march the last five mile into the Valley Forge. I can remember General Washington standing there. He was holding his cloak about him with one hand, and gripping Lord Stirling's arm with the other. He was shaking with anger and pity, watching the falling snow cover up a trail of bloody footprints that reached all the way back to Gulph Mills."

"We read of it," Elizabeth said, bending down and lifting her skirt from the floor, "but reading and seeing are different things."

"Aye, you've read of it." Jonathan's voice was bitter. "You read of it on the back page of the *Gazette* and the like. The front page was taken up with demands for Washington's removal and replacement by Horatio Gates, the hero of Saratoga. Every man jack of us knows that Schuyler and Arnold won Saratoga, that Gates arrived in time to reap the credit."

"All we can know is what we've read, Captain." She loosed the tapes of her bodice, one by one. "If you'll look out the window, I'll shed these for something more in keeping with a bed—in case the Redcoats come acalling."

Jonathan obediently stared out at the deserted pike. The wavy glass, backed by darkness, reflected a swirl of cambric as Elizabeth made ready for the night. Distorted as the image was, he could tell when she had put something on and, turning without any bidding from her, he found she was enveloped from neck to ankles in a shapeless thing of frills and bows that was tied about her waist with a belt of plaited ribbon.

Elizabeth took a tortoise-shell brush from her saddlebags, and seated herself on the bed. She pulled out the combs that prisoned her coiled hair, and it cascaded about her shoulders in waves of gleaming black. The wide sleeve of her robe slid up to her shoulder as the brush rose and fell, and the absolute jet of her hair heightened the whiteness of her arm and the warm pink of her face.

Tossing her hair to one side with a long sweep of her arm, Elizabeth gave Jonathan a steady, appraising look. "Why did Lord Stirling choose you for this dangerous business of going into Philadelphia?"

"That's a mite difficult to answer." Pulling off his coat and hanging it over the back of the rocker at the edge of the hearth, Jonathan sat in the chair and stuck his feet out toward the fire. "I'm from Virginia and that was a necessity if I were to pass as your servant. I can name places and people if I'm questioned. I'm well enough trained that I can assess the military value of what I see. Stirling trusts me not to send him worthless information—nor yet to let something of import happen under my nose unnoticed."

"Hardly reason enough, I would say." She laid the shell-backed brush on the bed cover, pulled her heels up onto the bed rail, and clasped her hands about her knees. "There must be other Virginia officers who know how to assess the military value of what they see."

"True," Jonathan admitted. "I said it was difficult to answer. I might ask, for why did the General decide on your house in Philadelphia?"

"And I'd find the answer easy to make. Lord Stirling has been a friend to my mother and father since afore they were wed. Despite what is said about most shipowners, he knows we are Patriot. And remember, I have this pass, although how the General found out about it I know not."

"Hardly reason enough, I would say." Jonathan gave her back her own words in a slightly mocking tone. "There are other Patriots in Philadelphia—among the shipowners. There were passes issued to other travellers. We knew about them, just as we knew of yours—"

"But how—and who?" she interrupted him, in surprise.

"Who he is? That I do not know. But he beats the very devil himself at ferreting out intelligence of that nature." Pulling his feet back from the fire, he stood up and faced her. "In all seriousness, Mistress Ladd, you voiced the reason for the General's choice of your family, and of me, when you said he was a friend. True, he hasn't known me for the years he has known you, but he's been closer to me than my own father since I first went to King's College."

"I didn't know that." Her voice held a new interest. "Lord Stirling would often talk to us about his 'boys' as he called them. He felt his responsibilities as one of the governors, and took his duties very seriously."

"He had to!" Jonathan said passionately. "We were cursed with a rabid Tory for a president until he was sent scuttling back to England where his writings and lectures were better appreciated. We had to bite our tongues, and hold on to our benches, and boil in silence while he lectured us on the evils of popular rule and the assumption of power by the Continental Congress. At nights, a few of us would gather around Alex Hamilton whilst he penned answers to President Cooper, and we fumed and spluttered like long-fused bombs because Alex dare not sign his name." He stopped, a little abashed at his outburst, and spreading his palms toward Elizabeth, he spoke softly. "I had not thought of being vehement."

"You told Lord Stirling of what went on?"

"We told him. Come Sunday, we would be at Lord Stirling's house in New York. Both he and Lady Sarah would listen to our outpourings. Lord Stirling would demolish President Cooper's arguments and, with a twinkle in his eye, he would suggest questions we could ask Tory Cooper the following week. Oft-times John Jay would be there with Mistress Jay, and that would be a day to delight any Rebel's heart." He laughed and pointed a wagging finger at Elizabeth. "Think on it, lass. Lady Sarah, sister to the Rebel Governor Livingston and wife to Rebel Stirling. Her niece, Livingston's daughter, married to John Jay. Alex Hamiliton and me. We had the Revolution started, the war over, and these Colonies free and independent afore Jefferson had written the Declaration."

With the suddenness of summer thunder, the hollow roar of horses pounding down the pike came through the front window. Jonathan swung about and bending low to stay out of the firelight, crossed to the dormer. He heard Elizabeth's bare feet pad across the floor behind him and felt her press against his back as her hair touched his cheek.

Together they watched the horsemen surround a small white house on the opposite side of the pike. Figures, indistinguishable in the dark, ran to the door, and the clank of a sword hilt being crashed against a door panel rang like a stroke on an anvil. A light flashed as the door was thrust open and a woman's screams tore the air. There was a confusion of red and white and black. Some Redcoats thrust aside a woman in a white shift. Others seized a struggling man in black, carried him through the doorway and on up the pike to where the trees overhung the stake fence of the last house.

The silence that followed was worse than the screaming, Elizabeth thought. Clutching Jonathan's shoulders she watched three officers follow the struggling men into the shadows. Even the clatter of the horses' hooves was dull and dead as the troopers slowly reformed into columns of fours on the narrow pike.

" 'Tis that such might befall you and me, lass, as had me worried this afternoon." Jonathan put his hands up and gripped Elizabeth's wrists.

"I know," she whispered, her lips so close to his ear he felt the warmth of her breath.

There was a jangle of harness and lifting of horses' heads as dim figures walked back from the shadow-hidden edge of the road, and climbed into their saddles. At the head of the column, an officer's white gauntlet was raised in command, and the patrol moved off in the direction they had come.

A light tap sounded on the bedchamber door.

"Yes?" Jonathan's voice was hoarse.

"No worries for the rest of the night I think." Calvit's voice was low and muffled. "They found the last of their deserters. Best you get abed. I'll wake you afore dawn."

Still crouched in the narrow dormer, Elizabeth and Jonathan listened to the landlord's soft footfalls as he went down the narrow hall. When they looked out the window again, there was nothing but a vague shadow, swinging back and forth on an invisible length of rope.

4 THE LESSON

O sweet name of liberty.——CICERO

The Red Lion Inn was three hours' riding behind them, before Jonathan and Elizabeth dared emerge from the narrow farm roads and bridle trails they had followed on Landlord Calvit's advice. Elizabeth, recovered from her fright of the night before, had been inclined to argue about the extra riding the longer route entailed, but Calvit's parting word had stilled her tongue.

"Better a sore backside for a day—than a stiff neck for all eternity!" Calvit had whispered, and sent them on their way through the woods at the rear of the Red Lion.

Eyeing Elizabeth as she jogged along at his side, Jonathan wondered if she were beginning to grasp the hard truth that the war, as she knew it from within Philadelphia, was somewhat different from the war as waged in the country. And that the same English officers whose spotless uniforms and flawless manners were the talk of the Indian Queen and other taverns were brutal, murdering fiends when they were on patrol duty.

Certainly this fiery, quick-tongued wench had much to learn. He in turn found his mind in a turmoil of doubts and alarms, as he thought back on the picture of life in Philadelphia, as she had unwittingly described it last night. After the Grenadiers had ridden off, neither had felt any desire for sleep, and he had sat in the rocker with his feet resting on the Dutch chest, while Elizabeth, propped up in the bed, had chattered on about family, friends and the shipping trade. What had alarmed him was the casualness with which she spoke of Redcoat officers, their visits, and what they said and did. As the hours passed, he had listened with growing concern to the pattern of life into which he was expected to fit himself as her servant.

She was Patriot, she was all for the Revolution, and she was infuriated at the treatment meted out to her father and her brothers. But her hatred was for some indefinite thing she called the "enemy," not for the individual enemy officers with whom she came in daily touch. Somehow it escaped her reckoning that the treatment she received at the hands of the Redcoat officers would have been very different, had she been some unknown country wench, instead of a well-known Philadelphia beauty.

It hadn't taken Jonathan long to recognize that she was not to be changed or swayed by words, so he had been at great pains to point to the signs of devastation as they rode along, their eyes alert for English raiding parties. Luckily, they had seen neither Redcoat nor brass-helmeted Hessian, and the closer they got to Valley Forge, the less likely they were to meet up with any. Perhaps, Jonathan thought, the Grenadiers' hunt for deserters last night had given them their fill of brutality for the time being.

Even on the deserted roads they had followed, he had been able to show Elizabeth what hate and fear and suspicion could do to a once-peaceful countryside. The grist mill on a little nameless stream that spilled into the Brandywine had been emptied of grain by English Hussars. But that had not satisfied their thirst for brutal destruction, and they had broken the buckets off the water wheel. In sheer viciousness, they had sledged out every cog in the mill gears.

Less than a mile from the wrecked grist mill, Jonathan had seen the look of incredulity on Elizabeth's face when they reached the tollgate. A gibbering little man, bereft of his reason, ran out from the tollhouse and waved them on with a grotesque flailing of his skinny arms. An inoffensive, sickly man he had been of no use to Rebel or Tory, but of no menace, either. He had been tardy in opening the tollgate for a squadron of English cavalry, and the Colonel had ordered him stretched on the bars of the gate and lashed with the troopers' belts as they galloped past.

One truth must be sinking in on Mistress Elizabeth Ladd, Jonathan thought, as he saw her glancing at the four walls of a mansion standing stark and roofless and fire-blackened. She must be beginning to realize that the tolerance with which the Redcoats treated Philadelphia was nothing more than a selfish desire not to foul their own nest. The English officers had to live there, and there was no gain in lessening their own comfort by destroying their billets or antagonizing the owners too much.

Every time their horses' hooves clattered loudly on a stretch of rocky road, Elizabeth could see the horrifying effect on the near-by villagers. The very sound drew people to their windows in an agony of terror lest it be another English patrol. Most of the houses had their downstairs shutters closed, as if that pitiful effort at defense would deter a marauding Lobster-back. Barn doors were wide ajar, a silent token that they were empty and not worth the raiding. Springhouse and smokehouse doors were left open for the same reason, and if a farmer had any cattle left, they were hidden in the near-by woods.

"This is not war as you read of it in the papers, is it, lass?" Jonathan waited till they had passed a small log farmhouse where an underfed woman, clutching a baby in her arms, was peering from behind a flimsy window curtain. "We don't know whether her fear is of Redcoats, and Tories—or whether she trembles at the sight of Patriots. Everybody has a fear, including the neutral-minded who take no side in the struggle, and express no opinion either whichway on this matter of Liberty or Death. The neutral-inclined are suspect and hated by both sides. Vengeful Tories report them to the English as Rebels, and the Rebels treat them as Tories if they won't take the Association Oath."

"It's horrible." Elizabeth shuddered.

"It's war, mistress, and when the English flee Philadelphia—God help any Tories they leave behind, for I do believe the Patriots will burn their houses over their heads or tear them to bits in the streets."

Elizabeth, turning in her saddle, looked at him in disbelief. "Won't —won't the Army try to keep order?"

"Should it?" Jonathan asked flatly. "Do you know any Tory you'd like me to defend? Nay, lass, we'll be too taken up with the English Army when it leaves Philadelphia to spend time defending Tories from Patriots."

In silence they rode along the edge of a sloping field that had lain fallow since the year before. The stubble and broken cornstalks, tramped into the earth by horses' hooves, told the story without the additional proof of tumbled and smashed corncribs outside the barn door. The corn had been too green for picking when the British had ridden through Valley Forge four months before the Rebels had made the Forge their winter quarters. And so the English cavalry had trampled the stalks flat with the ground.

Reaching the top of the incline, a horse's length ahead of Elizabeth, Jonathan reined in his mount and pointed. "That—is the Valley Forge encampment."

Elizabeth, looking directly into the morning sun, swept the bed of the Valley from its nearest western end to the mud-banked earthworks of Fort Moore at the far tip of the crescent hills.

" 'Tis not what I expected to see." Elizabeth dropped her hand to her saddle and watched the sun-splashed Schuylkill tumbling past the outermost trenches. "I'd not thought much of anything about the camp, but I had no inkling of a log town built around a grass square—and every hut like its neighbor."

"They're not all alike," Jonathan said as he spurred his horse forward. "The hospital huts are bigger—and more crowded than the usual order of twelve men to a hut."

"They don't look of a size that would house twelve men."

Jonathan nodded grimly as he looked at her. "There are nigh to a thousand of them—each fourteen by sixteen feet. Each hut supplies two men for picket duty. Then there's one to stand guard at the hut, one to tend the fire—there are six shelves to sleep on—the other two sleep on the tamped earth."

"And the green square in the center?" Leaning forward in her saddle, she pointed to the irregular stretch of grass lying between the hills and the company streets that fronted the rows of huts.

"That was where we cut the trees to build the huts," he explained. "Now it is the parade ground and General von Steuben's drill yard. But there'll be no parades or drill today—this is market day."

"Market day?" She twisted in the saddle to see if he were japing her.

" 'Tis the God's truth, mistress. Come the next bend in the road you'll see for yourself."

"But why a market day—in a soldiers' camp?"

"Why market day around the State House in Philadelphia—with all the fine shops and market stalls?"

"Well," she answered slowly, "we get our fresh fruit and greens at lower cost—and goods we're not like to find in the other shops."

Jonathan weighed his words before he spoke again. "We of the Army, mistress, have the same need of food."

"But the Army—"

He stopped her short. "Mistress, iffen I'd waited on Army food, Army clothes and Army money—I'd be dead o' starvation, naked as I was born, and without the cash to bury me."

"But the Congress—"

"Mistress," his voice was harsh as a whiplash, "the Congress passes resolutions, sets aside days for public worship—and demands the recall of officers who fail to win battles because they have neither arms nor ammunition—the word 'Congress,' mistress, in Valley Forge is on a level with a foul oath."

Feeling that he had said too much, and said it too strongly, Jonathan urged his mount ahead as though to end the matter. It was difficult for him to accept the idea that the civil populace in Philadelphia regarded the Redcoats in their midst as they would a swarm of visitors at a May Day fair, and that even the Patriots held daily converse with the enemy—and blamed the Rebel Army for the English presence more than they blamed the English. It angered him, too, to learn that they held Washington in no great regard, and sat back, enduring the discomforts of travel on passes and weakly enforced curfew, while trading with the enemy and waiting for Washington to deliver them.

Of course, he had to admit, his own harsh appraisal was weighted with the contempt every Rebel soldier had for those who were willing to compromise on anything connected with the English. He saw how matters in the city could hardly be different. With more than a third of the merchants in Philadelphia Quaker, a third Tory, and the Patriots enlisted in the Rebel Army, affairs were likely to take that shape. Certainly the womenfolk couldn't upbraid the Redcoats, especially if they had any satisfactory form of figure and any features short of ugly. The heat around his neck began to cool as more sober thoughts paraded through his mind. All Quakers didn't welcome the English: for there was Mistress Darragh who had spied on André, and there were others whose identities were known only to Washington and the staff. Then, too, there was no real way to know a Patriot in an occupied city, for the successful spy or informant had to hide his true inclinations if he hoped to continue with his task.

"What's that?"

He swung around at Elizabeth's cry and saw her looking toward the river. "As I told you, mistress, market day. These be the sutlers and hucksters on their way to set up the booths and stalls in the camp."

He watched the splotches of color move slowly over the bridge. Red and white covers on the sutlers' carts alternated with the blinding yellow of the hucksters', and dotted in and about, the multicolored bonnets of the tradesmen's wives bobbed up and down as they stepped along the split slab flooring.

Most of the tradesmen, their wives and their carts were over the bridge, and the men whipped up the horses in a mad scramble to secure the best trading places. Stalls were thrown up and goods displayed with astonishing speed—and within minutes the tin horns of the hucksters were competing with the banging and clanging of the sutlers' bells and drums.

As the ragged Rebels poured from the huts, their pinched faces and too-bright eyes telling the story of starvation and camp fever, Jonathan watched the effect on Elizabeth. He saw her face drain of color and the little white lines deepen at the side of her nose. She swallowed air and her quickened breathing set her breasts to heaving under her loose-fitting travelling dress.

"Not a pretty sight, is it, mistress?" He swept his arm outward. "With these skeletons, sound in heart, but lacking in flesh, we are supposed to free Philadelphia."

"I had no notion—" She dabbed at her eyes with the back of her hand. "We folks in Philadelphia heard tell—but not of this—"

" 'Tis scarce a condition we'd boast of or make known to the enemy," he admitted. "And for that reason you're blameless for not knowing. But we know, Mistress Elizabeth, and it irks us somewhat to read the *Sentinel* and the *Gazette* and the other papers with their outpourings. 'This war will not be won till we shoot a few Generals.' Who would they shoot?"—he turned and asked the question savagely. "Washington?"

The only answer he got for the moment was the crunching of her horse's hooves on the loose shale of the Yellow Springs Road. When she spoke, her voice was tired and mildly defensive.

"We have our problems, too, Captain. Not so serious, perhaps, and we are not starving. I'll remind you that my father would starve in the Walnut Street Prison, did I not take him food. And that I have two brothers, both prisoners, who may even now, for all that I know, be hanging from the yardarms of their own ships." A touch of defiance crept into her voice as she threw her head back and looked at him. "Had you two sisters and a mother in like fix—mayhap you'd be civil to English officers yourself."

" 'Tis a possibility, but an unlikely one. I'm not of a nature to hold my tongue, or be civil to my enemies. This venture we are undertaking will force me to keep my mouth shut, 'tis true, but I'm much afeared, mistress, any kin of mine would suffer, if their deliverance depended on my politeness to English officers."

"An easy speech to make, Captain, since your kin are far removed from milords Howe, Grant and Grey—not to mention the Warden of Walnut Street—Captain Cunningham."

"Your father's warden?"

Her nod was slow and suggestive. "Captain Cunningham is an ill-natured, detestable Irishman whose chief delight would seem to consist of kicking over a pail of soup or scattering a basket of bread under the noses of hungry prisoners."

"I've heard tell of some of the doings at Walnut Street. Captain Cunningham had best see to it that he's not the last man to leave Philadelphia when the English leave."

"You think they'll leave?" Elizabeth asked wistfully.

"They'll leave."

She saw his mind working in the changing color of his half-lidded eyes. When he'd determined how much he'd say, he reached out and placed his hand on her arm.

" 'Tis common knowledge that the French sent a fleet out to aid us at the time they took recognition of our independence. How long Admiral Richard Howe can allow for their arrival I know not. But 'tis obvious the Admiral cannot leave his vessels in the confines of the Delaware for long. When he moves, he leaves his brother Sir William in one devil of a mess—sitting in Philadelphia with the Delaware at his back and us at his front. 'Tis a situation Washington is not like to ignore."

"Then it's going to be soon?" Her face brightened.

"Soon and on the sudden. If the folks of Philadelphia have aught left that they value, they'd best batten it down tight or the camp harpies will carry everything they can lay hand to, when the order to move is given."

"Where will they move to?"

Jonathan grinned, looked at her and laughed, "Did I know the answer to that I'd write Congress myself and ask for the Chief's office." He stopped short and pointed. "There is General Stirling's headquarters, and Lord Stirling himself at the upstairs window. Ask your question of him, lass, and see if he has the right answer."

Wheeling their horses off the road, Jonathan led the way up the path at the side of the house to the shade of a big oak that spread its branches over the shed sheltering the back door and the cellar entry. Dismounting, he helped Elizabeth from her saddle, and slung the saddlebags over his left arm. Saying nothing but a subdued "Thank you, Captain," she plodded ahead of him through the kitchen garden, overrun by the weeds crawling down from the South slope of Mount Misery.

The kitchen door opened and Stirling stood there, hands outstretched. "Welcome, Elizabeth! Welcome to Valley Forge!" The General took her hands and drew her into the house. "I looked for you last night."

"Redcoat patrols, sir," Jonathan answered as he dropped the saddlebags in the corner of the back hall. "They blocked every road, and we waited till daybreak—at the Red Lion."

"Calvit took care of you?"

"He did indeed, sir," Jonathan answered emphatically as he followed Elizabeth and the General into the dining room.

"I'd have taken you both to the Bull Tavern for a nobler meal." Stirling drew a chair for Elizabeth and shrugged his shoulder at the table. "But we have to keep your visit here a secret from the camp. We'll hold a council after dark down at the Ironmaster's. 'Twas for that reason I waited you here. As you can see, my quarters have the advantage of being hidden from the encampment. Fall to, Jonathan, I've had my meal."

Unappetizing as cold pork was at mid-morning, both were hungry after their hours in the saddle. Stirling seated himself on the small bench at the side of the fireplace and waited till Elizabeth had eaten a few mouthfuls.

" 'Twas August last, I supped with your father, Elizabeth. I had little thought, then, that matters would change so. How does he bear up in Walnut Street?"

"He grows thin, General. He shares what he can with others in the prison."

[58]

Stirling sighed. "Had I but guessed the turn that affairs were to take —I'd have suggested that your father flee Philadelphia—"

"You'd not have succeeded, General."

Stirling rose to his feet, crossed to the table, and pressing his fingertips on the table top, he leaned forward and spoke softly.

"You are willing to risk yourself, Elizabeth, to help us?"

"I'll do anything I can to help."

"Good!—Good! I knew I'd not misplaced my belief." Quickly he pulled the bench toward the table, sat down and nervously clasped and unclasped his hands. "I'll not tell you in detail our stratagem at the moment—I'll give you that at the council tonight. But, in brief, Elizabeth, since you are—in a manner of speaking—free to move about Philadelphia, I want you to pay especial notice to certain movements Jonathan might not be in a position to watch. Discuss them together, and write them down in a cipher report to me."

Too anxious and taut over the scheme to remain seated, Stirling heaved himself from the bench and strode up and down the length of the room. "Our difficulties multiply more quickly than we can cope with. The Commissioners from England have done us more damage than we thought they would. Information comes to us too slowly, and when it does it is mostly bad. The truth is, from Boston to Philadelphia to Charleston, the Commissioners' promise from the English Parliament has caused some of the most Patriot-minded to feel that the Congress should accept the terms. And the devil of it is—" he stopped his pacing and leaned over the table—"we have some difficulty in making a plausible answer."

"They don't offer us freedom," Jonathan remarked.

"No, they don't. But they offer everything else. From every corner of the Colonies we get the same reasoning. What are we fighting for? Relaxing of port restrictions—representation in Parliament—repeal of the stamp tax. The Commissioners say the English Parliament agrees to give us these."

"Everything but freedom from the English King," Jonathan said contemptuously.

"Yes, Jonathan, but you see we lose the support of those who were angered at port restrictions. We lose the help of those who revolted because of the stamp tax. We are left with but one arrow in the quiver as it were—Liberty—where before we had a dozen."

"And Captain Kimball's journeying with me to Philadelphia will gain you information to counter that?" Elizabeth's voice showed her surprise.

"What we will accomplish by Jonathan's being in the city, I do not know," Stirling said frankly. "Between you, you may learn nothing, and consequently we will learn nothing. But the garnering of intelligence is like buying tickets in a lottery. If you buy one, you may win. If you buy them all—you will win. We are gambling that we will win something by placing the Captain in your home. Who can tell what it may be? It might be a fast ship arriving with news of the whereabouts of the French Fleet. Suppose it were forty-eight, or twenty-four hours' notice that the English were readying a full-scale attack on us here—or anywhere."

Stirling paused, put his foot on the bench, and looked into Elizabeth's face. "I tell you something, lass. General Wayne's lads were cut to ribbons at Paoli because one of our sentries took a pouchful of King's coin, not to give the alarm. We lost a battle—Brandywine—because of the treachery of Major Speare who reported to General Washington that there were no English on the road, when the truth was Howe was but a mile away. Who knows what you may find when you seek for it; an English officer who can be bought—a negligent or drunken officer in charge of the guard on the floating bridge near the mouth of the Schuylkill—or a whole regiment of discontented Hessians waiting to desert an important post?"

"I—I hadn't thought there were so many things that we—Captain Kimball could find out." Elizabeth pushed her plate from her, and looked wonderingly from the General to the Captain.

"You'll learn more at tonight's council." Stirling laughed at her kindly. "I hadn't intended to talk of it now. I do have a surprise for you."

"You do?"

Stirling leaned forward and gently pinched her cheek. "When you go upstairs to bathe and rest a mite, you'll find an old friend who has bathed you more than once."

"I know—I know." She clapped her hands. "Lady Sarah?"

"That's right, Elizabeth." He held her hand as she turned to go. "Just one thing more, lass. I'd not say this in front of the others at the council, so I'll say it now. You have a strong will, Elizabeth, and a mind of your own, but in this business we are embarked on, defer to Jonathan. You'll find that he values your life—and mine—more than he does his own."

5   QUICKSANDS

Our doubts are traitors.——Shakespeare

Completely exhausted, and racked with doubts and fears, Elizabeth twisted and turned on the high box bed in the upper chamber of Stirling's headquarters. For hours, ever since she'd waked from a frightening nightmare, she'd watched the slow, steady march of shadows across the white wall toward the door facing the bed. When the thick shadow cast by the bedpost reached the door, she would have to get up and dress herself for the evening council at the Ironmaster's.

But she was determined not to go to that council. Not for Lord Stirling or anyone else, was she going to jeopardize her family. She was going to dress and march downstairs and tell the General that she had been wrong in agreeing to his scheme. No matter how many whys Lord Stirling threw at her, she had an answer for all of them. Her first mistake was made when she hadn't followed her intuition and rejected the idea at the very beginning. If only she'd sent the polite little note she wrote immediately the General's letter had arrived at her uncle's.

Her reasons, then, had been good and sound. They were just as forceful now. Her mother's illness, the frequency with which the English officers called at her home, made the plan unworkable and dangerous. She clenched her hands into fists and beat the feather bed that plumped up on either side of her. The word "dangerous" was what had led her finally into this quagmire. Stupid, silly pride that wouldn't let her admit to Stirling that she was afraid to help because of the danger.

Throughout the afternoon, Lady Sarah had opened the bedchamber door and looked in to see if she were still sleeping. In these brief moments, Stirling's voice would drift upstairs, and she would hear a word or a sentence that told how much he was depending on the plan. She hated herself for deceiving Lady Sarah, but pretending sleep was the only way she could be left alone to think her way out of the mess she had made of things.

Without meaning to, she shook her head from side to side on the rumpled pillow. What was the General going to say when she announced that she was not going on with the stratagem? More than likely he would say nothing. He would nod his head slowly, turn his face away to hide his disappointment, and set about the task of devising some other scheme. But Lady Sarah wouldn't be able to hide her feelings. Good, kind, lovable Lady Sarah who had been like a fairy godmother to her when she'd visited the Stirlings at Baskingridge. She wondered if Lady Sarah would ever again invite her to the Jersey home to meet nice young gentlemen of marriageable age, or painstakingly try to show her how to hold an embroidery needle—so that she didn't look as though she were punching holes in sailcloth with a marline-spike.

All one night, down at her uncle's, she'd gone through the same self-torture as she was doing now; driving her mind in circles. She'd make her decision, then the same doubts and naggings would attack her from all sides. One thought, more persistent than all the others, would surge uppermost and bring her right back to the beginning of all her uncertainties. She shouldn't be arguing with herself about what Lord Stirling would say. She would make her decision on what her father, her mother, and her brothers would say were they in a position to give an answer. Frustration made her rigid, for there was no doubt as to what they would say. But that didn't make it any easier for her. She wasn't ill. She wasn't in prison, nor was she captive aboard ship as her brothers were. She could run and hide if things went awry—they couldn't. They were the hostages who would have to pay the penalty.

Vague, indefinable sounds from the encampment filtered through the louvered shutters. The clanging from the forge, the intermittent clomp-clomp of horses' hooves, and the threatening challenge of sentries, had all added to the terror of her nightmare. Tired from lack of sleep, she had plunged into a torpor that ended only when she had fought her way out of the dream and back to a shivering wakefulness. Tense, her hands clenched, her neck and hair bathed in the cold sweat of fear, she couldn't believe at first that it was only a dream. Her throat ached with pain and dryness from her fruitless efforts to cry out, and her knees trembled from the timeless running that had neither lessened the distance between her and her pursuers, nor brought her objective one half-step closer. All through the horrible dream she had heard her father's voice calling. In front of her, fixed in its distance, and hopelessly out of reach, was the Walnut Street Prison. Pursuing her, always gaining but never catching her, was a pack of Redcoats whose shouted threats were quite silent. She knew them all, from the gross Cunningham who led them, to a stranger Redcoat whom they called Captain Kimball. And all the time the drums were beating, the hammers were pounding on the gallows, and swinging from the end of an invisible rope was the shrieking form of her father.

She tried to sit up, but overcome by an uncontrollable flood of tears she threw herself about and buried her face in the pillow. Her mother, ill and in bed, had been unable to visit the Walnut Street Prison, and for weeks Elizabeth had kept the truth about her father's condition from her mother. After each visit to the prison, she'd walked the squares of Philadelphia trying to compose herself so that her mother wouldn't suspect. Even from herself, she'd tried to hide what was obvious, that a few more weeks in the Walnut Street hellhole would kill her father. Every night, before she fell asleep, the last thing she saw was the vacant look in her father's eyes, the wan slackness of his once-firm lips, and the palsied shaking of the hands that had been so steady and capable only five months before.

As far back as she could remember she'd taken great pride in her father's strength. At school she'd held the other girls spellbound, and gloried in telling them tales of her father's prowess at sea. In those days she'd been too young to distinguish seamanship from strength, and her father's battles with a wheel that had broken free of its lashings, or a sail that had become fouled in the shrouds by a gale, were triumphs of her father's strength over the ferocity of the ocean. When most of the girls she knew were playing house with rag dolls, she was learning to walk a tilted deck without sliding into the scuppers, or standing on her toes looking into the binnacle, and counting the number of turns it took on the wheel to move the compass card five degrees.

Her first memory was of the sea. Deep and green and frothy-white it had been as she looked down on it from the safety of her father's arms. He had carried her to the topmost crosstree so that she could watch a school of dolphins playing about the ship. With her eyes shut tight she could see everything as clearly as she had then; the black, gleaming bodies disappearing under the port bow and reappearing on the starboard as they leaped out of the sea, with the water rippling from their backs. And she could picture her mother, too, standing by the forward hatch, shading her eyes as she looked up, laughing and waving to her.

A sudden increase in the chatter downstairs caused her to raise her head and listen. It was Lady Sarah, telling the General's orderly what she wanted from the larder, as she spread the table for supper. Turning her head, Elizabeth looked at the window and saw it was almost dark. She pulled herself wearily from under the coverlet, and crossing to the wash-stand poured some water into the china bowl. Splashing her face, she wondered if she'd feel differently if Lord Stirling had chosen some officer other than this Captain Kimball for the task. There was no changing of her mind on that score. This Virginia Captain irked her. She had a feeling of being thwarted every time she made a suggestion. It was a sensation she didn't like, and she had no intention of allowing herself to be forced into a position where she had to endure it.

She rubbed her face with the towel, and her lips curled disdainfully as she compared Kimball with the English officers she saw daily. Maybe they were enemies, and maybe they did strut, and maybe some of them were cruel; but they were soldiers. They were the soldiers the Rebels had to outwit and defeat, and they weren't going to be outwitted by the likes of this timid, indecisive Kimball. In spite of herself she contrasted the Rebel Captain with the quiet but authoritative Major Broadmoor. Her ears reddened, and she tried to halt the guilty flush that suffused her neck and shoulders. She was behaving like a fool. She wasn't in love with Broadmoor—even if she knew he was in love with her.

Lifting her petticoats from the back of a chair, she thrust her arms through the billows of white and shrugged them over her shoulders. She tied the tapes quickly and struggled through the dark tunnel of her full-skirted travelling dress. Already the light from the campfires was pinking the window glass behind the shutters, and the voices of ten thousand Rebel soldiers gathering for their evening meal sounded to Elizabeth like the warning mutterings of a distant storm.

Standing on tiptoe, she looked down through the slots in the shutters. It was darkening rapidly, and the stream of indefinite figures passing the glow that bloomed from the forge gave her an eerie feeling of watching a scene from another world. Two officers on horseback, riding abreast, passed through the smoky-orange light, and their shadows climbed high, distorted and grotesque on the flat rock-face rising a hundred feet above the natural spring that bubbled and frothed its way to the Valley Creek. At the north end of the covered bridge leading to the headquarters, she could see two sentries passing and repassing each other, their legs making a wickerwork pattern as they crossed in front of the flickering lanthorn standing on the ground a few feet away from the bridge flooring.

Leaving the window, she reached in her saddlebags for her hair brush. Well did she remember the night of panic and downright terror when the word was received in Philadelphia that the Rebel Army had fled to the Valley Forge. No one that she knew could even tell where the place was, but everyone agreed that it was too far away to afford any protection to the city. The streets about the State House Yard were filled with Tories, openly jubilant that Washington was decisively beaten, and that Sir William Howe and the English would march in to find a ready welcome. Contrariwise, the Patriots were gloomy and angry, blaming the Congress, and Washington, and calling the Rebel Army names even her father said he'd never heard before.

That night was the first time she had ever seen her mother cry. Her father, too, had needed all his control to keep the tears from doing more than moisten his eyes. None of them went to bed, but, instead, they roamed the house, meeting together first in one room then in another, separating and rejoining, rejecting plans as fast as they made them. They needed no one to tell them what English occupation would be like. They'd seen it on their many journeys to Boston, but it was something the Philadelphians would have to taste for themselves before they'd believe how bitter tasting it could be.

Reluctantly she put her brush back in the saddlebags. She could postpone the ordeal of going downstairs no longer. If it were possible, she would do anything to avoid causing Lord Stirling pain or adding one extra worry to his load. It had been difficult to hide the shock she felt when she saw him, aged twenty years in a few months, and she'd hardly recognized Lady Sarah, who looked tired and wan and worried.

Almost hating herself, Elizabeth crossed the room, opened the door and stepped out to the small landing that was no more than a wide top step to the stairs. Her hand was on the rail when she heard Lady Sarah mention her name.

"Elizabeth is not fitted for the task, William. She's not been raised to be deceitful, or to say anything other than what is in her mind. And at supper, do use one of the straight-back chairs. Remember Doctor Shippen said it was better for you to sit straight."

"Yes, dear."

Elizabeth almost smiled at the meekness of the General's voice.

"Are you suggesting, m'love, that Jonathan—or perhaps I—was raised in deceit?"

"She's a young girl. You're both grown men. I have no fault to find with your choice of Jonathan. He's careful, shrewd, and possessed of a cool temper. I think he could cozen his way out of any dilemma. But I do think, William dear, that you placed too heavy a responsibility on Elizabeth— making her decide something as important as this—when she's almost alone in the house."

For a moment the only sound from the dining room was the soft thudding of the pewter platters as Lady Sarah placed them on the table. Elizabeth lifted her foot to go downstairs, but the General's voice stopped her.

"Elizabeth did not make the decision, Sarah my dear. Jonathan made that. I told the lad to decide for himself whether or not Elizabeth would be able to play her part. I was quite certain of her answer before I wrote her, but that was not enough. Jonathan was the one who had to be satisfied, for his is the responsibility."

"Why were you so certain that she'd agree, William? There are many Patriots who are brave enough, but who would refuse if their father and brothers were held hostage."

"Sarah, lass, it is because of her family that Elizabeth felt duty bound to agree. When the war is over, what think you would be Elizabeth's position, were her father and mother and brothers to learn that she had refused to help in working for their freedom?"

"But one false move, William," Lady Sarah's voice rose a little, "and Enoch Ladd would be hanged."

"Yes, m'dear. That is a fate that faces any of us—hanging or shooting or a bayonet—if we make a false move. But I think that Elizabeth realizes something else. If we do not get information that makes it possible for us to undertake the attempt on Philadelphia—Enoch Ladd will be dead from his imprisonment. And hanging or ill-treatment, a bullet or a cannon ball— dead is dead, Sarah."

Elizabeth waited to hear no more. Turning on the landing, she went back into the bedchamber and closed the door as quietly as she had opened it. Holding the latch in her hand, she pressed her forehead against the doorjamb. In all the turmoil of arguing with herself, she'd given no thought to what her father or mother or brothers would say if they knew that she'd refused to aid Lord Stirling. Deep inside, although she'd thrust the thought away half formed, she knew that the General spoke the truth when he said her father would die of imprisonment.

She squeezed her eyes tight and drew a deep breath. Intuition, premonition, whatever name it went by, again warned her that she was making a mistake, but what she'd overheard left her no freedom of choice. There was nothing for her to do but put on a brave front to hide her fears—and go on with the stratagem as though she'd never had a qualm.

6   THE CAST OF THE DIE

Ludwick—my honest friend.——GEORGE WASHINGTON

The Ironmaster's two-and-a-half-storied mansion stood at the intersection of the Gulph and Valley Roads, its western gable facing the Valley Creek. With the destruction of the forge, Ironmaster Dewees had left the huge house to the use of the Rebels, while he went about the task of converting one of the smaller iron mills to the output of small shot for the Continental Army. The rear of the mansion overlooked Washington's headquarters, and the lookouts posted at the dormer windows could see far and wide, from Sullivan's bridge guards across the Schuylkill, to the earthwork lunettes and redans that dominated the low-lying approaches to the encampment. Down in the cellar, the bake ovens were hot from day's end to day's end, as Christopher Ludwick, the Baker General, stood guard over the precious flour and even more precious salt that went into the Rebel Army's main food supply.

The hot enveloping moistness from a hundred loaves, fresh out of the brick ovens, drenched Jonathan when he opened the door to the cellar and waved a greeting to the Baker General. Many a time in the bitter cold of the winter, Jonathan had worked all night in the cellar, mixing and kneading and shaping the lumps of dough that were placed on the long-handled paddles, then shot into the inky blackness of the brick-arched ovens. "Honest" Ludwick could never remember Jonathan's name, nor could the baker forego the retelling of his tale—and the hearty laughter with which he told it—of the members of Congress who signed his commission with the demand that he produce one hundred pounds of loaf for each one hundred pounds of flour.

"Mein Gott!" he would laugh, punching Jonathan in the chest with a floury hand, "ditt they think I leaf mein fine bakehouse in the Letitia Court of Philadelphia to thief from them! I giff a hundred and thirty pounds of loaf for a hundred pounds of flour. They forget, these men, that water—salt—milk—butter—yeast, haff to go into the dough."

The weight of a hand on his shoulder drew Jonathan back from the cellar entry. Turning, he saw Mad Anthony. "Come, lad," the General whispered, and strode down the main hall. Closing the cellar door behind him, Jonathan followed the General to the back parlor.

The Ironmaster's Mansion had seen many strange meetings in the course of the encampment, but this council was likely to be the strangest for some time to come. The effect was anything but military, Jonathan thought, and would give much aid and comfort to the enemy were they to see or hear of it. That Stirling was holding such a meeting at all was the best proof of the desperate plight the Rebels faced. They knew nothing of what was happening in Philadelphia, other than the well-known truth that the English outnumbered them, outgunned them, and occupied the stronger defensive position.

One quick glance about this room was enough to justify the label of ragtag and bobtail, that the English gave the Continental Army. At the far end of the narrow room a stern-faced man, who looked ten years older than his thirty years, betrayed his impatience by continuously snapping his fingers. He was Captain Allan McLane of the Delaware Light Horse, and one of the Rebels' finest cavalrymen. His men boasted that in a sabre charge, the Captain's blade was too quick to be seen; but you could hear it whistle. McLane's uniform was made from pieces of table and bed linen gathered from his family's linen press on his last, quick trip home. Standing talking to the Delaware Captain was his Indian Chief of Guides, a copper-colored skeleton whose Oneida name had been changed to Call Me Chief, and whose uniform was a breechclout topped off with a pale green waistcoat that hung in tatters.

Bending forward from the waist, listening intently to the half-English, half-Indian conversation, La Fayette looked anything but a dashing marquis. Dressed in a uniform much too large for his frail body, La Fayette was all head and hands and feet. He had never recovered from the blood letting he suffered after Brandywine, and to Jonathan's eye, the young Frenchman was like a frail parchment-colored boy with feverish, glittering eyes sunk deep in a thin pinched face.

Incongruous in her well-fitted clothes, Elizabeth sat between the fire and the table lamp. The sweeping curve of her body, from shoulder to ankle, was sharp and soft by turns as the fire rose and fell. She looked so certain-sure of herself, while Jonathan, dressed in ill-fitting clothes like some country loon, felt tense and far from being at his ease. He would have liked, for even a few minutes, to have appeared before her in uniform, but that would have advertised his presence back in camp, and, anyway, she had been closeted with Lady Sarah all afternoon, as he had been with the General.

The small back door at the end of the room opened and shut quietly. Stirling, followed by Von Steuben, crossed quickly to where Mad Anthony stood studying a field map in his dispatch book. The Baron looked as if he had just shaved, as most likely he had. Shaving was a disciplinary ritual with the Drillmaster, and night or day his heavy square face was smooth as an apple. Jonathan had shivered, in the dead of winter, watching the Baron at his morning ritual. It had been Jonathan's week of orderly duty, and he had reported to the Baron's quarters at four in the morning. The Baron, dressed in breeches, plunged his face into a basin of icy water then scraped his face with a razor that sounded as if it were chipping icicles. He followed this with a mug of the blackest of coffee, and shaved himself again after a second plunge into the almost freezing water. Between splutterings and tortured gasps, he lectured Jonathan on the value of discipline, and at five of the clock, the Baron started on his tour of inspection as Inspector General.

Stirling and the Baron were of similar build, tall and heavy, contrasting with the wiry Mad Anthony. Stirling's uniform, like Washington's, was strictly military, snug and high-collared, with stiff white breeches and polished, black jack boots. Wayne was a farmer, and nothing would change him; not even his uniform, for he wore it loose and open, ready to be taken off the moment the war ended.

Turning from Wayne and Von Steuben for a moment, Stirling caught Jonathan's eye, and Jonathan drawing himself up quickly, saluted.

Stirling waved back, grinning. "A habit you'll have to rid yourself of for a few weeks, Captain."

"I'll try, sir."

Von Steuben turned and glared at him fiercely. "Better than try you should do, mein Captain. Ach! Do not scowl so." He stepped forward and shook Jonathan by the shoulder. "You are a brave man, and such a good soldier yet, you cannot break your good habits—ja?"

Stirling signed to Jonathan to join him at the table. When the room was still, the General placed his right hand on Elizabeth's shoulder, and his left on Jonathan's arm. "I have no need to tell you of what these young people are undertaking, but I want the sworn word of each of you that you will not disclose it to a living soul."

There was a murmured chorus of assent, and Stirling sat down. "I have, but a moment ago, told General Washington of what we purpose. As is his custom in matters of this nature, he does not desire to know the names of all the parties involved—but I had to obtain his permission for you, Captain, to remain out of uniform. He bade me tell you, sir, that you have his good wishes and admiration."

"Thank you, General," Jonathan said, and meant it fully.

"And of you, mistress—" Stirling inclined his head to Elizabeth—"General Washington took my word for your beauty and said your patriotism equalled it."

"I, too, thank you, General," she murmured, and leaned back in her chair.

"To the business at hand then." Stirling lowered his voice, and his sweeping arm invited everyone to listen closely.

"Mistress Ladd returns to Philadelphia and her pass through the English lines includes one man servant. Captain Kimball is to fill that role. The pass, I think, will not be questioned in the matter of getting into the city—but 'twill be known at once that Jonathan is not the same servant as the one she took with her. I suggested that you, mistress, get a letter from your uncle's medico, stating that your other servant was taken with the smallpox and you had need to fetch this Jonathan in his place."

"I have the letter, General."

"Good. Now to make certain that the English officers who visit Mistress Ladd's home will be overjoyed at her return, we have prepared a small wagon loaded with goods and stuffs she has brought back from Virginia for them." Stirling stopped, and searched his memory—"Tobacco, salt, a small cask of wine—ah yes—a delicacy they like, never having tasted it in England, Indian-dried deer meat—and other odds and pieces." He turned to Elizabeth, "You distribute your gifts in whatever manner you think will bring you the greatest benefit."

Elizabeth raised her hand, gesturing that she understood, and Jonathan nodded to Stirling, indicating that he would help.

"One think you make—what you say?—certainement of," Von Steuben interjected. "Do not giff these gifts till the English officers make the call at your house."

"Mistress Ladd's home," Stirling spoke to the group, "is located right in the midst of the houses commandeered by the English officers for their quarters—near Franklin Court and the Carpenters' Hall, fronting on Chestnut."

"In my daily marketing I pass Howe's and Grey's quarters." Elizabeth emphasized: "And I can watch the goings on at the Indian Queen Tavern from my bedchamber window." Pausing, she thought for a moment. "By varying my marketing, I could watch Cornwallis' too."

Shooting his arm out, the palm of his hand held as if he would crush the suggestion, Von Steuben thundered, "That iss what you must not do! Do nothing, nothing, nothing in any way differing from your usual habit." He dropped his arm and a twinkle came into his eyes as he tapped the side of his nose with his forefinger. "Such a change as you offer, Fräulein, is a—a—come, Jonathan, come, in English say it for me!"

"A certain way to arouse the English officers' suspicions," Jonathan supplied.

Von Steuben beamed. He strode forward, threw his arm around Jonathan's shoulders, and turned to Stirling. "Could I not have the Herr Captain when this little affair is finished? On the drill yard—he could swear for me in English when mein French und German are all failing for me."

When the laughter had died away, Stirling continued the Baron's warning. "Take no unnecessary risks—at any time. What would it profit us here at the Forge if you were to gain intelligence and be caught before you could communicate it to me?"

"How will we communicate with you, General?" Elizabeth asked. "All letters are taken to the British post—"

"We dispense with the usual post, Elizabeth," Stirling said, smiling. "We use our own—just as we use no words in our cipher—we use numbers." He reached over to the table and picked up a small dictionary. "Bailey's —not much of a dictionary—but compact and well suited to our use. 'Tis an innocent enough thing to be possessed of and will excite no suspicions if noticed by the officers who visit you. Jonathan will teach you the use of it when you have to send your first message."

Handing the dictionary to Elizabeth, Stirling took a small bottle from the table. "Even should your message fall into enemy hands 'twill do them little good, for you write the cipher in this colorless fluid instead of ink. We are beholden to John Jay for its invention. Unless the recipient of the letter has the proper fluid with which to reveal the writing—the paper remains blank."

"I understand that Captain Kimball will show me the use of the ink," Elizabeth broke in. "But how do we get the word to you?"

Stirling placed the bottle back on the table. "When you get home to Philadelphia, a tradesman will call on you. He will bring you a bottle of Jay's ink. He is the merchant who notified me that you were going to Virginia. Do as he says, and he will get your letters to me."

Von Steuben held up his hand. "In this matter of what to watch for and report upon—do not forget activities around the English ships. Water on board being carried—shortage of salt pork in the market it might be— night-working people at the ropewalks. Others you think of, Lord Stirling?"

"Yes, Baron." He turned to Elizabeth and Jonathan. "This you can watch for, from the uppermost windows of your house, no need to risk being seen—keep a constant eye upon the shipping in the river. As of now, the smaller vessels are downstream and the larger frigates—those mounting thirty or forty guns are anchored above Gloucester Point—"

[70]

"They were when I left Philadelphia," Elizabeth agreed.

"The English may change their positions—slowly and without fuss so as not to attract attention. But the moment you detect any movement of larger vessels downstream—"

"We'll notify you," Elizabeth spoke briskly. "'Twill be a token that they're readying for sea." She turned to Jonathan. "I know the signs. The smaller sails would get no wind were the frigates aft of them—not if they sailed in formation."

"Excellent, mistress." Stirling beamed on her. "Happen perhaps you'll make a sailor out of our Jonathan." He beckoned Captain McLane. "Tell us your part in the affair, Captain."

"Soon as this council be ended," McLane said, "I'll take me fifty of my guides, and push along Gulph Road to the narrow road that follows the Schuylkill on this bank. At Matson's Ford, using due caution, we cross the river and follow the road past the grist mill at the village of Spring Mill. We are to push on up the Barren Hill Road to the church and spy out the most favorable defensive position for a force of twenty-two hundred men, with the proper places all designated for outpost pickets."

"Correct but for a detail I have had to change—I will give you the change later." Stirling took Wayne's dispatch book and pointed to the field map. "The purpose of Captain McLane's effort is to prepare the way for General La Fayette and his men to occupy the Barren Hill area. 'Tis an area we know too little about, but it commands two of the five possible attack routes the English might use in leaving Philadelphia to fall upon us here—the Germantown Pike and the Ridge Road."

"The Ridge is the tricky one to watch, Marquis." Mad Anthony stepped into the light of the lamp. Towering above the pale Frenchman, he traced the Ridge Road with his fingernail. "This road emerges from the valley of the Wissahickon, and ten thousand men could be hidden from you till they burst into the open—right under your nose so to say."

"Is there any house, high on this Barren Hill the owner of which we may trust?" La Fayette, speaking slowly, searched out the English words he had learned, and rolled them out with relish and enthusiasm. "A place for a lookout?"

"The very best, Marquis." Wayne placed his finger on the crest of Barren Hill. "Here stands Saint Peter's Church—a full two stories high and with a square tower. The tower has two arched opening in each face and offers a view that reaches here to the camp itself." Pausing, he held up a warning finger. "But even from the tower, you'll see little to the east. The trees are so thick at the head end of the Wissahickon—'tis as I said, an army would be hidden till they appear suddenly on the road."

"There is a small churchyard, as I recall it?" Stirling asked.

Nodding, Wayne moved his finger to the west side of the church.

[71]

"There is, with a low stone fence—a good defensive position. And down at the foot of the hill on the same west side, where the Germantown Pike makes a somewhat sharp turn, is the Barren Hill Tavern. The host is Patriot, but he's in no position to give you any warning. He's too far down the hill. The English would be storming through his door afore he knew they were there."

Down in the cellar, the clanging of iron doors and the murmur of voices told that another batch of Ludwick's loaves was being drawn from the brick ovens. Captain McLane shuffled uneasily at the passage of time, and Stirling, sensing the unease, pulled his timepiece from his pocket and saw that it was nigh to nine of the clock. From the back of the Ironmaster's, a sentry's challenging "Stand! Who goes?" rang out. It was answered quickly by Knox's booming voice, and even Von Steuben shuddered and muttered, "Gott! The Herr General speaks louder than his own cannon."

Holding up his hand as a signal, Stirling waited for silence. "One more detail and I think we will be ready to move. Your arrangements, General La Fayette, we can examine later since you will not be moving to Barren Hill with your men till Sunday or Monday night—three days hence at the least."

"As you desire it, Lord Stirling." The Marquis smiled his boyish smile. "I am in attendance at this council to observe and to listen and to learn."

"Then to the final matter." Stirling slid Wayne's field map across the table and pointed to the converging roads at Barren Hill. "Captain McLane and his guides will take Mistress Elizabeth and Jonathan—no longer Captain Kimball, but Jonathan—with them, giving them safe conduct to the other side of Barren Hill. You, Captain McLane."

"Yes, sir."

"The change I spoke of a few minutes back. Do not cross the Schuylkill at Matson's Ford as you go down tonight. Keep on this side of the river all the way to a point opposite Spring Mill."

"I understand, sir." McLane inclined his head toward Elizabeth.

Stirling closed the dispatch book, and handed it back to Wayne. "Scan the crossroads well, and when you are satisfied that 'tis clear of English patrols, release Mistress Ladd and Jonathan to their own devices. Return to Matson's Ford and carry out your instructions as of before the change."

"Yes, General, I understand."

Stirling stretched out both arms and signed the group to gather about him. "This is a delicate matter. I intend it as a warning to Elizabeth and Jonathan. It is advice to all of you. The most ruthless English officer in Philadelphia is Major André. He is cruel, clever, and he holds an important post as Sir William Howe's Chief of Intelligence. André hates us with

[72]

an unbelievable, personal ferocity. He has hated us ever since we hurt his pride by making him prisoner." Stopping, and looking from face to face to add weight to his words, Stirling lowered his voice to a whisper. "During André's enforced stay with us, before his exchange, he made many friends by his gay, charming manner. Some of these friends have since deserted the Rebel cause, and it is my belief that André lured them away."

Wayne interrupted by smacking his palm on the table. "What General Stirling is suggesting—is true. We have officers in the Rebel Army whose disloyalty is no secret. We may have others whom we do not know, and who may be in secret correspondence with André."

"They are in secret correspondence with André," Stirling admitted. "That is why you, Elizabeth, and you, Jonathan, must not be lulled into placing too low a value on André because of his reputation as a fop and a rake. It is your wits against him and his spies. And it is your lives and our success that are the stakes."

"We'll be on our guard, sir," Jonathan said with more confidence than he felt.

"But not with such timidity that we learn nothing," Elizabeth cut in a little too suggestively.

Stirling waved a finger at her. "Timidity is a virtue in spying, lass. Be timid about what you undertake—but having undertaken it—be decisive in the carrying out of it."

He pushed himself up from the table and glanced at McLane to try and quiet the Delaware Captain's impatience. "I've not said much about the import we place on this venture. As matters stand with us, we are in an intolerable position—a stalemate. We do not wish merely to be successful in standing off an attack on us here. We cannot afford to lose the men and guns an attack on Philadelphia would entail—even were such an attack to succeed, which is doubtful. To do what we must do, we need advance intelligence of English plans. To satisfy, and answer, the rising clamor of the people, we need more than a victory of sorts—we must initiate the action."

Finished, Stirling led the way to the door, held his hand out to Elizabeth. "Thank you, mistress. Take care of Jonathan—he'll do the same for you. When Captain McLane leaves you, you'll be on a road you might well have chosen to return from the south—"

"I know the road." Elizabeth shook the General's hand. "I've travelled it afore."

"One thing, Jonathan."

"Yes, General?"

"Nothing—nothing at all is as important as giving us twelve hours' warning of anything the English are planning."

"I know, sir, I know."

"Then Godspeed to you both," Stirling said fervently as he opened the door and watched them file silently into the darkness.

7 DIAMOND CUT DIAMOND

Vain hopes, vain aims, inordinate desires.——MILTON

To say that Major André was furious was to give a new meaning to the word. André was enraged to a point of madness where he was unaware that his tunic collar was wrinkled. His pacing of the upper room in Mistress Darragh's was fast and slow by turns, and the clenching of his fists squeezed drops of moisture from between his trembling fingers. Each movement he made rustled the dispatch sticking from his tunic pocket; and each rustle goaded him to further inarticulate spluttering.

Impatiently—and senselessly, he admitted to himself—he crossed and recrossed the room to look through the slotted shutters of the balcony doors. Down below, Dock Street was empty, and he was waiting for General Grey, Colonel Monckton, Major Broadmoor and, ah, yes—that arbiter of the proper thing to do—Lieutenant Colonel Cosmo Gordon. Grey knew the horrifying news, and, therefore, had no need to hurry. But the others—he stretched his arms stiffly by his side and chewed his lower lip in sheer vexation.

"How dare His Majesty! How dare he!" Kicking at the heels of his own boots with every step, his anger against the King mounted. Mentally he cursed every stick of furniture in his "cell," as he called Lydia Darragh's front bedchamber. He had suffered capture and imprisonment in this wretched campaign against the Colonies. He had lived in quarters such as these, and some worse, he argued with himself. And now! Now when he was enjoying the confidence of Sir William Howe, acting as his Chief Intelligence Officer—and a colonelcy within his grasp—the King in one of his insane spells had ordered General Howe home.

He rubbed his dry lips with the back of his hand and tried to see some way of salvaging the patronage he enjoyed, and had to have if life was to be worth the living. To return to England with only a major's pay to sustain him was unthinkable. He had to have a colonel's rank, a regiment to command. He needed the money the sale of commissions to his regimental officers would bring, if he were to frequent the clubs and gambling houses he'd enjoyed only on a patron's card in the past.

"Something must be possible." He ran the words over and over in his

[74]

mind, and squeezed harder and harder on his hands as if to force a solution to his predicament. Catching sight of himself in the glass above the commode he stopped his pacing and regarded his features. He tried to smooth away the distortions with the flats of his fingers, and realized that this was no way to appear in front of the officers he had asked to come to his quarters. "Something must be done," he thought again, something that would be of such lasting benefit to General Howe that no matter the lapse of time, Sir William would be indebted to him, John André, forever.

Violently he pulled a dispatch case from the bed, spilling the papers over Mistress Darragh's well-scrubbed plank floor. The sight of them only added to his desperation. They were the secret papers Sir William was taking back to England with him, and Sir William had asked him—asked him, not ordered him—to look at them before they were sealed and taken aboard the *Andromeda*. These papers, the confidence Sir William had in him, marked the difference between his position now, and what it would be when General Clinton took command.

Sir Henry Clinton would take no pains to further the career of any officer. Clinton had no appreciation of a man's worth, nor the power to do anything about it if he had. André sat on the bed and stared at the shuttered balcony doors. If only he could return to England with Sir William his future would be assured. Sir William knew everybody, went everywhere, and it was no secret that the Howe family had greater wealth than the King, and wielded greater influence in the right places. In England, Sir William could obtain a full colonelcy for André or anyone else, and open the proper doors at the right time.

It was too late for that now, André realized. The very dispatches Sir William had sent to England praising his Chief of Intelligence removed any possibility of a transfer home. Whatever steps he was to take to assure Sir William's continued patronage must be taken now; and there was no time to lose. He had to devise something whereby Sir William would find himself indebted to him.

Bending down, he picked up a handful of the scattered papers and placed them beside him on the bed. One was a crude map of Washington's camp at Valley Forge; drawn by a Tory named Parker who had spent several days in the camp at the beginning of the year. He remembered seeing it before, and threw it aside. There were two or three cipher dispatches with their decoded messages attached. Notations in Sir William's hand showed they were from spies who had since been hanged. There was nothing here that gave him a glimmer of an idea as to what he could do to batten himself on Sir William's bounty.

Two or three squares of paper, stuck between a couple of dispatches, fluttered to the floor. They were filled with small firm writing by a hand he did not recognize. His first casual glance as he picked them up changed when he read the second line. Here was something that, surely, Sir William had not intended that even he should read. Here was a list of Rebel generals, with an assessment of their worth under each name. He scanned the paper quickly. The opinions were at variance with Sir William Howe's estimates of the officers, but the contemptuous undervaluations were vaguely familiar. He read them again. Washington: indecisive, and deficient in military knowledge. Sullivan: insolent, a poor lawyer, and a poorer general. Greene: a Quaker who suffers from gas in the belly. Stirling: a lordly dog doing his Master Washington's bidding. Wayne: not mad, not brave—stupid. André smiled. Now he remembered. These were the opinions of the Rebel general, Charles Lee.

Thoughtfully, he turned the next sheet of paper. Disbelief at what he read drove every other thought from his mind. Certainly Sir William had never spoken of this. It was a military plan, in detail, designed to cut the Colonies in two. The British Fleet would seal off the Bays Delaware and Chesapeake and establish a line of block forts extending west and separating the South Colonies from the North. At the same time, the Hudson Valley would be seized by British troops from Canada, and in a short time the Colonies, deprived of each other's assistance, would surrender.

Whose plans were these? André got down on his knees and gathered the papers together, hunting for the missing last square of paper which might contain more details; and what was more important, identification of the man whose plans they were. An illuminated banquet and ballroom programme caught his eye, and an idea began to form, diverting his mind. Sir William liked to dance, and he liked to gamble, and he liked blond-haired women—as witness Mistress Joshua Loring's name after almost every dance on the programme.

Kneeling where he was, André closed his eyes and allowed his imagination to run free. He would arrange a farewell party for Sir William. It would be the most stupendous farewell that ever was. He could see it, an all-day affair with the Fleet and Army taking part, and a banquet and a grand ball. A private chamber would be set aside for Sir William's gaming, and a golden-haired wench who'd not be afraid to gamble her honor against the General's gold could easily be found. Everything would be lavish, but the last word in good taste. It would all be to the honor of Lieutenant General Sir William Howe; something the General would always remember and in the remembering he'd not forget John André.

Opening his eyes, his mind returned to his search, he riffled through the sheaf of papers. Details of the farewell he would work out with Cosmo and the others when they arrived, now he'd like to find that missing square of paper. Only one piece remained on the floor. It was face down under the bed and all but hidden by the coverlet. He picked it up and turned it over. The hand was the same as on the other squares. His thoughts came to a sudden stop, and the shock of seeing the signature catapulted him to his feet. This—this was incredible. Small wonder Sir William had never mentioned it. Sir William must have forgotten the plan was among these papers. He carried the single square to the tallow dip to make certain his eyes weren't playing tricks. No. There was no doubt about it—the paper was signed by Charles Lee, General in the Rebel Army, and late prisoner of Sir William Howe.

The jangle and clatter of cavalry horses crossing onto Dock at the Two Street Bridge sent him flying to the window—Monckton and Broadmoor—with the rakish Cosmo bringing up the rear. As it always did, the necessity for action set his mind to functioning properly, and dashing back to the bed, he gathered the treacherous Lee's papers together and hid them under the bolster. Down in the street the ping of a scabbard point scraping the cobblestones told him that someone had dismounted.

Lifting a towel from the commode rail, he wiped his face, rubbed his fingers, and tossed the towel onto the small, black-painted settle in front of the balcony doors. Quick steps took him toward the upper hall, though he paused long enough to look in the glass. He liked this glass. It was the only thing in Mistress Darragh's house he did like. This glass rounded his thin face and shortened his long neck. It was on an angle, and made him look taller than his five feet seven inches. The front door banged, and he ran out and down the boxed-in stairs that led to the parlor. The rattle of chain spurs in the front entry warned him to compose himself. André bowed mockingly as the officers entered. "My apologies, gentlemen, for routing you out of your, or whoever's chambers you were in at this unwonted hour." He spread his arms as an invitation to the officers to seat themselves. "I have some distressing-bad news for you that can't keep till morning mess."

"I cannot endure bad news without liquid fortification." Gordon strolled to the side table, uncorked a decanter of brandy and poured himself a glass.

"Best swallow that one then and pour yourself another, Cosmo, for this is devastating." André waited for the dramatic length of suspensible time—

"Sir William has been sent down—called home—relieved of his command."

Cosmo Gordon choked on the brandy. Monckton and Broadmoor were obviously unbelieving. A tall figure appeared in the doorway and all jumped to attention and saluted.

"At ease, gentlemen." General Grey looked about. "I see John has loosed the thunderbolt."

"Who succeeds to the command, sir?" Monckton asked.

"You'll none of you like the answer." Grey lowered his voice. "Clinton."

"I'd hoped it would be Cornwallis."

"A vain hope, Monckton—" the General smiled faintly—"Cornwallis is too much like Sir William."

"Besides being a gentleman, Cornwallis has no more stomach for this miserable campaign than Sir William." Catching sight of his wrinkled collar, André smoothed it, then went on, "I think some reports have reached the Palace—through certain ladies—that we do more sporting than fighting here in Philadelphia." He flicked a speck from his white breeches. "Jealous women are the very devil—here or in London."

"You didn't ask us over here—at this ungodly hour—to tell us something we already know?"

"No, Cosmo." André fished the dispatch from his pocket. "I thought we ought to give Sir William a right royal farewell—and the time is short."

"The time is short for any entertainment of any sort." Grey seated himself on the corner of the table. "Our new commander frowns on social interference with garrison duty. Best you make all the hay you can while Sir William's sun still shines."

André saluted the General. "Sir, your thinking is so kin to mine that I am encouraged to make my proposal."

"Twaddle, John, you'd make your proposal no matter the odds."

"We are in agreement—" André shrugged—"we can scarce be otherwise, that we'll have no chance at the gaming tables once Sir Henry Clinton is in the saddle. What wenches we entertain, we'll entertain sub rosa—and the final tally will show that we have money in our pouches and naught to spend it on. My proposal, therefore, brothers in sorrow, is that we spare no shillings in giving Sir William such an embarkation that even Almack's couldn't match!" He stopped short, and a guileless smile spread over his face. "There! Unbidden, an idea from the brow of Jove himself. We take a leaf from Almack's, have the guests invited by a committee made up of Philadelphia's most charming ladies." His enthusiasm grew and he mocked a ballroom dancer in his capering about the room. "We'll have the Ladies Shippen, and Peggy Chew. And we must not forget Mistress Rodman or Captain Mathews' Mistress Bond, the Ladies Craig and White—"

"And what in hell do they issue invitations to?" Cosmo poured himself another brandy. "Do we take the flagship and sail them up the Thames, down Fleet Street and the Strand to St. James and unload them at Almack's Domino Room?"

André waved the Honorable Cosmo Gordon to silence with an imperious wave of his hand. "We'll out-Almack Almack's, as Johnson or

Fletcher or some playwriting fellow would say it. We'll have a King Arthur pageant affair, with a bit of Drake, so the sailors won't be nettled—you know, decorate the barges and the bomb ketches—give the ladies a water-parade first. Then on shore, perhaps down at Wharton's, hold an old-style jousting tourney—ladies' favors on our sleeves, emblematic pennants on our spears—blazoned shields—"

"And if we survive this—what of the midnight hours?"

"Dear Cosmo—" André looked at the Colonel in pity—"always worried about what to do nights. We'll have a grand ball, mask and costume, but we'll leave that a matter of choice. I'll design the committee costumes myself—Turkish I think, the two Peggys would be enchanting in Turkish array."

"And while we are so engaged," Colonel Monckton interposed, "the Rebels attack." He held his hand out, thumb down.

"Ah no, Colonel, we want no second Trent's Town." The humor was gone from André's face. " 'Tis here that General Grey is to use his persuasive powers—to suggest that General Grant and a strong party finish the afternoon festivities with a march past of two or three battalions—and leave for a sortie on some hamlet on the outskirts of their Valley Forge encampment. We'll publish it about so that word of the attack will reach Washington—he'll stay awake and make the Rebels stand to all night. We'll have no surprises from that quarter."

"The stratagem has merit—" there was admiration in Grey's voice—"and might be worth more than a mere sortie. We might get some horses and fodder—we've not been up Crooked Billet way since the first of the month. I'll talk with Sir William—'tis his farewell affair—he can talk with Grant."

"Whom do we ask to this mixture of lavishness?" Major Broadmoor tried to sound casual.

"We," André emphasized it, "do not ask anyone, therefore no one can feel insulted by us. We cannot invite all the Loyalists in Philadelphia, therefore we will not ask anyone. That will be the duty of our committee of hostesses—just as it is at Almack's. We will provide the entertainment, the food, the, ah—gentlemen. The ladies will invite the ladies, and we may be assured they will ask the desired ones."

"Here, Major." Cosmo pushed a full brandy glass across the table to André. "Drink to the child of your brain. 'Tis a better way to say farewell to Sir William than any I'd thought on." He raised his own glass. "To Sir William, one of England's gentlemen. And to the affair in his honor—what will you call this all-day mixture of festivities?—has to have a name, you know. Once this blighted war is over and we are back in dear old London—must have a name so we can talk about it at the club. Might even have a small club within a club—the Almack's of Almack's—"

"To avoid any more disturbin' tales reaching the ladies in London, I will design a programme—dignified and military-looking—with the tokens and salutations in Latin."

"Good!" Cosmo beamed. "I pray your Latin is better than mine—God knows what might come of my Latin if it reached the ladies in question—they'd be most like to meet us at the boat with broadswords in their hands or put poison in the wassail bowl."

"Might be that we give the whole affair a Latin name," André said thoughtfully, "one that is scarce heard at all. I have recollections of an affair held in northern Italy—a medley of divertisements—'Mischianza' 'twas called—"

"How do ye spell it?"

"Have no worry about the spelling, Nap—" Cosmo laughed—"just so we can pronounce it. Mischianza—" he mouthed it reflectively. "I like it. Sounds like the name of a good wine."

"You've not much time to make your preparations, John." General Grey rose and stretched his legs. "Sir William goes aboard the flagship any day after the twentieth. That, of course, is confidential till Sir Henry Clinton assumes official command."

"And leaves us but five days," André counted on his fingers. "We'll hold our farewell on Monday the eighteenth—we can make ready."

"Aught that I can do?" The decanter clinked against the glass as Cosmo poured himself a stirrup cup.

"Yes, by God, you can. Talk Wharton into the use of the place for the grand ball and dinner. It has the most spacious rooms of any house along the river."

"I shall call and pay my respects to Mr. Wharton." Loosening his sword belt and hitching the frog over his hip, the Honorable Cosmo Gordon looked in the mirror and cocked his bearskin hat at a more elegant angle. "I shall report progress tomorrow at the Indian Queen," he said, eyeing the group in the mirror, "and failing to find you there, I shall adjourn to the cockpit. Join me, Nap?"

Major Napier Broadmoor assented by slipping the chain of his Grenadier's helmet under his chin, and both saluted themselves from the room.

"I will see Sir William at breakfast." General No-Flint Grey turned toward the door. "I think it best, John, that we post some more cannon round and about—one pointing at the State House—another at Christ Church—"

"Perhaps one at the entry to Franklin Court," André suggested. "These natives hold Franklin's house in much regard."

"We'll make use of your Grenadiers, Monk." Grey waved to the door. "Come along and we'll give the bomb-throwers a chance to show themselves in some of the important places around town."

André watched as Colonel Monckton followed the General through the door. He felt a sense of superior satisfaction that his plan had ripened so quickly. Sir William would be flattered mightily. It had to be so. One day this war would end and John André could benefit far more by the patronage of the Howes than by the fickle smiles of an insane monarch. Now he could sleep, and in the morning—in the morning he would set about the tricky business of soliciting information from General Lee. André laughed quietly to himself as he turned back upstairs. Lee would be surprised. Lee might balk. But Lee would co-operate when threatened with the exposure of his plan to separate the Colonies.

8   DEFIANCE

*'Tis not Howe as captured Philadelphia, but Philadelphia as captured Howe.——*POPULAR SAYING, 1778

It was no mere idle boasting when the inhabitants of the largest city of the Colonies called Philadelphia "great." Long before the cupolas and spires of the State House and the numerous churches came into his view, Jonathan had marvelled at the docks and yards that stretched along the Delaware, above and below the place where he swung onto the road that ran along the river's bank. As he bumped up and down on the seat of the wagon Stirling had prepared for Elizabeth, he found his eyes darting from the forest of shipmasts to the sheds and storehouses and ship chandleries. In and about the wharves and slipways, an occasional Redcoat could be seen; mostly, Jonathan thought, checking goods ashore and assigning boxes and bundles to the wagons drawn up between the buildings. There were few of the townsfolk abroad so early.

Elizabeth nudged his arm, and then opened the small silk bag she carried suspended from her wrist by the drawstring. She pulled out her pass and held it in her hand as they rolled closer to the squat blockhouse that stood at the edge of the road.

"This one has a four-pound cannon as well as the usual two dozen Lobsterbacks." Jonathan grunted between closed lips. "How many more sentry posts do we pass—I've lost count of them?"

She whispered back without turning her head. "Unless they've changed things, this is the last one. We'll soon be in the city."

Pulling reins, Jonathan halted the wagon and sat staring about him as a humorless-looking Redcoat, with half his front teeth missing, came up to the horse's head. In all the British Army, no worse man could have been detailed for this task, Jonathan thought as he listened to "Path, mithtreth, pleathe," whistle through the gap in the sentry's teeth.

The lisping sentry took the pass and disappeared into the block-house. Mindful that someone inside the place might be watching, Jonathan showed all the interest that a gawky country lad might show on his first visit to Philadelphia. He looked behind him at the beautiful mansion houses all but hidden by trees, and he had no need to feign admiration for their velvet lawns that stretched like widespread green aprons almost to the water's edge.

The lisping sentry came back, followed by a quick-stepping Guards' captain who nodded briefly to Elizabeth and proceeded to look in the bed of the wagon.

"Your pass, Mistress Ladd, says nothing of a wagon—or provisions." He spoke behind her back, poking about in the bundles.

"The wagon is borrowed from my uncle in Virginia. I had to use it to carry these gifts. They are odds and ends that I thought Major Broadmoor and the mess might like as a change."

"I'll accept your word for it, mistress." The Guardsman stepped back and gave a perfunctory salute. "You may pass."

Jonathan shook the reins and the wagon rumbled forward. Elizabeth's voice had betrayed no hint of fear, but Jonathan felt her knee trembling as it pressed against his. He decided to say nothing, to give her a chance to get her nerves back on an even keel before he spoke to her again. She was hardly to be blamed, he thought, for the Guards' officer had shown suspicion in his attitude and tone of voice, if not in the words he used.

Looking around him again, Jonathan saw that they were in the city.

"We turn left at the next cross street." Elizabeth pointed to a cob-blestoned street curving to the left. "We follow the curve, along Dock Street and over the Two Street Bridge."

" 'Tis a right proud city—" Jonathan inclined his head—"bigger than I'd thought to find, even from what I'd heard tell." He dropped his voice. "But I had expected to see more English."

"We missed the big encampment because we came in by the Balti-more Pike. Had we come up from Port Chatham direct, on the River Road, we'd have passed Gloucester Point, and 'tis said the English have between twelve and fifteen thousand men in and around there, close by to where the Schuylkill runs into the Delaware."

"But right here, in the middle of the city—"

"There are enough. They're camped along the Callowhill with can-non every few rods. They say that two thousand are camped in the State House Yard, and most-like that is true, since the seven-foot brick wall around the yard makes a good defense."

The light wagon rattled its way over the corner at Dock and Spruce. The street was narrow and Jonathan was glad that the two drain gutters fitted the span of the wagon wheels, else the slightest turn, one way or the other, would have sent a wheel hub crashing through the little bow windows that bulged out from the houses, much in the manner of blisters on a cottage loaf of bread. On his left a house—different from any he had ever seen before—caused him to crane his neck. The gable faced Two Street, and it was more decorated than most houses were on the faces that fronted the street. A richly carved coping, so deep it was more like a valance, covered the join between the walls and the steeply pitched roof. At the second story a broad balcony stretched the full width of the gabled wall and two full-sized doors, with a window between, opened onto the balcony. On the ground floor two huge windows with leaded lights, flanking the main door, gave the house more of the look of a shop than a dwelling.

"What is it?" Jonathan asked, sensing that Elizabeth had seen him looking at it.

"Loxley's house," she hissed, "and don't stare at it. 'Tis the home of Mistress Lydia Darragh! Major André has his quarters there. You'll see soldiers enough heading this way when the Major holds his daily questioning of the poor wretches caught during the night by the Provost Marshal's guard."

"What hour of day is that?" Jonathan fixed his eyes dead ahead.

"Any hour that doesn't interfere with André's pleasures." She held her arm low, and pointed ahead. "We turn left at the big house—the one with the slate roof."

" 'Tis a big place." Jonathan eyed the massive front, broad wings, and chimneys. "Builded more like barracks than a house. With bars over the windows, 'twould make a good prison."

"The English have prisons enough. That was William Penn's city mansion. We used it as the town hall till the Fathers put up a combination court house and market at Two Street and High."

"So that is the house we watch for the comings and goings of Sir William Howe." He pulled the wagon around the wooden stanchion that served as a hub fender on the sharp turn from Dock Street onto Third.

"Sir William has his headquarters at Richard Penn's house, not Billy Penn's," Elizabeth said under her breath when Jonathan had cleared the narrow corner. "That we can only watch from my bedchamber."

There was a sudden rattle of drums and the shrill piping of fifes. Jonathan swore and pulled the horse up quickly as a regiment of British Foot, their Colonel at their head, marched along Chestnut. The white skins of the side drums shivered under the perfect rhythm of the sticks, and the polished-brass drum barrels swung on the drummers' legs in time with the faultless "quick march" step. The red and blue uniforms were spotless, and the pipe-clayed cross belts and pouches were as white as the commanding Colonel's French chalked gauntlets.

Sitting hunched forward on the wagon seat, Jonathan knew that Elizabeth was comparing, as he was, this display of British military might with the ragged, unarmed mob the Rebels called an army. The shouldered muskets, black and gleaming clean, were tipped by glittering bayonets that made a continuous line of shimmering light as they flashed past the sunlit corner of Third and Chestnut. Exactly twelve paces to the rear, a drummer lad led the Colonel's horse, fresh curried and well fed, with the Colonel's gold-hilted sword and scabbard clanking against the empty saddle and burnished steel stirrup.

Elizabeth waited till the last marching footfall had died away before she turned to Jonathan and asked dryly, "Convinced there are soldiers in Philadelphia?"

"God A'mighty yes!" Jonathan lifted the reins and guided the wagon onto Chestnut.

"That's the house." Elizabeth indicated a red brick house with a double mansard roof of tiles broken by four dormers on the street side. A weather vane in the shape of a four-masted schooner rose from the wrought-iron railing that guarded the flat top of the oblong roof. Admiring the polished glass lights in their leaded frames, Jonathan reined the horse to the left and followed the carriageway to the combined stable and carriage house at the back of the plat.

"Best we begin our play-acting," Jonathan whispered. "Go to the house without speaking to me. I'll stable the beast and wait you in the kitchen quarters."

Elizabeth climbed down from the wagon and Jonathan walked to the stable doors. Swinging open the split door he saw with the tail of his eye Elizabeth run along the bricked path and disappear through the side door. Only one horse was stabled in the four stalls, so Jonathan quickly unhitched the horse from the wagon, and lowering the shafts to the ground, led the beast into the nearest stall. A shake of the crib above the manger dropped ample green feed into the trough and while the horse snorted and pulled at the fodder, Jonathan slipped the halter rope through the hitch ring and made it fast to a cleat at the back of the manger. The wood-stave bucket was full of water, and satisfying himself that the oat bag hanging from the stall side was well filled, Jonathan closed the door.

Although he'd known from her bearing and the clothes she wore that Elizabeth was wealthy, he'd not expected to see such a house as this. The back windows, which he took to be kitchen windows, were levelled and leaded just as were those in the front. The red brick walls were laid in

English bond and the white lines of mortar were as straight as taut strings. The back door opened at a touch on hinges that were noiseless, and he stepped into a kitchen that was bright with polished copper and pewter. Pots and pans and skillets of every size and shape hung by their handles from the mantel or sat on trivets on the wide hearth. The heavy oak kitchen dresser was weighted down with lustre-banded ironstone, and blue plates that Jonathan knew did not come from England or the Colonies.

Jonathan turned as an inner door opened and Elizabeth entered.

"Maggie—our combined housekeeper and cook since the English came—has gone marketing, Mother says." She stopped and her brows furrowed. "I don't see how we can keep up this deception without Mother being given some sensible knowledge of it." She gestured upstairs. "Mother is over her vapors—brought on mostly I think by Father's being in prison—she's talking of coming downstairs for a spell each day. We've got to speak together—work together—we can't stop her from thinking, and she's most like to think the worst if she catches us in odd corners deep in converse. And talk—Mother would talk if the house were being blown apart by English cannon."

Jonathan turned the thing over in his mind. To his way of thinking, a secret shared ceased to be a secret. And yet he had to admit the truth of what Elizabeth said. He did have to work and talk with Elizabeth, and that was going to be a mite difficult with Mistress Ladd herself out of bed and around her own house.

"If you're not of a mind to do it, I'll say naught and let her think what she will, even if she thinks I've lost my wits and more to boot."

"I've no more liking for that notion than you have," Jonathan said soberly. "Should she harbor such an idea—she'd be right quick to order me from the house."

"What would you expect her to think? Where do we write our messages—in my bedchamber or yours? Mayhap we can sit at Father's table in his room of an evening and 'twill seem plain ordinary. 'Tis something neither you nor Lord Stirling added up in your reckoning," she finished a trifle sarcastically.

"In that you are right—for 'twas our belief that your mother was too unwell to be about. I'll remind you, mistress, that you had your chance to speak on that—in our council at the Forge."

"I didn't know then—"

"And neither did the General! Debating in circles about who forgot what, brings no answers." He grinned at her. " 'Twould seem I'll get my ears boxed, and you'll get your bottom warmed for dallying with the bound servant—lessen we speak with your mother—so let's at it."

Elizabeth led the way into a main hallway where two wide staircases with mahogany balustrades, wide as ship's rails, went up the side walls to the upper floor. Niches, alcoves and shelves were filled with small replicas of every build of ship afloat, Jonathan noted as he trod the heavy-piled red runner that ran the length of the hall and climbed the stairs. On the stair turn a brass eagle with wings outspread hovered on the newel post, its gimlet eyes of ruby stones staring fixedly at a slender clock case showing two polished-brass weights hanging behind the glass door.

Light, broken into jets of color, shot through the stained-glass skylight set in the long oblong top of the mansard roof. In the center, a square pane of sea-green glass had wrought-iron numerals arranged around three sides. A long pointed shadow thrown by the slanted rod of a gnomon on the outside of the glass pointed to the Roman VIII as the clock chimed the hour in the manner of a ship's bell.

" 'Tis the only glass sundial I've ever seen." Jonathan looked up admiringly.

"And the most accurate—when Father is here to move the gnomon about—according to the season. Father set about making it the day I was born, and 'tis not adjusted to his liking yet."

On the plain plastered wall behind the balcony that led to the bed-chambers, Jonathan saw a series of well-executed portraits. Elizabeth, catching his eye, moved to the end of the balcony and slowly pulled a tasselled cord. Shutters on a louvered window in the opposite wall, directed the light at the portraits, and she pointed.

"Grandfather, Father, Mother, my brothers and Elizabeth in her first low-necked dress. They were done by Master Peale," she added.

"I know Master Peale's hand." Jonathan surveyed the oils. "General Washington and Stirling and others have sat for him at Valley Forge this past winter."

Elizabeth crossed the balcony and opened a heavy oak door. "You have company, Mother, from Virginia."

Looking past Elizabeth standing inside the doorway, Jonathan saw the foot of a four-poster with deep ruffles of blue and white around the stretcher. Beyond was a large gilt mirror above a brass-bound sea chest of silken smooth walnut. He could have sworn that the face in the mirror, framed by lace-edged pillows piled and propped at the head of the bed, was staring straight at him. Mistress Sally Ladd wasn't, of course. He knew that, so he enjoyed the undetected scrutiny he could give her, and took his time entering the room.

"Jonathan Kimball, Mother, of Kimball, Virginia."

It seemed to Jonathan that Elizabeth, despite her prideful declarations about what she would or would not do that night on the tavern road, was somewhat afraid of her mother.

Sally Ladd looked at Jonathan, then at her daughter. "He cannot be as bad as you make him sound, Elizabeth."

"Truth is—" Elizabeth started.

"Truth is—" Jonathan echoed.

Sally Ladd waved them both to silence. "Your introduction, daughter, savors more of a judge sentencing an abandoned criminal to transportation for life. This Jonathan Kimball of Kimball, Virginia, is either a gentleman masquerading as a cutpurse—or a cutpurse with most gentle airs—"

"Madame." Jonathan bowed, kissed the veined hand that rested on the white dotted-blue coverlet.

"Proof of nothing, young man. You're clumsy at it, which the young men of Virginia are not—"

"Mother, please. Jonathan is our new servant. He worked for Uncle—"

"That he did not!" Mistress Ladd sat bolt upright. The pillows collapsed all around her. The lace capelet about her shoulders slid off, and Jonathan could see whence Elizabeth inherited her white skin and flowing curves.

"The young man has neither cracked finger-tips, as he would did he work on the salt farm, nor 'baccy stains under the fingernails—and he's too skinny for one of your uncle's bound men. Your uncle always fed his men and his animals too much for their own good health."

"Madame—" Jonathan stepped close to the bed, picked up the capelet and placed it about Sally Ladd's shoulders. "I am in truth from Kimball, Virginia, but I am a captain in the Continental Army. Your Elizabeth and I have a chore to do for Lord Stirling—'tis for that reason I masquerade as your servant."

Jonathan watched Mistress Sally close her eyes, and sink back on the disordered pillows. Where he'd expected to see the lines deepen in her face, they smoothed out, and the tightness about her lips slowly changed to a ghost of a smile.

"Dear Will," she said softly, "one of our dearest friends. You know, it makes no difference how often I see him, I always think of him as I first knew him—handsome and kind, one of the kindest boys who ever lived." Opening her eyes, she laughed aloud. "When I was a lass of ten years, I was so much in love with him I vowed every night before I fell asleep that I would wed with him." A long sigh escaped her lips. "But he was twenty-three, and a colonel in the Militia, and as brave a looking officer as ever you saw—"

"Who was?" demanded Elizabeth.

"Will—William Alexander—Lord Stirling, of course." Sally Ladd raised herself on one elbow. "Never once did he say he was too old for me. Nor did he suggest that I was a foolish little girl. He treated me like a young lady and always bowed more deeply to me than to any of the grand young ladies who fluttered about him."

Jonathan burst out laughing. "Nobody loves the General any more than I do, but to be truthful I can't imagine him ever being twenty-three—"

"He cut a better figure of a man than you do, Captain. He was over six foot and his uniform fitted like a French glove." Placing her hands behind her, Mistress Sally pushed herself up in the bed. "But why do we chatter of thirty years past—tell me, how do I give aid in this scheme of Will's, whatever it be?"

"By accepting me as a servant—"

"Tush, lad." Mistress Ladd drew her knees up under the covers and clasped her hands around her legs. "I remember when Elizabeth's uncle took you under indenture. A gangling boy you were then, like a colt with wobbly legs—leastwise, so we'll tell any who ask. But you'll have to tell Maggie the truth when she returns with her basketful of wilted greens and the leavings of the market. She's too inquisitive not to find out."

"What about this talk of yours—of getting out of bed?" Elizabeth walked to the window and pulled aside the thick blue drapes.

Sally Ladd lowered her chin to her knees, and chuckled in the bed-clothes. "I could have risen any time I'd a mind to. 'Twas my belief that if I suffered from vapors no medico could cure, the English would be afeared to quarter their officers here."

"And you didn't tell me—you let me think—" Elizabeth stamped her foot.

"Aye, Beth, that I did—and see that you don't undo the good work now. You've been a dutiful daughter, showing the proper concern for an ailing mother. Your visiting English officers are all of the opinion that I'm at death's door; see to it by your anxiety that they still believe so."

"The best way I know to keep up the pretense is for you to stay abed, madame." Jonathan took hold of the bedpost and leaned down. "Any change that comes coincident with my lodging here may make the English suspicious."

"Baron von Steuben said the same thing, Mother. He told me not to make the slightest change from my marketing habits."

" 'Tis easy for you two who are up and about to prate of not making changes." Mistress Sally turned to one side and thumped the feather-filled mattress. "I'll lose the use of my legs if I lie here much longer. God knows 'tis a relief to know we have a Rebel man about us again—and that this house can serve some useful purpose—"

"Now, Mother, you know I have had to do—what I've done—"

"I know it, Elizabeth, but knowing it does not make me like it one whit better. Leastwise, in this new venture, you take some affirmative part, in the stead of being a sweet morsel for these English jackanapes to ogle of an afternoon."

"How much can a body see from the window?" Leaving the bed, Jonathan walked around the foot of it and, hiding behind the drape, looked out.

"That's the Indian Queen Tavern on the next square." Elizabeth inclined her head slightly to the north. "Most of the high-ranking British eat there—and gamble—and drink."

"Which is Howe's quarters?"

"You can make it out, and no more. 'Tis the second house on the second square up from the Indian Queen." Jonathan had walked back to the center of the room when the sharp rattle of tight-braced drums—a sound that caused Philadelphians to stop whatever they were doing and run to a window—rose from the street. Jonathan followed Elizabeth, and peered around the edge of the drapes. A company of Grenadiers, formed in a hollow square, marched along the High Street. In between their ranks, a lone figure, arms tied tight behind his back, stumbled in an unbalanced gait over the rough cobblestones.

"On his way to Howe's headquarters!" Elizabeth spoke to her mother as much as to Jonathan.

"Sir William bothers himself with prisoners?" Jonathan raised his eyebrows. " 'Tis not what I'd been told."

"Prisoners, no matter what the charge, are fortunate when they have Sir William or the Earl Cornwallis, for their judge. They may go to prison, but—" Elizabeth shuddered—"they're likely to get the noose from Tarleton or André."

Hidden by the drapes, Jonathan watched the double file of Grenadiers stop opposite Howe's quarters. The prisoner marched forward, disappeared and the roll of drums stopped.

"A warning to us to be careful." He turned back to face Elizabeth and her mother. " 'Tis not our necks we have to worry about alone, for we might be able to escape—but we have your husband, madame, and your sons to think on." Turning directly to Elizabeth he asked, "What of your father—who takes food to him when you are gone?"

"Last week and yesterday, Maggie stopped at the prison after her marketing." Deep lines crossed Mistress Ladd's forehead, and she leaned against the head of the bed. "One visit a week is all the bountiful Cunningham permits."

"When do you report your return to the city?" Jonathan turned to Elizabeth.

"She has no need to report," Mistress Sally answered him. "Major, the Honorable Napier Broadmoor—familiarly known as Nap to his gambling intimates—calls here almost every day, either alone or with his cronies, to inquire if the beautiful Mistress Elizabeth has yet returned."

Jonathan watched the burning red mount Elizabeth's neck and climb her cheeks at the goading sarcasm in her mother's voice. Elizabeth moved her lips, then biting the lower between her teeth, she stood silent.

"The wind blows that way?"

"It does, sir." Sally Ladd pounded the pillow at her right. "Were I up and about I'd order the perfumed puppy from the house."

"I can't do that." Elizabeth turned pleadingly to Jonathan, "Major Broadmoor has much influence with Colonel Monckton and the Colonel has a like influence with Cunningham."

"For which your father would care not a jot, lass. When he gets out of Walnut Street—" Mistress Ladd wagged a finger warningly—"he's like to forget your age and take a leather door hinge to your bottom when he hears you've been primping and scraping and curtseying to an English grenadier."

" 'Tis a delicate matter, madame, where much can be gained by some primping and curtseying, and everything can be lost by a too stiff back. Irksome it may be, and that I grant you—" Jonathan sat on the edge of the bed speaking softly—"and more irksome 'twill become as we engage in this business we are embarked on. If I'm to get the answers I want I'll have to do a might of bowing and bootlicking, and be all for the King when the English are around."

"It may be so—"

"Just as you, madame, have warded the English off with feigned vapors, Elizabeth and I have to do the like in what manner we can."

"It may be as you say, Captain, but I lie here abed, listening to the simpering of these scarlet-clad simpletons till I'm like to burst my spleen."

"Yes, madame. But these same simpletons have kept us sewed up in the Valley Forge for five months."

"Not the Macaroni Club wasp-waists who shake their hips around her." Mistress Ladd poofed and snapped her fingers. "They couldn't fight their way through the haze from a bumper of brandy."

" 'Tis far from my mind to debate the matter with you—and God knows I have no love for the English—but I do say, madame, that these wasp-waists can ride a good horse, shoot a straight shot, and are not to be taken lightly with either a sword or a bayonet in their hands."

"Jonathan was wounded at Chadds Ford on the Brandywine," Elizabeth spoke up, "and some of these baby-faced English, as Mother calls them, have fought in Canada afore coming here—"

"So some of them can fight," Mistress Sally interrupted, "but am I to lie abed for the rest of my life—with your father in prison, and my two sons slaves aboard their own ships—because some of them—some of them can fight?" She sat bolt upright, her eyes blazing. "In God's name, what are Mister George and Will Alexander and Mad Anthony doing out there on the Schuylkill? They should be here—throwing shot down the streets of the city. Are there no farmers in Pennsylvania—as there were at Lexington?"

"Madame!" Jonathan held out his hand defensively. "You read somewhat like the front page of the *Pennsylvania Journal*. Till this month past, we have had neither arms nor flint nor ball with which to fight anybody. Nor have we had food enough to feed every man every day. You ask: What make we out on the Schuylkill? As to that, I refer you to Philadelphia's Supreme Executive Council which told us that were we to move more than twenty mile from the city—they'd remove their aid, their finances, and their men from General Washington's command—although," he shrugged his shoulders, "what aid they've given or withheld, you'd be in a better position to know than I am."

The crash of a slammed door downstairs brought the battle to a close. There was a second thump and the sound of something rolling across a planked floor.

"Maggie—she dropped a turnip." Reaching above her head, Mistress Sally pulled a braided cord and the faint tinkle of a bell came from below. Before the bell had stopped its ringing, Maggie's footsteps clumped across the floor and fell to silence as she stepped onto the red runner.

"She'll have word of something." Sally Ladd moved her head in the direction of the bedchamber door. "It will be powerful dire, but don't believe it, Jonathan. Maggie's had General George killed, taken prisoner and dead of the fevers ten times a'ready—and Philadelphia's been fired by the Tories every time a chimney smokes."

Maggie bustled into the room. Her face, flushed from climbing the stairs, was freckled as the day she had left her Scots seaport town of Leith more than fifty years before. She opened her mouth, snapped it tight when she saw Jonathan and folded her hands under her apron as if to hide their slightest movement from this ill-kempt stranger.

"How is Father?" Elizabeth asked eagerly.

"Who is yon?" Maggie jerked her bonnet at Jonathan.

"Jonathan Kimball," her mistress answered. "He is really a captain in the Rebel Army, but we are pretending he is one of the servants from the plantation. You understand?"

"Aye, I understand. But where's Brodie?" Every "r" rolled like the turnip she had dropped downstairs.

"Brodie is supposed to have been taken with the smallpox."

Maggie shook her head at Elizabeth's answer. "There's no a body who knows Brodie will believe that. Brodie is a muckle too mean to get any kind of pox. Leastwise I'd always a-thoughten so."

"Now tell me—" Elizabeth left the window—"how is Father?"

"I didna see him, Mistress Beth." Maggie choked.

"Didn't see him—" There was sudden fear in Elizabeth's voice. "Why, Maggie, why?"

Jonathan looked at Mistress Sally Ladd, white-faced, trembling, all her bravado gone. Suddenly he saw a side of life in the occupied city he'd never thought of. This silence had revealed a desperation that was different from anything he had ever known. It was as though pretending that everything was all right would make it so. Mistress Sally, forcing herself to be sharp tongued and pert and a little cynical, was trying to hide the hurt and fear that was deep inside her.

"Why, Maggie?" Elizabeth's voice was sharp in tone and pitch, near to cracking.

Jonathan placed his arm about Mistress Ladd's shoulder. "What is it, madame?"

"We—Maggie and I—weren't going to tell Elizabeth—"

"I couldnae lie, Mistress Sally," Maggie said defensively. "I've not seen your father since you left, Elizabeth. They took the food, but they'd no let me in. Yon English will no let any but kin in to see the prisoners."

Elizabeth looked from one to the other in angry bewilderment. Her eyes grew big and round and bright with combined anger and terror. "Then —then for aught you know—Father is dead?"

"No, lass." Maggie shook her head vigorously. "He's no dead. I speered that from Mistress Darragh last week, and I saw Mistress Priest yesterday. They let her inside tae see her man, and I speered from her when she came out. Your father's alive—but he's sick—verra sick."

Elizabeth ran to the door, and Jonathan sprang from the side of the bed.

"Where are you going, lass?" Jonathan asked as he reached her side, and gripped her arm.

"And where would you think I'm going?" She wrenched her arm free and faced him. "I'm going to the prison. I'm going to see my father if I have to bribe every sentry on duty."

"But, Mistress Beth, today's no a visitin' day—" Maggie stopped, wringing her hands in despair.

"Wait, lass, and listen to me." Jonathan tried to calm her by keeping his voice low and level. "You gain nothing by going to the prison. Could you take a medico with you it might be different, but you'll not better your father's plight by going there. You may wreck all our plans, and find yourself in the prison with your father if you try bribing sentries—"

"Plans!" she snapped at him, stamping her foot. "That's all you care about. You have no understanding of people's feelings. What care I for plans with my father ill and dying in that pesthouse!" Her finger shook with unreasoning rage as she pointed it within an inch of his face. "If a spineless Congress hadn't abandoned us—and you and your ten thousand Rebels hadn't turned tail at Germantown—my father wouldn't be in prison. I'm going to see him. And not you, nor Lord Stirling—not even General Washington himself could stop me."

9   HIATUS

To-morrow to fresh woods, and pastures new.——MILTON

Rodman Alley, running at right angles to the Delaware and ending in a long irregular yard, was surrounded by all the activities for building and furnishing ships, and was a bedlam of every known sound. Where the alley continued out into the water as Rodman Wharf, a ropewalk joined the shipyard with Dock Street. Narrow lanes, blind alleys and even narrower courts made the place a human rabbit run.

In the days before the occupation, the yard had been the haunt of cutpurses and footpads, and if ever a rogue reached the alley or the ropewalk, the night watch gave up the chase and reckoned there was no profit in a cudgeling that brought him neither pence nor prisoner. If the yard and its network of crooked and sharp-angled streets had been a thorn in the side of the City Fathers in the days of peace it was more than that now in the occupying British, for in the windowless shed that housed the ropewalk wheel more than half the accidents that befell the British fleet had their beginning.

Aaron Cults, shipmaster without a ship, sat on an upturned pitch keg, shredding and teasing at bits of frayed rope, and stuffing the fluffy fibres into a wide-mouthed net bag that hung on a cobwebbed stanchion on his right. When the bag was filled it would be carted off to be used as caulking to close the seams of one of the new hulls down on the slipway —and he would get one shilling for his broken fingernails and blistered fingers.

Although he himself sat in darkness, he could watch everything that went on through the opening where the ropemaker spun the big wheel that twisted fibres into strands, strands into cords and lines and ropes. And while his fingers worked quickly on his chore of rope teasing, his mind worked more quickly on schemes that gave His Majesty's officers worrisome days and sleepless nights. At the moment, he was wondering who could be placed aboard Admiral Lord Richard Howe's flagship *Andromeda* for just one hour, and how it could be accomplished. An ordinary deck hand wouldn't do, for it had to be somebody who would be allowed below decks, someone who could enter the afterhold without arousing suspicion.

Behind his impassive face, Aaron Cults gloated over the latest tool of destruction his lads had fabricated. It was nothing but a short, thin, broad chisel as sharp as a razor, but it was the correct size to slip in between the joints in the wooden drum underneath the *Andromeda*'s wheel. There it would remain hidden by the turns of the rope that ran from the wheel to the drum and on to the tiller. Once at sea, with the quartermaster turning the wheel to keep the *Andromeda* on her course, the sharp edge would gradually cut into the steering-gear rope, and it was to be hoped that when the rope parted, leaving the flagship rudderless, it would be at a crucial moment of high seas or heavy winds.

It must be nigh to eight bells, Aaron thought, rising to his feet and stretching his angular six feet and a bit to rid himself of the cramps in his legs. His net of caulking stuff was full. He should take it down to the slipway. Yes, he should take it down there, but he wouldn't—not till Parson Poole and Peter Febe and John Norris reported on the morning's doings. Some of the others might come too, instead of waiting till night, for there was a deal of activity aboard the British ships, and it wasn't all because of the farewell sea-parade nonsense for Howe that everybody was talking about.

A bomb ketch throwing a load of fused shells into the middle of the city couldn't have made as much of an explosion as Howe's reported return to England was causing. Boiling, spluttering mad the Tories were, and threatening dire vengeance on His Majesty if this recall of Howe foretokened the removal of the English troops from Philadelphia. All last night rumors had flown from one end of the town to the other like bats on a summer's evening. A deputation of the most loyal Tories had chased Sir William from tavern to tavern till they found him at the Three Tuns, a mile out Old York Road, and so much in his cups that most likely he'd told them the truth when he said he had no notion of what His Majesty intended.

The deputation had lost no time in wording a strong letter to the King warning him that after giving him their loyalty in the matter of the Revolt, they weren't in the frame of mind to be left to the mercy of the Rebels without the protection of the troops they'd fed and housed and paid taxes on for half a year. Aaron knew the letter had gone, for Ebenezer Kittle was master of the sloop the deputation had commissioned to make the fast run to London, and Ebenezer, though counted a Tory, was a Patriot. He had lifted the fancy red seals and shown Aaron the letter.

Aaron kicked the pitch keg out of the way when he saw the ropemaker wave an arm to let him know that somebody was coming to the shed. In a moment, Parson Poole followed by John Norris slid round the edge of the shed opening and came toward him.

"Town's bubbling like a kettle o' hot pitch," was Poole's greeting.

"Them Tories is so thumping mad they've not got enough sense to be real scared," Norris added.

"Got ye a lad who's going aboard the *Andromeda* tomorrow, Aaron." Poole lifted the corner of his mouth and closed one eye in the same movement. He'd been half strangled in a mutiny and couldn't wink without working his lip upward.

"Who?" Aaron asked eagerly.

"Peter Febe hisself."

"How's he getting aboard?" Aaron was surprised.

"Going aboard as an apprentice to Toombs, the ship's carpenter. They're putting a partition in the afterhold so Sir William's gear can be locked up."

Aaron reached above his head and lifted a pair of rope-soled shoes from the rafter. "The blade is inside the sole of the right foot. Tell Peter he'll have to slit the sole to get it out."

"Right smart ye are, Aaron—right smart." Poole took the shoes and looked at them closely. "They'd never guess—never."

"Rufus Ladd is coming ashore," Norris said quietly. "I saw him and his English guard putting off in the long boat. Peter Febe is watching to see where they go."

"His sister Elizabeth is home from Virginia, too," Poole said sourly. He looked up at the tall Aaron and shrugged his shoulders. "I know you don't read the same storm signals in that quarter that I do, but I tell you I don't like it. A Patriot lass don't have to put up with them backside-swinging cronies of André's lessen she wants to." He held up his hand as Aaron opened his mouth. "I know—I know—you're going to say she does it for her pa and her brothers. Well now, I'll ask you, what's it got her pa? Nothing, I tell you, nothing—and by God, iffen Rufus finds out he's like to keelhaul her."

"She's trying to keep her father's shipping business afloat till he gets out of prison. I told you that afore, Parson—a dozen times if I told you once."

"And her pa and brothers would rather sink their ships than give the English the barnacles offen the keel, and you know it, Aaron."

"I don't know it, Parson. You and me will have to disagree on it. If Rufus Ladd, or his younger brother Matthew, wanted to sink their ships instead of sailing them thither and yon at the orders of the English, they could do it—and you know it."

"And I know we gain nothing by this talking yes and no." Norris tried to laugh the two men out of their argument. "I'd thoughten that the duty of keeping a weather eye on Shipmaster Ladd's youngest was Dan Jarrett's concern—"

"It is," Parson Poole snapped. "'Twas him as told me this morning that she'd come back—bringing a different servant from that old fool Brodie she took to Virginia with her. A long-legged, hook-nosed buzzard according to how Jarrett described him. Spite all you say, Aaron, I don't like it and I'm all for keeping a slight closer eye on her—and him—than we did afore."

Aaron reached out and put an arm about Parson Poole's shoulders. He hugged the little man to him as he spoke softly, "Parson, there just isn't a more Rebel-hearted man than you about these parts."

"Glad you think so, Aaron."

"And aboard His Majesty's ships, when you get a job on one of them, you're all for the King—and the English officers stand around laughing at your description of the ragged Rebel rascals you saw three month back at the Valley Forge."

"That's true—"

"And André was like to split his skintight breeches down on the wharf one day when you mimicked Mifflin in his cloak made out of an old rose-colored blanket?"

"Yes?"

"And yet, Parson, you're Rebel. Think about it, lad. Wait till you hear Jarrett's report on Mistress Elizabeth's new servant. And instead of boiling over when you hear of her playing coy with English officers—remember your own antics when the English are near by."

"You're right. I'm wrong," Parson Poole assented and shook Aaron's blistered hand. "I stowed cargo on the troop ship *Effie* last night. I'm thinking that she'll heel to starboard first time they have to tack. Second tack, the cargo will shift I'm afeard, and the troops will have to come topside and stay there till she makes port—unless they've a mind to be crushed by casks and cases sliding about below."

Aaron laughed. "Good. I always did say that you were the best hand at stowing cargo I ever had on my ship—when I had a ship. What about you, John?"

"Not much today. I spent the morning on the *Lizard*. Most I was able to do was loosen the leather flaps on two of the bilge pumps. Won't do no harm I know, but the deck hands will break their bloody backs carrying bail buckets afore the carpenter finds what's amiss with his pumps."

Aaron nodded. "I can see them. Water sloshing around in the bottom—'All hands to pumps'—everybody sweating blood pushing the pump beam up and down. More water, and the deck officer yelling at all hands to fall to and bail. Like you say, John, no real damage unless they should hit bad weather, but it will make good telling around the ale pots some-time."

"There's one thing certain sure." Poole chuckled. "The next revolt the English have, they'll bring their own lads to stow cargo and do their shipwrighting and rigging. They won't never use Philadelphia's crews again."

Before Aaron could say anything, the waving arm of the ropemaker sent them to their knees, and they were busily teasing at the rope ends when an undersized English lieutenant, followed by Rufus Ladd, ap-proached the opening of the shed. Reaching above his head to pull a length of tarred twine from a wooden peg, the ropemaker shot a quick questioning glance at the Captain. But Rufus, his full six feet of sea-weathered frame held stiffly erect, stared straight ahead. Unlike most Philadelphians, the press-ganged Captain kept his black hair short cropped, and the severe line of the Puritan-like trim was paralleled by the furrows that creased his forehead. Deep-tanned from wind and spray, Rufus looked older than his years, and the network of wrinkles spreading out from the corners of his gleaming gray eyes to his high cheekbones made a changing pattern as he spoke.

"This is Leftenant Benbow," Rufus said loudly.

"Morning to you, Leftenant." The ropemaker leaned on his wheel, inclining his head as though hard of hearing. He looked at the spindle-shanked Benbow encased in his fashionable too-tight scarlet tunic and white breeches. "What do you lack that I can furnish?"

"Captain Ladd needs some ropes or something." The officer waved contemptuously. "Not being a sailor I don't know the strange names he calls them. You'd best explain in your own seafaring tongue."

"I need them for flying the extra bunting in the sea-parade."

"Ah, yes." The ropemaker beamed. "I'd heard. A grand affair I imagine it will be. You'll need extra line, Captain Ladd?"

"Yes. Twenty fathom of gun's line."

"Aye aye, Captain."

"It will have to be reeved through a loaded eye block."

"I'll see to it." The ropemaker nodded in rhythm to his words.

"Twenty fathoms should do—trained as it will be from bowsprit to peak," Rufus said thoughtfully.

"On the *Sally E* it should be the right length." The ropemaker cocked his head to one side and moved his lips as if counting. Satisfied with his calculation he nodded solemnly. "Yes, Captain. On the *Sally E* and any of the others."

"Yes," Rufus agreed. "That's all. Can you get it aboard by tonight?"

"I'll bring it myself. I'll have to make up the ends myself, but it will be aboard before dusk."

"Is that all?" the Lieutenant asked disgustedly. "Do you mean to tell me a ship's captain has to come ashore himself for drivel like this? We could have sent one of the crew."

"But Leftenant," the ropemaker's voice was ingratiating and explanatory, "if I had no line such as the Captain desires—a crewman would not have dared take anything else. The Captain and I could have reached an agreement on a substitute."

"If that's all then, let's be on our way, Captain Ladd. The smell of this place sickens me."

"It's the pitch, Leftenant, it makes many a landsman sick." The ropemaker's voice was full of sympathy.

"If you'd choose to, Leftenant Benbow, we could stop at my home and—"

"I don't choose to, Captain Ladd," Benbow cut in insultingly. "And you, sir, know it is strictly against orders for you to talk to anyone."

Lieutenant Benbow stalked off along the ropewalk, Rufus Ladd following at his spur-clanking heels. Samuel Moxley, the best rope spinner on the Delaware, leaned on his big twining wheel and watched them pick their way along the tow-strewn walk. The broad-shouldered, sea-weathered Rufus towered above the shrimp of a redcoated Benbow. Rufus' powerful hands could wring the English officer's neck as a housewife would wring a pullet's, and yet there he was, forced to act like a lackey to a sword-toting boy hardly old enough to blow his own nose.

Judging they were out of earshot, Moxley turned to the three hidden in the darkness of the shed. "Whoreson English popinjay! I hope Rufus splits his thick skull with a belaying pin afore he drowns him. You get the message?" he asked, walking inside the shed.

"I did," Aaron said glumly. "I reckon we'll have to forget our plans for the sea-parade."

"There was no mistaking what he said," Parson Poole agreed. "The words that made no sense were 'guns,' 'loaded,' 'trained.' "

"And I asked him if he meant the *Sally E* and all the others, and he said yes," Moxley pointed out.

"We'll drop the plans for wrecking their sea-parade," Aaron said bitterly. "No sense to getting our own ships blowed out of the water. We'll meet again tonight and try and work out something new. Oh, well!" he tried to lighten his voice, "we can't do everything we want to. But I'd sure have liked to seen Admiral Howe's face when his first line of ships got fouled on our underwater boom."

10   QUALMS

Not guilty is not enough, she must be above suspicion!——CAESAR

From where Jonathan lay on the roof of Enoch Ladd's house, he could see most of the city spread out under him. Dusk had fallen before he'd dared climb out on the narrow ledge that kept loosened slates from falling to the street. The ledge jutted out at such an angle that it couldn't be seen from the ground, but that afternoon, when he was making certain that all the neighbors knew who he was, and that he was the hardest working servant the Ladds ever had, he'd realized that there must be something for the shipmaster to stand on when he adjusted the gnomon on the sundial; or cleaned the glass pieces that made up the skylight.

He had always considered himself even-tempered and slow to arouse to real anger, but today he had suffered every kind and degree of resentment that his nature was capable of feeling. A fine creel of eels Stirling had dropped him into with this Elizabeth Ladd running amuck the very first day. Of course she was worried about her father, and he could understand that, but to explode like a short-fused bomb and rush out talking wildly about bribing Redcoats was likely to bring an end to their spying before it was started. And where was she now? Here it was night, and not a word from her since morning.

Again the thought flashed into his mind, as it had throughout the day when he was going from chore to chore, that perhaps she had been able to bribe her way into the prison—but had failed to bribe herself out again. "It just couldn't be," he muttered, trying to reassure himself. If the English had caught her, they would have come to the house. But the other side of his mind argued that it need not be so. More than once in the past, the English had taken prisoners and made no report of the capture. It had been weeks before they admitted that they'd taken General Lee prisoner, and a goodly number of those they arrested as spies were hanged without a word being said by the Redcoats.

Perhaps, he thought grimly, he'd wasted the day trying to establish his identity and reputation as an industrious servant. He'd certainly made enough noise and fuss carrying out the fireplace ashes, and he'd polished every bit of brass he could find on the front of the house where every house-holder on Chestnut Street could see him. The windows on Four Street hadn't needed cleaning, but he'd taken a wood-stave bucket and a sponge and made certain that his energy was noticed, especially by one vinegar-faced wench who snooped from behind her back fence.

Certainly his efforts were vain if Elizabeth had been trapped. It made little difference what her offense was, for once she was suspected, everybody in the house would be watched, and his role of servant would come under closer scrutiny than he had any liking for.

He tried to quiet his anxiety by paying heed to what he had come up on the roof to do: to get himself oriented to the plan of the city. As he lay now, stretched out looking down on Chestnut, he could separate the ships in the Delaware. On the ground, or even from the upstairs windows, the shipmasts were a maze of spars and rigging with no pattern to distinguish one from the other. Up here, he shifted his chin on his clasped hands, although it was dark, the running lights, topgallant lanthorns and dolphin-striker flares, outlined one vessel from another so that he could pick out a ketch from a cutter or a schooner.

Only a few minutes before he'd been facing the opposite way, watching the English officers in their scarlet and blue and gray converging on the Indian Queen Tavern, and every once in a while a burst of laughter, loud and sustained, was carried upward to him on the faint breeze that blew his hair into his eyes. That it was a right smart city, he had to admit, and 'twas better lighted than any he'd seen before. Like the City Tavern, the Indian Queen had two lamps on posts set outside the front door, and these, with the candle flames reflected in the windows, lighted the street and were reflected again in the water running down the center drain. While he watched, pine-knot flambeaux and rosin torches sprang to light beside the chandler stores and open-fronted sheds that stood along the Delaware's bank.

He did wish that he knew more about ships, their trim and their signals. Some sort of activity was going on aboard the frigate *Andromeda*, for the shutter-like slots that opened and closed to show alternate squares of black and white had been signalling their messages since he'd watched Elizabeth fly off down chestnut Street that morning. It was impossible, lying here on the roof, to form a clear picture of the lay of the streets, for he couldn't tell which of the alleys ran from one square to another, or which might turn out to be cul-de-sacs and, therefore, traps to be avoided when he went venturing after curfew.

Thinking of traps gave him an unpleasant twitching in his stomach. If indeed Elizabeth had been caught, and the English should come to the house, he was in the worst kind of a trap; on a roof, with no other roof close enough to jump to, and no way to get down except the way he came up—through the dormer window. He shifted his weight and wondered if he should get down from the roof while he had the chance. The longer he waited without any word from Elizabeth, the less he could reckon on what to do. There was nothing he could achieve by going to look at the outside of a prison, and he could search the streets of Philadelphia for a week and not set eyes on Elizabeth.

The sight of a patrol of Hessians, led by a burly sergeant carrying a spluttering link, decided him. The patrol was marching along Three Street toward High and Arch, but the next one might come marching up Chestnut and surround the house. Raising himself to his knees and gripping the ledge tightly, he moved closer to the corner of the roof. A tedious and worrisome matter, this business of spying; and he was not of a disposition suited to it. His stockinged toe caught on a loose slate, and he held his breath waiting for the thing to slither down the roof and crash into the street. He heard the slate thud into the ledge behind him, and breathed again when it hung there, wedged between the roof and the slate-rail.

But he couldn't shake the feeling that there was something wrong in the whole affair, and it irked him mightily because he couldn't fathom what it was. It was something more than mere annoyance at Elizabeth's self-will and determination. He could cope with these, even though it meant bickerings and splutterings such as she'd displayed on the road to the Red Lion. Today's outburst was a different matter. She'd been afraid for her father, and she'd lost her head. That he could understand, and he was sorry for her. But she'd refused to listen to reason, and that was something that sapped the confidence out of him. For himself, if he were to tally all the stupid things a spy could do—trying to bribe a British sentry would be at the top of the list.

Ahead of him was the dormer he had left open, and holding tight to the ledge, he turned around and sliding his feet through the opening, dropped to the floor. Closing the window softly, he picked up his boots and crossed the room to the doorway. With a stunning sense of shock that stopped him in the middle of a step, he realized what it was that didn't fit into the scheme. He didn't trust Elizabeth! Her casual acceptance of the work to be done, back at the Silver Dolphin; her defense of English officers, her contempt for his wariness on the road, her blushes when Broadmoor's name was mentioned, and her complete disregard for everything but having her own way this morning, all added up to something less than the patriotism he looked for in a wholehearted Rebel.

And yet, he stood irresolute, Stirling couldn't be wrong in believing that she was Patriot. The General had known her since childhood and if there was one man in the Rebel Army who judged character aright it was Stirling. But Stirling didn't know about Broadmoor; and who could tell what changes might take place in a wench when she fell in love?

He stood there, in the doorway, with a sourness in his mouth that warned of physical sickness. The half-formed doubts and fears swelled about him like engulfing waves that he had neither the strength nor the skill to combat. Pounding at the seat of his brain was one dominating thought—the lives and fortunes of the Rebel Army weren't going to depend on any such milk and water patriotism as this lass made manifest.

What was he going to do? He couldn't tax the girl with being Tory-inclined, any more than he could tale up her deficiencies in patriotism and hand them to her like a tallied bill. Nor could he accuse her of being overfriendly with the enemy officers, without having her father's plight being thrown in his teeth again. He couldn't do any of these things; but, by God, neither was he going to disclose the General's secret cipher to her —leastwise not till she'd proved him wrong.

Somewhere, downstairs, a latch clicked, and he heard a footfall as if someone had come in the back door. He sped down the staircase and came face to face with Elizabeth as she walked into the big hall from the back of the house. She stopped when she saw him and waited for him to speak.

"You saw your father?" he asked with as calm a voice as he could muster.

"I saw him." She swept her hair back from her face with the gesture he already recognized as one of her habits.

"Then he is alive. Mistress Darragh and Mistress Priest told the truth?"

"Yes."

"You bribed your way into the prison?"

"Yes. I bribed my way in," she spoke slowly and turned away.

Suddenly, he knew she was lying. The elusive something that had nagged at him all day was clear in an instant. In the morning, when she had swirled out of the house, he had watched her walk along Chestnut, and she had worn neither cloak nor bonnet. Nor was she carrying the little silk bag with the drawstring in which she kept her money. It was still lying on the commode in her mother's room. She'd not had cash with her to bribe anybody.

11   STRETCHING THE NET

All is fish that comes to the net.——ENGLISH PROVERB

Midnight in Philadelphia found the streets bare of civilians, except for the trusted Loyalists who carried "certificates of loyalty" signed by Sir William Howe. Some of those had learned too late that their certificates were a liability. Trusting to the protection of the General's signature, they had ventured out on one last night, never to be seen or heard of again, and certain Patriots moved about the city satisfying challenging sentries with the stolen papers.

Behind the chamber doors and draped windows of the Indian Queen and City taverns, English officers drank, gambled, or wenched the nights away as suited their tastes and pockets. In Sir William's headquarters, portraits of the Penns looked down on scenes of revelry that rivalled the clubs of London and the debauchery of Bath. Roman in his tastes, Sir William liked music with his gaming, and the plucked harp strings and tinkling harmonium sounded no less sweet because the instruments had been stolen from Benjamin Franklin's home.

Down in Moore's Alley, the subalterns, whose pay didn't permit the faro tables, gambled their pence at the cockpit till the last feather had flown, and then made their way to one of the waterfront coffeehouses where the coffee was stronger and cheaper than the thin ale the Colonists' tastes ran to.

The well-known Tories kept their lights burning in defiance of the curfew, especially when entertaining English officers, and Von Knyphausen's surly, black-uniformed Hessians, who had taken over the duties of the night watch, did no knocking on doors when they saw British uniforms through the chinks in the shutters. Patriots obeyed the curfew, and spoke in whispers. They knew that a Hessian house inspection was only an excuse for petty pilfering under the threat of a report to the Provost Marshal.

Some who were counted as Patriot but who were soft-voiced in their opinion were given special permits to ignore the curfew. They had work to do, filling Army needs. Mullins, the little tailor up on the corner of Arch and Five, had a permit. He cut a fine uniform, and needed the night hours to keep up with the orders he had from the officers who liked to ape Colonel Cosmo Gordon's style in high-waisted breeches. He had keen ears and a memory, and much of what he heard had reached Valley Forge in the days before André's order went out to the officers to watch their talk.

Cobblers who could fit a jack boot that would slide on and off and still be snug around the ankles straddled their short-legged benches and worked till their eyes could no longer see the waxed points on the stitching threads they poked through the holes made by the awl. One of these, Abel Voss, the cobbler, lived almost opposite the floating bridge that crossed the Schuylkill just before it flowed into the Delaware. The English maintained their biggest permanent duty guard on both ends of the bridge; five hundred men it was said, and nobody crossed over except strong patrols under the command of a colonel. But Abel Voss could get messages over, when there were any to send. He and Dan Jarrett had worked it out, and they were mighty proud of it. A weighted length of signal flag line was tied to a heavy pig jug that was wound with rope to protect it. The line, wrapped about with lead foil from old tea chests, was sunk in the Schuylkill, and when there was a message to send, Abel pulled the cork out of the pig jug, put the message inside, and lowered the jug in the water. Sooner or later, one of Jarrett's lads, Abel didn't know who, would slowly pull the jug across the river bottom and up the bank at the opposite side. But, Abel shook his head, as he laid aside the boots he was working on, no messages had gone over for nigh a month now.

On South Two Street, Quakeress Lydia Darragh was thinking much the same thoughts as Abel Voss. She was standing on a stool in the kitchen, with her head close to the ceiling rafters, trying to overhear what André, in the little room off his bedroom, was saying to the disagreeable man who reported to him every night at about this time. She wasn't very tall, and gripping the broad rafter with her fingers, she stretched herself to the limit of her aching toes.

There was no doubt about it, André was being careful. For all her straining to hear, she couldn't make sense out of the rumble that leaked through the plank floor. Deep in her bones, she knew that this big, bestial-looking Tracy Quimby, with his rude manners and his spiky rim of red hair around his bald pate, was some kind of informant; and she had tried, in vain, to find out whom he informed on.

Loosening her grip on the rafter, she dropped her arms and flexed the cramp from her fingers. Nothing was to be gained by listening any longer, she decided, and climbed down from the stool. The voices were unnaturally soft, just as they had been for weeks past, and it could only mean that André was warning his visitors to keep their voices low; a sure sign that he suspected her.

It was odd, but in keeping with the kinks and twists in the business of spying, that André should suspect her now, when she had learned nothing for months, yet fail to suspect her when she had warned General Washington of the impending attack on Whitemarsh. André had a reputation for being right smart, but looking back on last December, she saw only a young pipsqueak being outwitted by an older woman. Some day she'd tell her children how André had come into the kitchen one night, and, right in front of this same fireplace, had told her that some important officers were calling on him and he wanted everyone in her household to be in bed before they arrived. She'd done as he ordered, but once the officers had settled down to their council in André's room, she'd stolen from her bedchamber, crept along the hallway, and listened outside his door. Much of what was said made no sense to her, but just about the time her feet were ready to freeze and she was sure she was going to sneeze, she heard enough to know that they were planning to attack Washington at

Whitemarsh. She'd crawled back into bed and when André came to her bedchamber and knocked on the door, she let him pound away before she made a show of waking from a sound sleep.

The officers had left, and André it seemed couldn't turn the key in the front lock, so she had to get out of bed and pretending to be half asleep, grope her way downstairs and lock the front door. Next morning, announcing that she had to take a sack of grain to the Frankfort Mills to be ground into flour, she obtained a writ from the Provost Marshal to pass beyond the line of English sentries, and with the sack on her shoulder she set off through the snow on the five-mile walk to the grist mill. While the grain was being ground, she walked to the Rebel outpost and gave her warning.

Lydia stopped her reminiscing when her eye caught the half-empty distaff on the flax wheel. She decided to finish her spinning. Carrying the wheel over to the fireplace, she stood it where the fire would give her a better light than the lone candle on the table. Right where she placed the low, rush-bottomed chair, was where it had been sitting the morning after the Whitemarsh debacle, and André, dispirited and disgruntled, had thrown himself into it and described how the English, expecting an easy victory, had found instead very wide-awake Rebels. "How could they have found out, Mistress Lydia?" André had asked, trying to warm his frozen feet at the fire. "You, Mistress Lydia, were asleep, for I had the devil's own time waking you."

André still hadn't learned the trick of locking the front door, so she must needs stay up till he went to bed. She drew and twisted some strands of flax from the roving and threaded them through the end of the spindle. Yes, she thought, some day she'd tell her children, and putting her foot on the treadle, she set the wheel to spinning.

Upstairs, Tracy Quimby lowered the report book he was reading from, and looked at André. "What in hell is that tapping?"

For the moment, André didn't answer. He was putting the last delicate touches to a sketch he had made of what the Whartons' withdrawing room was going to look like after he had hung it with mirrors and installed the imitation marble columns that would give the hideous room an oriental effect. He propped the sketch against the candlestick on the table, and turned to Quimby. "The tapping is nothing but Mistress Lydia's spinning-wheel treadle touching the floor. Now you see why I tell you to keep your voice low. If we can hear that—she can hear us." He picked up an elaborate drawing of the Mischianza invitation, and studied it critically. It was a shield with the upper-left quarter showing a setting sun—emblematic of Sir William's recall—and crowning the shield was a stylized fleur-de-lis with laurel wreaths dropping around the edges of the shield. The whole device was surrounded with staffed flags, pointed spears and broad-bladed spattons jutting out from behind the body of the shield. And giving balance, at the bottom of the shield, a balance which pleased André's artistic leanings mightily, was a pair of heavy cannon, pointing outward, with two side drums to fill the space below the gun muzzles.

Still engrossed with his own handiwork, he spoke to Quimby. "Go on with your report, I'm all attention."

Quimby lifted his report book again and angled it to catch the light. "We caught a deck hand this morning. One of those, I suspect, who has been harassing the shipping. He was taken slashing the ropes or lines or whatever they're called that keep a sail furled."

"And?" André laid the Mischianza invitation on the table and leaned back in his chair, viewing the sketch of the Wharton place.

"And what?" Quimby said irritably. "Cunningham will hang him tomorrow after breakfast." He turned to the next page in his report book. "I told you before that we had some suspicions of a man named Jarrett?"

"Vaguely. I remember something. What about him?"

"Yesterday, he was seen following Mistress Ladd."

"The wench Major Broadmoor has picked for his inamorata?" André was surprised.

"Yes."

"Why should he follow her?"

"That I will discover. The Ladds have a neighbor who hates them venomously for having blocked her view of the river by building their house three stories high—"

"I know her. An utterly unattractive bitch who makes the Provost's life miserable with her hourly reports on who takes a physic and when." André shuddered at the memory of her needle-nosed, sharp-visaged face mounted on a scrawny neck.

"Her news this morning might interest you. She was watching—"

"I'll wager she was. I don't think the witch ever sleeps."

Quimby went doggedly ahead. "She says that the Ladds have a new servant. A tall, oaflike critter who works like a dog and has the appearance of being lacking in sense."

"I'll be sure and report it to Sir William."

André's sarcasm nettled Quimby and he slammed the report book shut and jumped to his feet. "Perhaps at the same time you'd do well to tell Sir William that his officers allow a pretty face to influence them in their duty."

"What the hell do you mean, Quimby?"

"Do you want my report—or shall I send it to England with Sir William on the *Andromeda*?"

"Don't be so bloody touchy. I'm listening to the tale."

"According to my informant," Quimby continued stiffly, "Mistress

Ladd ran out of the house in what the informant described as a state of alarm. Coming along Chestnut was the man Jarrett whom my informant knows. When Jarrett caught sight of Mistress Ladd, he turned and followed her—as did the woman you pay so little heed to."

"And Mistress Ladd went where?"

"She went to Major Broadmoor's quarters. The Major left his quarters almost an hour afterward, but Mistress Ladd stayed most all day." Quimby opened his book again. "Broadmoor, from what I've pieced together, hunted for General Grey. When he found him he persuaded the General to give him a special pass allowing Mistress Ladd to visit her father in the Walnut Street Prison."

André stretched out his legs, clasped his hands behind his head and looked at the ceiling. " 'Tis natural enough for the woman to want to see her father. But I thoroughly disapprove of Broadmoor's actions."

"There is more," Quimby said pointedly. "Broadmoor hired a carriage at the Logan Mews, and took Mistress Ladd to the prison. After the visit, he escorted her home. The man Jarrett was outside the prison, he had obviously followed them, since there was no one else to follow, and he definitely did follow them to her home."

"It will bear looking into." André was thoughtful. "Put a more constant watch on Jarrett."

"What about the new servant?" Quimby closed his book again and stuffed it into the wide pocket of his floppy coat.

André grinned. "I'll order Broadmoor to ask his mistress where she got her new servant. 'Twill give me an opportunity to reprimand him without seeming to. He's close to Grey—both Wadham men you know—Oxford ties are very close, so I can't bear down too hard."

"We should place a watch on the Ladd home." Quimby was emphatic.

"Why?" André raised his effeminate eyebrows. "Broadmoor may be enjoying an amorous Rebel wench, but he's not fool enough to talk, and he knows nothing to tell. Suit yourself, Quimby," he added when he saw his informant's jaw tighten.

"I'll watch the house." Quimby's eyes narrowed, and he turned to go.

"There should be something to report soon on my efforts at effecting a link between us and Valley Forge," André whispered as he followed Quimby to the door.

"You place more faith in that matter than I do."

"You're wrong, Quimby. Lee is an Englishman. He is a soldier of fortune fighting on the losing side. A commission in the British Army and a pouchful of gold are bait beyond his refusing. He'll not be the first Rebel General nor the last to desert their cause for a price."

Quimby turned at the doorway. "Use all the bait you wish, Major, and pay out all the line you like. I'll do my fishing around the Walnut Street Prison and the corner of Four and Chestnut—and I'll catch more fish. Good night."

"'Night, Quimby, I wish you luck, but I'll wager you a hogshead that I land the biggest fish."

12   A PROMISE! A TOAST!

Patriotism is not necessarily included in rebellion. A man may hate his King, yet not love his country.——SAMUEL JOHNSON

Elizabeth stared at the small French timepiece on the mantel of her bedchamber as its dainty hammer struck the thin, silver bell seven times. The tinkling sound barely carried across the room and into the deep alcove she called her chartroom, but she hadn't needed to hear the chime to know what hour it was. Most of the day had been divided by looking out one window after another to see whether or not Jonathan had returned, and watching the clock tick off the longest hours she'd known in her whole life.

When she'd come downstairs for breakfast, Jonathan had already left the house. When he had left or where he had gone, she had no idea. She had hunted the house over to see if he had left a note, and after looking in every impossible place so many times that she couldn't remember the number, she'd come to the conclusion that he was giving her a taste of the same medicine she dosed him with the day before.

Not only was this one of the longest days she'd ever lived through, but last night had been a torment of sleeplessness and self-censure. Why had she been so hopelessly stupid as to lie about bribing her way into the Walnut Street Prison? And her lie had been useless, for Jonathan hadn't believed her. She had read the disbelief in his face even while she was telling the lie.

Close to blushing at her own folly, she picked up the polishing cloth from the table in front of her, and rubbed furiously on the brass barrel of the sextant she had been cleaning. Always in the past, when things upset her, she could find a kind of relief in cleaning and adjusting and handling the things in her chartroom; the things that were tangible evidence of her accomplishments. The sextant she was cleaning—her sextant—had been ceremoniously presented to her by her father in front of the whole crew of the *Sally E* when she had "shot the sun" and charted the ship's position accurately every day on a voyage to Cape Charles and back.

She looked over at the two globes sitting on the combined bookshelf and chart chest under the window. The terrestrial globe had been her reward for the most accurate dead reckoning on board, when they'd seen neither sun nor stars for three days, in the densest fog that ever followed a ship north from Hatteras. And the celestial globe had been more in the nature of a double award, for she'd been allowed to take the wheel of the *Sally E* and pilot her through the channel between Appledore and Smutty Nose, and the globe was for "keeping the tiller from slopping," as her father said.

Her mother's remarks had been different. "Keep it up, lass, and you'll scare every man away from you. A good sailor doesn't need another sailor for his wife, and a landsman wants a good cook, not a master mariner."

There was a deal more truth in what her mother had said than she'd realized at the time, Elizabeth admitted ruefully. If she knew as much about handling men as she did ships, she wouldn't be in the mess she'd cooked up for herself. Half a dozen times during her restless night she'd wanted to get up and go to Jonathan's room and confess that she'd lied. She hadn't gone, because she knew it would only involve her in more deceit.

She pushed her chair back from the table and threw the polishing rag across the room in a burst of anger. Just what words was she going to use to tell Jonathan that when Broadmoor had said he would get a pass, she'd fallen sobbing into his arms and ended up by letting him kiss and fondle her? In her mind, it was easy enough to say, and to justify. What was a little kissing and fondling in exchange for seeing her father?

Clenching her fingers till she felt her nails digging into the palms of her hands, she paced the room like an angry cat. She'd not made one real effort to check Broadmoor's advances, and at the time she hadn't seen how she could. She was the one who had gone to his quarters, he hadn't asked her. She'd gone to him to beg a favor when she knew how he felt toward her. He had soothed her and quieted her when she sobbed out her relief, and she hadn't paid any heed when he sat on the edge of the bed and put his arm about her.

In her pacing, her toe touched the polishing rag, and, bending down, she picked it up and placed it back on the table. She was disgusted as well as angry. She was disgusted with herself for having thought that Broadmoor would seek out General Grey and obtain a pass for her the instant she asked for his help. And she was disgusted with Broadmoor for having tried to make love to her when she was distraught about her father and had no mind for anything but to visit the prison as quickly as possible. Her despair and her tears had been real enough, but she could have reined them in more quickly than she had. Instead, when she found the Major persisting, she had pretended to see nothing more in his advances than an effort to console her. At last, after an hour of getting nothing but continued sobbing, and trembling lips in response to his caresses, Broadmoor had left his quarters to try and find General Grey.

Abruptly she stopped her marching, and looked helplessly about her room. In her present mood, she'd give anything to get out of Philadelphia and go where nobody even knew her name. She was sick of the whole business, from stem to stern and deck to kelson, she was sick of it, and if it weren't for her father, she'd take her mother—

"Where?" She'd spoken aloud without knowing it. She couldn't leave, and there was no sense in even debating it with herself. She stamped her foot in anger and looked at the compass, and the dividers and the sextant lying on the table. Was she, a lass who could make a fix from a star, and read a log, or take her trick at the wheel, going to go below because the weather was turning rough? So Broadmoor was likely to be a little difficult, and Jonathan needed handling like a whale in a herring net. They weren't difficulties that had no solution. Looking at it, now that she'd chided herself all day, Jonathan was more of a problem than Broadmoor, for there was no question but what the Captain had doubts about her patriotism.

How she would go about proving her patriotism, she didn't know. She was as loyal to the Rebel cause as Jonathan, but unlike him, she couldn't find the words to talk about it, and all her upbringing had inclined her toward hiding her fears. That was something else in which she'd copied her father, for it was his belief that the worse the storm and the closer the danger, the more confident he must appear in front of his crew.

At the sound of a knock at the back door, she ran out of her room and down the stairs. Maggie was in her mother's bedchamber and hadn't heard the knocking. It could hardly be Jonathan, she thought as she crossed the hall, and none of the officers came to the back door. Pausing at the kitchen window, she looked out. There was something familiar about the man who stood there, although she couldn't say for certain where she had seen him before.

In the dim light he looked short and round shouldered, and he glanced about him as though he were afraid of being seen. He had no peddler's box or tradesman's basket slung on his drooping shoulders, and the broken-brimmed tricorne crammed down to his ears all but hid his face. When he raised his hand to knock again, Elizabeth noticed a livid scar running from his knuckles to his wrists, and that his right thumb was missing.

His hand had been mangled by a cut from a cutlass, Elizabeth guessed as she went to open the door. She'd seen such markings before on men who had been set on by pirates.

"Mistress Elizabeth?" he whispered as she opened the door.

"Yes."

"I'm Dan Jarrett. I have something for you, and Jonathan Kimball."

He came in without waiting to be asked and shut the door behind him. Opening his coat he reached in his breeches pocket and pulled out a small bottle. "This is the writing fluid Stirling said would identify me. Where's Kimball?"

"I don't know. He's been gone since before breakfast."

"You don't know?" He sounded and looked incredulous. "He's your servant—and you don't know where he is?" He brushed past her and went into the kitchen, beckoning her to follow. "Listen, Mistress Ladd. What kind of an answer do you think that is? Do you expect an officer of the Provost Marshal to be satisfied with that—should one come calling?"

"What else can I say?" She looked at him blankly. "He didn't leave word. Of what use would it be to lie to the Provost guard when I've no notion where he might be? I could put a rope about his neck if my tale didn't agree with his."

Dan Jarrett shook his head slowly as he rebuttoned his coat. "For him to be missing at night, mistress, is one thing. He might be out sampling the taverns. But for him to be missing in the day, without your permission, is enough to hang him."

"Then don't prate at me." She flung the words at him. "He's the one who left—not me."

Jarrett turned and faced her. His round shoulders seemed to straighten. He pulled off his tricorne and crumpling it in his hand, pointed it at her. "You can tell Kimball what I said when he comes in. But let us understand something, mistress. In this business, whether we be Captain, Mistress of the house, river rat or General, our necks are all on one string, and it's short shrift for any who jeopardize the others. Think on that, mistress, the next time you call on enemy officers for help." His voice was flat and harsh as he finished, and holding out his hand, he gave her the bottle of writing fluid.

The latch clicked, and the door slowly opened. As though he'd been shot from a bow, Jarrett crossed the kitchen and crouched, tensed and ready, against the wall. Through the widening opening, Elizabeth saw Jonathan's face.

"You're back." She forced herself to sound calm and casual. "There's someone to see you—behind the door."

Jarrett stepped out and shook Jonathan's hand when the Captain had closed the door again. "I'm Dan Jarrett. I brought the writing fluid. Use it sparingly, it is hard come by and costs as much as a case of tea."

"Where do we put the messages?" Jonathan asked.

"There's an old brick watering trough out by the stables. Walk out casual-like, as if you were checking the stable doors. On the inside of the water trough, the fourth brick from the top end in the bottom course is loose. Slip your message in there and I'll pick it up and see that it gets across the Schuylkill to Stirling."

"How long—after we—after a message is placed there?"

"Stirling will have it before breakfast the next day, Captain—much before breakfast." Jarrett turned to Elizabeth. "When you have a message for me, do as your father did—"

"My father?" Elizabeth was taken aback.

"Yes, lass, afore he was arrested. Put your mother's sewing basket on the table in the east window—I can see it as I walk up Chestnut. If the basket is there, I come back later after dark and get the message. But every night, last thing, I check in case there is a message."

Jarrett crammed his battered tricorne on his head and put his hand on the door latch. "Best that you two do a sight more lacing your stories together. I don't know what ails you, but this is one business where the right hand has to know what the left hand is doing. Good night."

Standing together in the kitchen, they waited long enough for Jarrett to walk out the driveway and onto Chestnut. When they heard no challenge from any patrol, Jonathan pointed to the fluid. "Where shall we hide it?"

Without answering, Elizabeth led the way out of the kitchen and across the hall to a door under the first stair landing. Following her, Jonathan found himself in a room that was of a different world. A four-sided ship's lanthorn, burning whale oil, swung from a crosstree lashed to a pine mast that rose from floor to ceiling. Around the mast, a polished mahogany table, with compass, sextant and parallel rulers, heightened the illusion of being on shipboard. Maps and charts dotted the panelled walls, and the street and houses were shut out by green porthole curtains hanging from rings that slid on a brass rod across the window.

"Father's chamber," Elizabeth said unnecessarily. "Everything, mast, panelling, cabin table—all came from the first *Sally E* when she ran aground at Whitehaven the year I was born."

Elizabeth placed her right hand under the table and, pressing a catch, pulled the top of the table with her left. The top slid around, disclosing a hollow in what looked like solid wood.

"Father used to keep privateer log and manifests in here."

"As fine a hiding place as ever I saw." He watched her lay the bottle in the hollow. "Where is the catch?"

She slid the table top back in place, and the catch clicked as the top came level with the deep sides. "Here is the catch, a forearm's length from the edge, and opposite the cleat on the mast."

Jonathan bent down, slid his hand under the table, felt for the slight depression in the wood and pressed. The catch lifted, and fell again as he withdrew his hand. "Simple." He straightened his back. "But unless a body knew the secret he'd never think to look."

"And a room where we have no need to talk in whispers." Elizabeth walked to the wall and rapped the panelling with her knuckles. "There are two-inch battens behind this, as well as a double course of brick. The windows are thick green glass and no one could see inside if the curtains were left open."

"Your father's love of privacy stands us in good stead."

"Father has no liking for privacy. Truth is—" she half smiled— "Father loved company too much. The window lights are green for the same reason this room is furnished as it is, because it reminds him of the sea." She leaned on the back of the captain's chair that stood beside the table. "Dan Jarrett gave me a tongue-lashing—and bade me tell you that —well, you heard him. It was more of the same."

"Yes, lass. I'd not have left you all day if I'd not felt there was need to teach you a lesson. You pay no need to what anyone says. Your own will is your law, and that is something that cannot be, in an affair of this nature."

"But—"

"Hear me out." Jonathan waved her to silence. "I have all sympathy for your father's plight, as I've said before. But you and I took in hand to do a duty, and having taken it in hand, it comes first. There is no reckoning what trail of damage you might do, were we in the midst of something, and you threw everything to the wind because of your own whim and self-assertive will. You left me sweating yesterday, not knowing whether you were in the prison or out of it. Perhaps I was wrong in leaving you today, but it did seem to me that since you wouldn't listen to words—you might pay heed to deeds."

"I was wrong yesterday. But can you not understand that when Maggie said she's not seen Father, I lost my head and nothing mattered but that I convince myself that he was still alive?"

"I understand it. What you, mistress, must understand it that you may lose your head once too often, and that might well be the next time." He put his hands on the table and leaned over it, looking at her. "Stirling doesn't expect you to go about spying on gun positions, strong points and weak ones, or on the lax habits of the officers. That is my task. But I must have a cover—a blind from which to work—and it must be secure if I'm to succeed. What happens if the English put a watch on the house and Jarrett can't pick up messages?"

"I know." Her shoulders drooped and she went on miserably, "I said I was wrong, and I'll mend my ways. But I'd like to say something, too, Captain."

"Say on, and speak as you please." He grinned at her. "My shoulders are broad."

"Your attitude toward me is irksome, and not reckoned to make me feel kindly toward you." She held the chair by its back and rocked it on two legs as she tried to frame her words. "Without saying so, you manifest your belief that I am not Patriot enough for your liking. 'Tis true I've not wintered at Valley Forge, nor fought at Brandywine—"

His raised hand stopped her again. "'Tis the wrong tack to take, lass. We've not asked the women to winter at the Old Forge, nor yet to fight in the battles. As for your patriotism, Lord Stirling is your sponsor, and I took his word. What change has taken place in my mind, you've wrought yourself. I've spoken to no one, and no one has spoken your name to me." He paused, and the edge in his voice was sharper. "Nay, Mistress Ladd, if—as you think—I have doubts, recall what you have said and done to put them there."

"But I am right, am I not?" she persisted. "There are doubts in your mind. In this matter of loyalty, you find a difference between you and me?"

He looked at her long and hard, considering, weighing his words in his mind before he answered. "I think there is a difference."

"What is it then?" She loosed the back of the chair and the legs chattered on the floor as she walked around the table and came closer to him. "If you know there is a difference—you must know what it is?"

Again he looked at her, forcing her to keep her wide-open, gold-flecked eyes on his. Her face was all honesty and forthrightness, though the sharp arch to her eyebrows gave her a worried, quizzical look. She was intense and eager, and her faster breathing could be seen in the pronounced rise and fall of her breasts as she waited his answer.

"You make it hard for a man, and your question is a mite unfair." He sat on the edge of the table and his long legs dangled as he clasped his fingers over one knee. "Nor is your question to be answered in one word, but I'll try, and if my answer displeases you—remember you sought it."

"I'll remember."

"By your own reckoning, you are doubtless Patriot. But for me, that is not enough."

"Why not?"

"Because between Patriot and Rebel there is a difference of sorts. I'm a Rebel and I'm dissatisfied and angered, and have no stomach for trafficking with those who are not. There are Patriots aplenty who'll welcome freedom—but who do nothing to bring it about. There are Patriots

[114]

who give help here and there, and still others who'll do much. But a Rebel —a Rebel in mind and soul and body—will stop at nothing."

"And you're a judge?" The surprise in her voice had a touch of acid in it.

"Of what I see and hear, I am a judge. And if I am suspicious, I have a right to be." He closed his eyes, and his leg stopped swinging. "We have been betrayed by men who were officers, who had taken an oath of loyalty. We have been ill served by generals who were perhaps not traitors, but who were not Rebels, for they placed their personal fortunes above those of the Rebel cause. Patriots may feel angered when they hear of some cruelty wrought by the English. But a Rebel feels the hurt as much as though the injury had been to himself."

"But you are no judge of another's feelings. You don't feel the imprisonment of my father as I do. If I am lacking in the words to speak my mind or expose my soul on how I feel about the war, how can you judge?"

He opened his eyes and looked at her. "I was not thinking of words. 'Twas not the words, 'Give me liberty or give me death,' that made Patrick Henry a Rebel. 'Twas because he was Rebel that he said them, and meant them, and he proved that he meant them when he marched against the Royal Governor Dunmore."

Jumping from the table, he paced the polished floor, and waved both arms at the walls and furnishings. "You live amidst surroundings that make it hard for you to see this war as it is. Here, in Philadelphia, the English are on their best behavior. They are held back somewhat by the brothers Howe, and Cornwallis, and Leslie. But were Philadelphia left to Grant of Ballachulish, and André, and No-Flint Grey—'tis a dozen hangings a day, and a fire-gutted house in every square you'd be looking at. And it would not be willing Tory wenches that they'd have for bedmates, but Rebel women, dragged screaming from their homes." He stopped and nodded his head. "I'll give even the devil his just due, Howe and Cornwallis permit no rape if they can prevent it, but André and Tarleton and Grant come from a different litter. Blood is to their liking, as it is to their hireling Hessians."

Abruptly he stopped his striding, and pointed at the panelled walls and the array of luxuries. "I am reminded of what General Washington wrote to the Congress just afore Christmas last. He said 'twas much easier and less distressing to draw remonstrances in a comfortable room by a good fireside, than to occupy a cold, bleak hill and sleep under snow, without clothes or blankets. What Washington said was true, for such comfort as you have here is what makes it possible for your mother to ask what in God's name we are doing at Valley Forge—as though Valley Forge were our choice."

"Now you are being unfair," Elizabeth flared up.

"Am I? I told you you'd not like my answer."

"Your reasoning is unfair. My mother said only what every Patriot in Philadelphia said."

"And what did I say to begin with, mistress?" Jonathan walked to Elizabeth and stopped, standing over her as he looked down into her anger-flushed face. "I said there was a difference between Patriot and Rebel. Rebels don't cast Brandywine and Paoli and the loss of Philadelphia in our teeth, but Patriots do. Rebels think of Trent's Town and and Princeton, and hope and pray for another day like them. Patriots are like eggs in the nest, some will hatch out into Rebels, others will not. There were Patriots at Trent's Town, they sent us bits of information they came by, and it was valued by us. But the Rebels tramped the ten miles in the snow at our sides and acted as our guides. 'Tis difficult to explain the difference since it is more of spirit than anything else. You said I couldn't have the same feeling for your father's plight that you do—"

"I did," she spoke up into his face. "And whatever you think of me, my father is as Rebel as Stirling himself—and so is my mother."

"I said no word about your father. I have no doubt he is in the Walnut Street Prison because he refused to comply willingly with the English."

"He told them to go to hell—and they were afraid he'd order my brothers to scuttle the ships. And had my mother not pretended illness, as she told you, we'd have Redcoat officers quartered here the same as the other 'Patriots'—since you'll not allow we're Rebel."

Jonathan pushed his hands into the top of his breeches, and twisted his shoulders into an expressive shrug. "I knew better than try to explain, but I made the effort, lass. Did you and I have the same feelings about the Revolt, we'd have no need to be talking as we are—we'd know we were of a like mind."

"I said I'd mend my ways," Elizabeth reminded him as she crossed the room to a heavily carved armoire standing against the wall opposite the window. "But I'll do more, Rebel Jonathan Kimball, I'll prove myself as Rebel as you, and make you eat your words." Putting her fingers behind the beading of the armoire door, she pulled it open and lifted a long-necked bottle from the shelf.

"Oporto." She held the bottle up carefully. "Vintage of the English Factory, and scarce as tea since the Boston Party."

"This map of Philadelphia—" Jonathan studied a highly colored map above the mantel, as Elizabeth took two long-stemmed glasses from a slotted rack in the armoire and carried them to the table—"how old is it?"

"Not too old." She poured the wine. "Father had it made when the house was finished; just twenty-four years this February past."

Jonathan turned at the clink of the glasses and took one from her outstretched hand.

"To my newly mended ways. I hope they'll merit your approval." Elizabeth touched his glass and sipped the ruby liquid from the rim.

He watched her and saw no sign of sarcasm in her glance. "As fine as ever crossed my lips." He bowed and turned again to the map. "Mostly regular streets all crossing at right angles—all except Dock Street."

"They were supposed to run north and south—and east and west—but they don't, leastwise not a mariner's North." Joining him at the map, she drew her finger along Dock Street as it curved from Three Street between Chestnut and Walnut, over Two Street and out to the riverfront on Spruce and Front. "Because of Dock Creek, I suppose the bridge runs that way and the street follows it."

Seems as though Proprietor Penn—or Logan, his Secretary—intended that the east and west streets should all be called after trees—"

"Such was the thought." She placed her glass on the table. "Times change and new names come along. Already the High Street is being called Market because the City Fathers builded a town hall and market at High and Two. The old folks never cease complaining about it—though it was built before most of them were born."

"And the east and west streets are all numbered—except One and that is called Front—natural I suppose, since every river town I know of calls the riverfront street 'Front.'"

"The rivermen call it First, River, Wharf—what they've a mind to."

"It will do me no harm to study this map." He spoke more to himself than to her. "There's no such thing as knowing too much about enemy territory, and that's what Philadelphia is right now."

Almost as a period to his sentence, the vibrant rattle of a side drum came faintly through the window. It was followed by the beat of heavy boots, and the night guard marched past the front of the house on its way up Chestnut to the State House.

"A quarter before nine." Lifting the lid of a small box, she looked at the chronometer suspended in its glistening gimbal. "From the parlor on the other side of the hall, you can hear the guard-change. They make somewhat of a to-do about it, the English do."

She crossed to the door and opened it. Jonathan, putting his glass on the table, followed her into the hall. As she reached the parlor, the big knocker on the front door fell with a heavy-handed crack that echoed in the house like a cannon shot. Jonathan wheeled about, ran back into Ladd's room, seized a wine glass from the table, and ran out to the hall again, closing the door behind him. He signalled to Elizabeth with the glass and sped down the dark passageway that led to the kitchen.

"Goddamme," he muttered below his breath, "my tricorne—I left it on the table near her father's door." There was no use to go back for it now. A mixture of voices, raised in greeting, was proof enough that Elizabeth had already opened the front door. He stood where he was, just outside the kitchen door, and held his breath to listen. The sharp English voices accompanied by the inevitable clatter of side arms and spur chains left a trail of sound that he could follow with his ears, across the hall and into the parlor.

"Thank God." They hadn't gone to her father's room, else they'd have seen his tricorne. Cut-off sentences and words piled one on the other made it impossible to sort out what they were saying. It did sound as though they were genuinely glad to find Elizabeth home, but her voice, lost in the babel, gave him no hint as to her response. At least, he contented himself, up to now there were no harsh questioning sounds as there would be if suspicion existed about her new servant.

There was a lull, and he heard her saying something that sounded like "wagon load." A burst of "hip hip" and "Spicey" followed, and he nodded to himself in the dark—"so she had mentioned the wagon." Again the voices fell and he heard the names Howe and André, and a mention of the Mischianza the whole town was talking about. Now the tones were different, low and angry, and carrying the unmistakable quality of an explanation, and he heard Clinton's name spoken with contempt. Elizabeth's voice sounded surprised—and he risked a step along the passage to try to hear the better. His step closer was a vain effort, for at that moment the parade-ground voice of a Grenadier officer rang out from the State House Square.

The post duties were shouted for all to hear, "To shoot on sight any who failed to give the countersign—to walk the post in a soldierly manner—to report all suspicious persons and disturbances—and to guard His Majesty's port and property."

The "sloping—ordering—inspection arms" of the guard-change became hazy and indefinite as Jonathan moved cautiously along the passageway that ran between the front hall and the kitchen. The passageway itself was in darkness, but the parlor door, at the front-hall end of the passage, was in the full light of the hall lamp. With his back to the wall, Jonathan sidestepped his way as close as he dared to the parlor. The last officer to enter the room had failed to drop the latch, and as Jonathan moved within a few feet of the parlor door, it opened far enough for him to catch a glimpse of the room. In the light from the four-branched candelabra on the parlor table he could see a splash of scarlet tunic and the silver basket hilt of a sword. The owner was speaking, and Jonathan watched the heaving out and in of the gilt facings on the tunic.

"'Twill be the biggest thing ever seen, m'dear—" The voice came faintly, and the end of the sentence was cut off by a chorus of agreement. Jonathan's ears throbbed with the strain of listening, but through the chattering voices, breaking up the flow of words, he caught the drift of the conversation. "Grant . . . the Forty-second, too bad Erskine would have to go with them . . . he loves to dance . . . two or three battalions . . . enough to keep Washington and his vagabonds alerted all night . . . no surprise attacks to spoil the night's festivities—"

The door opened farther, and Jonathan stepped backward down the hallway. Now all he heard was a jumble of sound, but it seemed that they were saying their good nights, for the voices grew louder, and shadows darting along the wall and disappearing into the blackness told that the officers were crossing the hall from the parlor to the front door. The outside door slammed, and Jonathan started back to the front of the house. Just as he reached the big hall he heard voices in the parlor. One was Elizabeth's, and she had at least one English officer with her.

The other officers weren't waiting, for he heard them still laughing and talking as they turned north at Four Street, on their way to the Indian Queen, Jonathan had no doubt. They were a carefree group, much in contrast with the officers in the Rebel Army who had nothing to laugh at, and who had to spend what little money they had on the food that the Congress didn't seem able to procure.

Jonathan drew himself back into the shadows again. Whoever this Englishman was, he took his time about his good night. And the fact that the others had left without him indicated that it was somewhat of an expected thing. Most likely this tardy officer was Broadmoor, Jonathan thought, and found himself incensed that Elizabeth should be alone with him for even a moment.

From out on the street came the sound of a passing patrol. The boots fell on the cobblestones as one step, and his mind drifted to the patrols he had seen in his day's round of the city. Philadelphia was well patrolled; not with a corporal and six men as the Rebels counted a patrol, but with companies of fifty men under a commissioned officer. Even the guard-mount he had just listened to was impressive. If he judged aright, the number of men marching past the house to take up the duty couldn't be less than fifty. That meant eighteen sentry posts around the State House Yard and two men for the main post. The old guard and the new guard together tallied over a hundred men—Valley Forge couldn't spare that many for Washington's headquarters.

There was as much truth as irony to what Alex Hamilton had said at a council, when he exploded and shouted that the English could have taken Valley Forge any afternoon they'd a mind to—if they hadn't been so damn lazy—thick-skulled—and too fond of Philadelphia and its pretty Loyalist women. At the same time, he had to smile when he thought of Washington's reply; that these were English Army traits, as much to be taken note of as their unaimed shooting from the hip and stupid adherence to fighting in mass formation.

The parlor door opened again, and Jonathan heard Elizabeth give a half-smothered laugh. Something boiled inside him when he heard her easy familiarity with this enemy officer—

"Good night, Major. You'll not forget to send your men for the wagon."

They were at the front door now, Jonathan reckoned.

"Shan't sleep for thinking of you m'dear. Be along with the men m'self to fetch the wagon, if it's pleasing to you?"

"Do, Major. I'll be here."

There was a long pause, and Jonathan waited for the door to close. Only the sigh of the wind and the rush of cool night air bending the candle flames down to the wax told that the door was still open and that Elizabeth hadn't come back into the hall. So faintly that he couldn't be certain he'd heard aright, came the sound of a muffled whisper.

Jonathan gritted his teeth and tried to swallow back the tempest that raged in him. A quick rush of air warned him that the door was closing, and, making an effort to calm himself, he walked into the pool of light made by the candles in the hall. He stopped short when he saw Elizabeth. Her face was flushed, her hair in disarray, and the dress was well nigh off one shoulder, as if an arm about her had suddenly been withdrawn.

Elizabeth had been kissed and fondled by the departing Englishman and had not had time to repair the damage.

"God A'mighty, mistress, have you taken leave of your wits?" Jonathan rasped harshly.

"He took me—I was surprised—I couldn't help it—we—" she stuttered to silence, and, trying to regain her composure turned her face away and made much of adjusting her bodice.

Jonathan stood still and waited.

"He, Major Broadmoor, has fallen in love with me." Her hand went up and she swept her hair back from her face, as she always did when she was at a loss for words. "I can't help it—if Broadmoor loves me."

"Any woman can help being kissed and mauled." Jonathan's voice was contemptuous. "All the women I've known hitherto could."

"You blind fool." Her eyes blazed with fury and she was close to tears. "You stupid blind hidebound fool of a Rebel." She advanced on him, hand raised as though she would strike him across the face. "Has no one told you that you catch no bees with vinegar? You prate of wrecking our plans. Would you have me wreck them by slapping Broadmoor's hands away; or would you have me making my father's imprisonment worse by presenting Broadmoor with a pair of Puritan-cold lips? By your reckoning 'tis all for the cause if you watch me undress, in the darkened window of the Red Lion, and spend the night with me in the same bedchamber— but 'tis contrary to the cause if an English officer from whom I might gain some intelligence kisses me."

She whirled her skirts at him and, with a back as straight as a mast on one of her father's ships, she marched to the stairs. Gripping the newel post with a hand that still shook with rage, she turned and her glance searched him from his feet to his face.

"Major Broadmoor may be English, and an enemy, but he is not a boor."

Jonathan let her go without an answer. He stood quite still in the pale circle of candlelight, and watched her climb the stairs. His eyes followed her slim ankles as she turned on the stair landing and continued on to the second floor. Hearing her bedchamber door close, he walked slowly to her father's room. His mind wasn't on what she had said, but on what she had not said.

Pushing the door open, he walked to the bookshelf and took down the dictionary Stirling used for cipher messages. Carrying it to the table, he pressed the catch, slid the table top aside and took out Jay's writing stain. In addition to the cannon locations, the size of the permanent guards, and the disposition of troops which he had to report, he had a warning to send. He must warn Stirling of the conversation he had overheard, that General Grant with his Highlanders and two or three battalions were to make some sort of attack—somewhere in the vicinity of the Forge on the night of Howe's farewell party.

It was vital intelligence and might mean the saving of uncounted Rebel lives. Yet Mistress Elizabeth, in her singular self-sufficiency, had stalked off to her chamber, and said nothing of it. He pried the stopple from the bottle of fluid and picked up a quill. It was a matter he'd settle with her tomorrow morning, and settle it for good and all.

13   INVITATION TO THE DANCE

Women are troublesome, and hinder us in the great march.——John Suckling

For all their vaunted military superiority, the English officers were unbelievably stupid, Jonathan thought, as he crouched in the thick rushes that covered the low-lying lands close to the ferry across the Schuylkill.

Hidden by the screen of rushes, he watched the South Ferry boat leave the landing and slowly make its way to the opposite bank of the river.

Carrying an old market basket on his arm, Jonathan had made a pretense of gathering wild mosses and lichens as he skirted the marshes, searching for some weak spot in the ring of guard posts that circled the city. The whole area, from behind Ben Franklin's hospital where it fronted Pine Street and was flanked by Eight and Nine Streets, down to the Schuylkill, had been smothered in a boiling, swirling white marsh mist that had swallowed him one moment, then left him standing in clear morning air a dozen paces later.

Since before daylight, Jonathan had doubled back and forth through the marshes with his half-filled basket of water greens. Once he had been challenged by a sentry, but the Redcoat, from Yorkshire, had only smiled at Jonathan's explanation of gathering wild herbs for his sick mistress, and waved him on his way with the advice that water greens held no cure unless they were gathered in the light of a waning moon. And in any case, nothing could equal the mosses gathered on the Yorkshire moors when it came to curing the vapors and such like unwellness.

Crouching where he was now, Jonathan satisfied himself that the English did have a five-hundred-man guard posted between the floating bridge a mile upstream from where the Schuylkill joined the Delaware, and the South Ferry. These English had men to spare. Jonathan shook his head as he watched the ferry draw closer to the far bank. Here they had five hundred men on guard at a place the Rebels would never dream of crossing the river. Added to that, they had more than a thousand men entrenched behind the brick wall around the State House; another point the Rebel Army wouldn't attack, since they'd be within English musket range on three sides.

How often such a fog as this could be counted on was something he had to find out. He turned and looked back at the smokelike curtain that draped everything. Though the clang of the bells was dulled by the thickness of the mist, Jonathan heard a ship's afterdeck bell ding-donging six bells in answer to the lighter taps on the bell on the quarter-deck.

"Seven by the clock," Jonathan muttered, and watched the two horses that operated the ferry stop in their circular track as the boat reached the opposite shore. An old man came out of the ferryhouse and unhitched the skinny beasts from the toggle-bar that dangled from the end of a long pole. The mechanism for operating the ferry looked to Jonathan as if it had been put together from pieces of an old mill, for the rope that pulled the ferryboat ran down a stone-lined sluiceway with tallow-soaked logs laid at intervals in the bed to keep the rope from chafing against the stones. A pair of bevelled mill gears, mounted at right angles to each other in a heavy wood frame, wound the ferry rope around a wooden drum as the horses, trudging in a circle, pulled on the long pole which turned the mill gears.

Picking up his basket, Jonathan glanced about to see that the path behind the ferryhouse was clear. The sentry on duty travelled back and forward across the Schuylkill with the boat, so there would be no one to challenge him, Jonathan reckoned, if he returned to Philadelphia by the path along Dock Creek. As he stood up, he noticed the weather vane atop the ferryhouse. Five minutes ago the arrow had been pointing inland. Now it pointed across the river. The wind hadn't changed. It still blew in his face.

Jonathan thrust aside the fog-drenched rushes and stepped out into the open space about the ferryhouse. The two horses were teddered to a feed trough at the side of the muddy circle made by their hooves as they pulled the windlass pole. The old ferry master, bent shouldered and bandy legged, with a big earring of Spanish gold glinting through his straggly gray hair, stood staring across the river at the boat being reloaded on the opposite bank. His right foot rested on one of the turns of rope about the drum, and his right hand, clenched so tightly that it looked as though the weathered skin would crack across the knuckles, was pressed down on his knee.

"Your weather vane stuck." Jonathan didn't look up, but twisted his head to one side as he spoke.

"It's allus sticking. Don't work no more, it don't." The ferry master didn't take his eyes off the boat.

"It was pointing right way, five minutes back." Jonathan, watching the back of the ferry master's hand, saw the sudden pulse of blood in the upraised blue veins.

"Real observing critter you be." The long leather-like face turned toward Jonathan. "Must be a stranger to these parts. Everbody as used this ferry for ten year knows the vane don't mean nothing."

"A Redcoat officer might think it meant something." Jonathan looked at him significantly. " 'Tis an old device—"

" 'Tis no device," the ferry master burst out angrily. "Now be on your way or I'll turn you over to the Redcoat sentry when he reaches this side."

Jonathan made no move to go. "I heard tell of a Rebel lad who used the same trick for nigh to a year. But he was right sly about it." Jonathan held his hand out, fingers extended, and moved his hand like a fish waving its tail. "This Rebel lad I heard of, he left a bit of slack in the vane—just so's to make it look natural like. A weather vane swinging free in the wind one minute and stuck fast the next—well, like I said, might make an English officer suspicious."

"And just what messages did this Rebel lad you speak of send by this device of his?" The ferry master fished in his pocket and brought out a stump of yellow-stained clay pipe. "Damn little a body could say with a busted weather vane."

Jonathan leaned close to the old man and closed one eye. "They do say that he signalled across the Hudson at Dobbs Ferry to let the Rebel spies know when the river was safe for them to cross."

"Hell's fire!" The ferry master snorted and threw his head back, laughing. "There's no spies here-a-bouts as need warning." He placed his hand on Jonathan's shoulder and spoke kindly. "You're a good lad—but I think somewhat addlepated."

Slowly Jonathan turned away. He felt a little chagrined that he had prodded the old man as much as he had about the weather vane. Evidently the rusty vane was stuck, and just as certainly the old ferry master was no Rebel spy, for Jonathan had given him every encouragement to disclose himself. The truth was, Jonathan thought guiltily, he'd said more than he should, but he'd been so certain that the vane was a signal.

"I had a lad like you oncet," the old man drawled slowly, as he dropped his hand from Jonathan's shoulder. "Cabin boy he were to me—but back in 'forty-six he went and got hissel' drownded."

Jonathan drew a long breath and closed his eyes. He multiplied forty-six by two and subtracted ten. Then he turned back to face the ferry master. "Old witch woman back to home told me I'd be drownded—in 'eighty-two—iffen I didn't hang afore then."

The ferry master looked about him quickly. "You one of Mad Anthony's lads?"

"No." Jonathan dropped his voice. "I'm with Stirling."

"The vane shows the lads on the other side that heavy raiding patrols crossed the floating bridge. Gives them time to warn the farmers to hide stock and grain and the like—and get their womenfolk hidden in the woods. I'll take your advice, too—about giving the vane more leeway to swing."

"How does a body get across on the ferry?"

"A body doesn't." The gold earring shook as the old man turned his head to look at the boat. "You need a pass signed by Howe and countersigned by André—and the Royal Marine guard stays aboard the ferry and collects them. Best, too, that you be on your way afore that bastard of a Marine comes back—for that's what he is—a bastard."

"But at night a man could cross over by hanging on to the rope—if the need was urgent?"

"And he was willing to hazard being shot at." The ferry master kicked the drum with the rope coiled about it. "Them English ben't stupid altogether. They makes me leave the boat in midstream, with lanthorns fore and aft, and they has two of them Marines with loaded muskets aboard for such as tries to get over that way."

Jonathan grinned. "Then I'll try some other road happen I have to cross—sudden-like."

"Best you leave sudden-like now. The ferry is close to being loaded again. Officers from the night guard coming over for their breakfast."

"I'm gone," Jonathan whispered, and stepped back into the cover of the rushes. So that was how the farmers were warned about raiding patrols. As he pushed his way through the rushes his mind went back to the evening he had ridden from the Silver Dolphin to the Red Lion with Elizabeth. Long before the Lobsterback patrols had shown up at the crossroads, the farm fires had been out and the farmhouses deserted. He smiled to himself, and climbed from the marsh to a bridle path that led towards the city. A simple enough device, the stuck weather vane, but it seemed to give sufficient warning to the Rebel farmers.

Thinking of the Silver Dolphin and the Red Lion made him recall Elizabeth, and the talk he intended to have with her when he got back. He gritted his teeth. Time enough for her when he saw her, just now he'd best keep his mind on the sentry posts and where they were located. The English sentries walked their posts in a right smart manner. Their muskets were shouldered at the proper angle, and they made their about-faces at the limit of their posts as if they'd been born standing on one heel. But they were so damned certain they'd not be attacked that they listened for nothing, and looked nowhere but straight ahead as they tramped up and down in front of their guard positions.

Just like the two sentries in front of the hospital which now loomed up ahead of him. By veering to the right, he would avoid them altogether. So assured were they of their own superiority, they'd not even bother to challenge him. Their confidence was galling, and it was everywhere apparent. Last night, lying in bed, he had listened to the roistering officers in the Indian Queen. Mingled with their liquored, cackling laughter, was the silly giggling of Tory wenches, who openly boasted that it was their duty to make the tiresome occupation as pleasant as possible for the invaders. With his hands clasped behind his head, he had listened to the inane giggling as some half-drunken wench, accompanied by her escort, went seeking a quieter spot for the continuation of their amorous dallying.

Turning the corner at Eight and Walnut, he looked sideways at the watch box standing one square away from the Logan house. The light still glimmered in the slotted lantern-like top of the box, but the English Dragoon, who had been on guard inside the shelter during the night, had been replaced by a Hessian Yager with his tallow-plastered hair slicked down under his brass-fronted leather helmet. The Hessian's moustaches were fiercely pointed, and his heavy bullet pouches hung on him like saddlebags on a horse, but his eyes stared uninterestedly along Walnut as though his two-hour guard-mount were a waste of time.

The closer Jonathan got to the Ladd house, the more he dreaded his coming talk with Elizabeth. He was irked at himself for allowing her so much space in his mind. Each time he tried to think out what he was going to say to her he would see her in his imagination, just as she was last night, standing in the hall, her dress half off one shoulder, her hair all askew—flustered and dishevelled and standing tiptoe on her dignity.

The more he thought of women, the less he could follow their reasoning. Even Sally, an honest-to-God Rebel he believed, threw her taunts about the Rebel Army in his face. Most likely these Philadelphia Patriots woud be the first to run to the papers and scream to the Congress were Washington to do as they asked. Couldn't they understand that nothing was to be gained by wresting the city from the English? Food, they might answer. But the food would feed the Rebel Army for a day, mayhap a week, and after that, hunger for the civil populace as well as the Army. 'Twas the lack of ability of the Congress, whose duty it was to buy food and transport it to where it was needed, that left the Army starving. Likewise, it was the Congress' duty to buy arms and clothes, but by the time the committees had haggled and bargained with the contractors, the battles were lost for the lack of arms, and the food and clothing arrived at one point after the Army had left for another.

Jonathan turned north on Six between the State House and the old Logan home. Ahead was Robert Morris' mansion and beyond that Mistress House's comfortable lodgings. If these outspoken Philadelphia Patriots were to try some thinking instead of talking, they might pipe a different tune when they reckoned what would happen to their beloved buildings, should Washington attack the city. Devastation would come, not from the puny two-, four- and six-pounders of Knox's batteries, nor yet from the English or Hess cannon within the town, but utter ruin would be wreaked on home and church as well as defenses—as Baron von Steuben had so often told overanxious officers—by the massive blasts of the British frigates' twelve-pounders and the searing flames born of the nine-pound shells tossed high in the air by the bomb ketches.

No seacoast or river town held by the enemy would be retaken by Washington if the Commander-in-Chief would avoid it. He had said over and over, with more vehemence than he usually displayed, that the destruction of their countrymen's towns and homes had no place in the Rebel Army's planning, nor was such action likely to enlist more citizens to the cause. It was bitter swallowing, but true. For if the Revolt succeeded, they'd have their homes and freedom. Should it fail, they'd have their homes at least. Better that, the Chief argued, than liberty in the midst of chaos, or failure and no roof to weep under.

Turning right on Chestnut, Jonathan was jolted out of his ambling gait at the sight of a beefy red-haired man obviously watching the Ladd house. Jonathan's shoulders tightened. Quick successive waves of skin-tingling alarm signals ran up his spine and hackled the nape of his neck. Stretching his steps and walking more quickly without seeming to, he advanced on the redheaded watcher.

Startled, the man looked up and saw Jonathan. Pulling his broad-brimmed black hat down over his red hair, he turned his back and walked hurriedly toward the Delaware. Coming to the Ladd carriageway, Jonathan stopped and anxiously waited till the stranger reached the corner of Three and Chestnut. Stepping back out of sight, Jonathan saw that the man was more concerned with hiding his features than afraid of being seen. Halting at the corner, the man turned, and concealing the lower half of his face with his hand, he scanned the street with a pair of piercing eyes before he darted off down Three. Standing just at the mouth of the driveway, Jonathan cursed under his breath as he watched the black hat bobbing up and down behind the stone wall till the inquisitive stranger disappeared beyond the first house.

His mind racing, Jonathan walked up the driveway and round to the back door. Now he had to face the disaster he had feared but never really believed would confront them; the reality of someone watching the house. He lifted the latch and went into the kitchen. Maggie, kneeling by the fireplace among her kettles and trivets preparing breakfast, didn't look around, so he went on into the hallway. There was no use deluding himself with the false hope that perhaps the red-haired man was doing nothing more than admiring the house. Had that been all, he'd not have moved off when he saw Jonathan, nor would he have turned to look back.

At the foot of the stairs he stopped, looking at the door to Enoch Ladd's room. He thought uneasily of the dictionary sitting on the bookshelf, and the secret writing stain in the hollow top of the table. Could he have been seen placing the letter in the horse trough? He shook his head and started up the stairs. No one had seen him. It was inky black, and he had been as cautious as a man could be. If the English were suspicious, why had they not placed a sentry on duty instead of a man with conspicuously red hair who scuttled away in such an obvious effort to avoid recognition?

The more he tried to lessen the seriousness of his discovery, the deeper the calamity seemed to grow. A watch might have been put on the house because he was a new servant—a possibility that had been reckoned in their planning. But he was convinced that this was desperately different. An English spy set to pry on a servant would watch the back of the house, not the front.

As he approached Elizabeth's room he tried to be fair. Despite his efforts to drive it away, the most likely explanation was the one that came to his mind most often and with greatest insistence. Elizabeth was the one under observation, and it was because of her ill-advised visit to the prison. He had no notion as to how she had succeeded in visiting her father, but it hadn't been by bribing sentries. Whatever the method, it had entailed grave risks and this cursed watch set on the house was the outcome.

"Damn women anyway," he thought savagely as he raised his hand to knock on Elizabeth's bedchamber door. Women had no place in war, unless it be in tending the sick and wounded. He didn't even know whether to tell her of the red-haired man. She might fly to pieces again, and spend the day running from window to window, advertising to the whole town that she knew the house was under scrutiny. Deciding against telling her, he dropped his knuckles against the door panel.

"Come in." Her voice was surprised.

"It's Jonathan."

"Oh!"

He heard the ropes of the bed creak on the side rails as she moved about; putting something over her shoulders no doubt.

"Come in now."

Opening the door, he went into the bedchamber. Elizabeth, still half asleep, looked at him wonderingly. She had some sort of shawl thing about her, he noticed, but for all it covered she might as well have left it off.

"What is it?" She yawned, and in spite of her wide-open mouth, still managed to look alluringly pretty.

"Why did you not tell me about the attack General Grant is planning on the outskirts of Valley Forge? Didn't you think it of enough import?" He kept his voice low, but for all his effort there was stinging rebuke in the tone. "Could you not guess that it is the very intelligence we should forward to Stirling?"

She looked at him, half amused. "I have no doubt Stirling knew before I did. The officers told me they were going to noise it abroad so that Washington cannot fail to hear of it. It is their intent that he should hear of it—what need then for us to send word?"

"There is need, mistress. Washington, hearing the rumors, will have no way of determining whether they be planned to draw him off, leaving part of his encampment undefended, or whether they are only a device. In either case, some of our lads might be killed, and it behooves us to let Stirling have the straight of it."

"I'm sorry." She frowned and looked straight at him. "I see where I was at fault. I'd thought since the English were making certain that Washington would hear of Grant's attack—there was no need for us to write. If you'll leave me, I'll dress and we can send the message."

"I sent it last night—from what I heard outside the parlor door." He walked to the window of the bedchamber and looked down into the street.

"I heard but little. Perhaps it's best you tell me all that was said. I'll know then if we need to send more."

Pulling her feet up, she rested her chin on her knees and wiggled her toes under the covers. The shawl fell unheeded from her shoulders as she tried to recall what was said the night before. Up Four Street, the Indian Queen was coming alive after less than five hours of silence, and the Hessian bandsmen, already rehearsing, struggled remorselessly with "Rule, Britannia."

"Number one," Elizabeth started. "Howe is going back to England, and Clinton, not Cornwallis, is taking his place."

"I doubt if that makes much difference to us." Jonathan turned from the window. "Unless it is preliminary to the English leaving Philadelphia."

"The officers didn't hint of that." Elizabeth shook her head and her hair fluffed up in its tantalizing way.

"Who did call last night?" Jonathan tried to laugh politely. "Besides your—Major Broadmoor?"

"Colonel Gordon and two lieutenants—Smythe and Bygrove. And Major Broadmoor is not my—" she came down heavily on the "my"— "Major. André and a group are preparing a farewell for Howe. On the eighteenth it will be, and in the nature of something big, from what Colonel Gordon said. A day and night of revelling—with Philadelphia's finest ladies—"

"You'll be asked?" he said quickly.

"Not me," she said. "Remember I'm Rebel—if a weak one in your tally. With the ladies who'll present the invitation list—the Shippen girls and Margaret Chew—I'm a Rebel."

"I'd give my soul to get near enough to that ball to overhear what's said by the officers." Jonathan paced the bedchamber impatiently. "A man might learn a lot in a few minutes—scraps of converse between half-drunken officers—or a word here and there from a fuddled groom or batman."

"But what would you expect to learn?"

He paused in his pacing, and faced her. "Who can say? A colonel or a general holds his tongue no better than a Lobsterback private when he's drunk. I might learn the reason for Howe's recall. It might be, as some of the Tories say, that the General's recall is but the first move in the withdrawal of the English from Philadelphia." He laced his fingers and pulled on the knuckles. "Again it may be that the English Government thinks that Sir Henry Clinton will push the war with more vigor than Howe. There is no limit to what a man might learn—if he could get close enough to hear. I wonder—" He stopped and stared at nothing.

"Wonder what?" Elizabeth prompted him, seeing his mind was far away.

"I was wondering," he spoke slowly, "if I could go there disguised as a coachman. Or if I could get a night's work as a scullery boy, scouring pots and kettles—"

"And you think that as a scullery boy you'd get close to generals?" She laughed derisively. "Nobody with any wits would try."

"I was but speaking my thoughts aloud. Once inside the place, I'd have to guide myself according to the shape things took."

"And the most likely shape would be a cross-beam with a dangling rope—or a musket ball in the back as you ran away. You're haverin', as Maggie would say, and if you don't know it, haverin' is opening your mouth and talking without thinking." Elizabeth folded her arms on her knees and rocked slowly on the bed. "Last night, the officers said nothing of the reason for Howe's recall—or why Clinton had been chosen for the command instead of Cornwallis."

Jonathan looked at her significantly. "Neither a pair of slim ankles, nor a low-cut gown, will cozen intelligence of that nature from them. That takes liquor. As for Cornwallis' not being given the command, I know the answer myself—even if they don't."

"And what might the answer be?" She moved her folded arms higher on her knees.

"The English Parliament thought that their Commissioners would succeed in seducing the Congress and enough of the people with their promises. Cornwallis was to have accompanied the Commissioners back to London in triumph—therefore he wasn't expected to be here. Don't forget that Cornwallis is a Member of Parliament himself." Finished, Jonathan pulled his eyes away from Elizabeth's bare shoulders, and walked back to the window.

"All of which doesn't get you into the Wharton mansion for the ball," Elizabeth reminded him. "You'd be more likely to get in there in an English uniform than as a scullion. Even as a coachman, you'd not be allowed to stay in the grounds."

"Are the officers to wear masks?" He swung quickly from the window.

Elizabeth shook her head slowly. "Only the ladies who may want to, according to Colonel Gordon. All the invited officers, except André, will be the Honorable So-and-So, or Captain, Sir Somebody-or-Other—all too well known to each other to accept a Virginia-spoken Englishman."

"Don't gloat over the difficulties, lass. I can think of a thousand lads out at the Forge who'd risk a hanging for but five minutes at that ball." Jonathan stamped angrily to the bedchamber door.

"I'm not gloating." Elizabeth sat upright. "One minute you take me to task for not telling you things—the next minute I'm gloating because I give you details. You veer like a rudderless ship. Don't blame me because you don't know your course."

"I'm going down to the waterfront. Anything I can buy as an excuse for being down there?" He turned in the doorway and smiled at her, all flushed with her anger.

"Get some saltwater fish if you can. I'm tired of the taste of these river fish. They've got no fight in them and they're flat."

Elizabeth watched him wave a farewell, and heard him run down the stairs. Of course, he'd left her door open, so she swung her feet from under the covers, got up and closed the door. It didn't take any imagination, she thought as she pulled her nightdress over her head, to reckon what was to be gained by secreting somebody at the Mischianza. But nobody was going to get into the Wharton place without one of André's invitations.

Halfway to the washstand, Elizabeth's knees buckled under her with the thought that flashed into her mind. Shaking, she went back to the bed and sat on the edge, while she tried to sort out the possibilities from the impossibilities. More than one Loyalist lass would be denied permission by her parents to attend the ball. Many of the more discreet Tories would be masked. Who would recognize her in costume and her face half covered?

Jonathan couldn't go. But she could. She felt the blood begin to course and tingle in her naked body. It was almost as if she'd been rubbed with one of the rough towels her father used aboard ship. Aglow now with an eagerness that surprised her, she jumped from the bed and started to dress with all the speed she could muster. The risks involved seemed to disappear one by one as she planned her moves. So she wasn't a Rebel by Jonathan's gauge? Well, she was going to do something he couldn't dare attempt.

She looked thoughtfully at her reflection in the mirror as she twisted her dress to tie the tapes. Every step was clear in her mind. She'd get Maggie to fashion a Mary of Scotland costume. The high, ruffed collar would hide the back of her head and her neck as effectively as the mask would hide her face. The long trailing skirt would hide her feet and ankles, and some padding would provide her with the hips she didn't possess.

Not for a moment would she let her mind dwell on the possibility that she might not be able to get a Mischianza invitation-ticket. Trivers, the printer, would be printing them. No one knew for certain whether he was Loyalist or Patriot, but he was the best printer around, and André could be counted on to give Trivers the work. The manner of stealing an invitation would have to wait till she was in his print shop. Then she could determine what was possible, what was safest and least likely to be detected.

She went to the clothes press, opened the double doors, and chose a deep bonnet that hid most of her face. Stealing the Mischianza invitation was fraught with more hazard than going to the ball. Trivers was no drunken officer to be won by fluttered eyelashes and provocative promises. Trivers was a cold little man who had defied efforts to label him as being anything but neutral.

Going back to the mirror, Elizabeth slipped the bonnet over her hair, tied the ribbons, and looked long and steadily in the glass. Were she to be caught stealing the invitation, her scheme would die aborning—and she'd not live much longer herself. For one brief instant she thought of telling Jonathan what she was planning, but pride wouldn't let her. She'd tell Jonathan in good season, she assured herself as she turned from the glass, and went to the bedchamber door. She'd say nothing till she had the stolen invitation in her hand to show him. Half-hearted Rebel was she? She'd show this Virginia Captain how she stood—and make him swallow every last one of his ill-spoken words.

14   BATTLE PLANS

In war trivial causes produce momentous events.——Julius Caesar

Muffled against the night air, which bored like gimlets into his stiff joints, Stirling slid from his saddle and teddered his horse behind the Ironmaster's Mansion. Less than an hour before, a dispatch rider had brought him word that Washington desired a council with the general officers, and that, as always, the Chief wished to consult with him before the others arrived.

These private conferences could not continue for many days longer, Stirling mused, as he waved a salute to the sentry walking his post before the row of log huts that housed the Life Guard. When Charles Lee returned from York he would be Senior Major General, as he had been before his capture, and Washington, always scrupulously correct in such matters, would not keep Lee out of his confidences.

Lee was never completely absent from Stirling's mind, and advices from York about the exchanged General's behavior disturbed Stirling mightily. That Lee would be boastful, and accept the Congress' flattery with his usual haughty disdain, was to be expected. But Stirling's sources of intelligence in York had informed him that Lee was corresponding with too many English officers. It was natural that Lee should write Howe and Cornwallis, and perhaps Grant, since they had been his enemy hosts while he was a prisoner. Other captured officers, like Sullivan and himself, had written formal letters after their exchange, but Stirling's information was to be the effect that Lee had posted two letters in one day to Major André; a completely unnecessary and questionable gesture that sharpened all Stirling's suspicions of the braggart General.

The situation was fraught with danger, yet he was powerless to correct it. The members of the Congress who believed that Lee was the Rebel Army's outstanding general would shrug off the suspicions he could not prove, and they would be quick to say that he was jealous because Lee had superseded him as the ranking Major General. He shook his head grimly. There was nothing he could do. There was nothing Washington could do either, even if he wanted to, so long as Lee could have his way by going over Washington's head, and appealing directly to the Congress.

As Stirling walked down the path between the Life Guard huts and the stone stables that did duty as one of the camp hospitals, he wondered what disclosure of bad news Washington would have for the council. He drew his chin down on his collar and lifted his shoulders, but the ills that had been their lot in the Valley of the Forge weren't to be shrugged away so easily, and he felt suddenly tired; tired of jealousies, and plans that failed, and officers who weren't to be trusted.

In a hut at the far end of the Life Guard, a perforated tin lanthorn hanging from a peg shed an uncertain light over the plank table where Caleb Gibbs sat working on the drill problems Von Steuben had given the Guard commander for his "night work." The yellowish glow also lighted the flagstones that led up to the back of Washington's headquarters, and, turning left, Stirling followed them to the back door.

Jutting out from the back of the headquarters was a log hut similar in design to the soldiers' huts, but twice as long. Here, in this mud-chinked lean-to without a window, the staff did its planning, and the Commander-in-Chief held his councils. Hardly the best of council chambers, Stirling had thought more than once when the snow was piled high on the split slab roof, but then it was better than trying to fit a dozen officers into the tiny parlor that was scarce large enough for Mistress Deborah Hewes to move about in: and especially so since Washington, Wayne, Greene and Cadwalader were over six feet, and his own bulk, added to that of Knox and Steuben, made any ordinary room too crowded.

"Good evening, General." Colonel Harrison, Washington's military secretary, greeted him as he opened the door.

"Good evening, Colonel." Stirling took off his tricorne, and pulled the slab door shut behind him.

"The Chief asked me to be certain I gave you this." The Colonel placed a sealed package on the long table. "He asked me to extract from his papers all the correspondence concerning the Cabal, and he said you should make disposition of them as you saw fit. The General never wants to see them again."

"Thank you, Colonel. Don't tell the Chief I'm here, if he should still be supping with Mistress Washington."

"I won't if you say so, General." The Colonel walked from the hut into the house.

Taking off his deep-collared cape, Stirling hung it with his tricorne on a wooden peg at the end of the hut. He knew, without opening the package, what it contained, and all the revulsions he had felt months ago welled up in him again, almost as though he were learning of Conway's Cabal for the first time. Distastefully, he picked up the small sealed package and placed it inside his tricorne, wondering if he could ever erase from his memory the shocked, stunned look on Washington's face when he presented the Commander-in-Chief with the proof of the conspiracy to remove him from command of the Rebel Army.

Stirling walked slowly to the end of the table and sank into the straight-backed chair that stood against the wall. Not even the vilest intrigues of the worst court in Europe exceeded the meanness with which Washington's enemies had tried to discredit the General. It seemed incredible, as he looked back on it, that such a conspiracy could have continued so long without coming to light. And it was just as incredible that men of such repute as Doctor Benjamin Rush, Samuel Adams, and Burke of Virginia could induce such generals as Mifflin, Gates and Conway to turn against their Commander.

The sealed package, hidden though it was by his tricorne, seemed to have the power of compelling him to look toward it, and think about it, even while he tried to forget it. That Washington hadn't resigned his commission and retired in disgust to Mount Vernon was proof, if any were needed, that the Chief placed his own interests last. That in itself, Stirling thought contemptuously, should have shamed the conspirators who scrambled for position and promotion like urchins after halfpence, and with no thought of the near-fatal blows they were dealing the country. How long could such a man as Washington be expected to endure the insolent slurs and lack of ordinary courtesy on the part of fools in and out of the Congress?

Even now, with all the proof in that hateful package, Stirling found it hard to believe that men could descend to such depths with the deliberate intent of ruining an honorable gentleman. The packet contained letters with Washington's name forged to them. Diabolical letters, supposedly written to Mistress Martha, and to Lund Washington; letters written implying that Washington was not wholeheartedly at one with the Rebel cause. There were unsigned letters too. Hateful, spiteful letters

[134]

written to the Congress accusing Washington of talking disparagingly of the Congress and of insulting Patrick Henry, Governor of Virginia.

Stirling closed his eyes and forcibly turned his head away. Washington had said to make what disposition he wished of the package. Well, the seals would never be broken by him. His own letter to the Commander-in-Chief, exposing Conway and Gates, was in the package, too, he had no doubt, and he needed no rereading of that any more than the others to remind him of the whole dastardly business. No. The package would go, unopened, to Baskingridge, to join the rest of his private papers.

"William!" There was consternation in Washington's voice as he came into the hut from the house entry. "No one reported to me that you were here."

"I asked Colonel Harrison not to tell you, sir. You have too little time with Mistress Martha as things are."

"The Colonel gave you the package?" Washington looked at the table.

"Yes, sir. I will send it, unopened, to Baskingridge."

Washington sat at the table. "It contains your letters to me, with copies of my answers. Colonel Harrison has also enclosed in the package all the forgeries that appeared in the newspapers, and the anonymous letters sent to members of the Congress—at least it contains those that the members forwarded to me. William!"

"Yes, General?"

"Apart from never wishing to see them again, it is time to clear the dispatch cases for more important correspondence."

"Meaning?"

"We must bring on an action, William."

Stirling half rose from the chair. "Bring on an action—how, sir?—an attack on Philadelphia?"

"No, William. I am convinced from all the intelligence we have received that an attack in that quarter is impossible. Your last report confirms that. Captain Kimball draws a correct conclusion when he says that an attack on the city could mean nothing but disaster. With three quarters of the English Army encamped at Gloucester Point waiting to attack our flank—we'd be marching into a trap if we made an attempt on the city."

"My thoughts exactly, sir." Stirling leaned his arms on the table and rubbed his thumbs together. "And any attempt on the troops at Gloucester Point is equally futile. Either the English Fleet sails downstream, and we have to face their guns, or they turn the guns on the city and flatten it. I'd thought, sir, that you were going to await the withdrawal of the English Fleet. They'll have to leave before the French Fleet arrives, and Howe or Clinton—it makes no difference—can't remain in Philadelphia without the support of the Fleet."

"That was my intent, William. But several things have forced me to alter my opinion. I am alarmed at the successes the British Commissioners enjoyed in stirring up a desire for peace, before we have gained our freedom. They have started rumors, dangerous rumors, William, about who, or what, is the Government."

"Intended to raise doubts as to who actually determines the policy of the country?—the Congress, or you as a general commanding an army?"

"More than that. That if I were removed, some other Commander would accept terms agreeable to both the English Parliament—and the Congress."

"Another effort, sir, to get you to resign," Stirling burst out. "Pay no heed to it, sir. They couldn't force you to resign by insults, so now they try the bait of peace in the trap. There have been times when I've had grave doubts as to our final victory—or that I will live to see it. You, sir, and you alone give me the assurance that my doubts are groundless. You may know it, or you may not, but this freedom we seek will not be found —unless your hand is in it. For that reason I resent, most vehemently, the patronizing casualness of the Congress toward your needs, and their demands for the dismissal of some officers and the promotion of others."

Washington leaned back in his chair; pushing his long legs under the table, he folded his arms and spoke seriously. "You and I, William, have no desire other than to live under a civil authority free from military domination. But to win that freedom by means of military domination of the Congress is to admit that the goal we seek is unattainable."

"Even so, sir, others, besides the English, wonder how long it will be before you say, 'Satis superque!' "

"It will not be said by me." Washington's eyes glittered and his jaw firmed. "The Congress may request, nay, demand, my sword, but I will be neither taunted nor insulted nor wheedled into saying, 'It is enough.'" The Commander-in-Chief reached out and tapped the pile of correspondence tied with the tape and daubed with the sealing wax that proclaimed it came from the Congress. "This is a symbol, William. If ever we expect to establish a government of these separate states that will be answerable only to the people—the acceptance of public censure will be necessary for its continuance. Who am I then, to escape it? Since I have accepted the trust thrust upon me, I must needs accept the criticism that it brings— merited or otherwise."

"But when the Congress demands the impossible—"

"The Congress may say that we demand the impossible."'

Stirling snorted. "The Congress has as many opinions as it has members. Which is right?"

"It would seem, William, that the Army has almost as many opinions as it has generals." Washington smiled thinly and reached for a square of paper. "I requested written answers to a question I asked at our last council. Should we attack the English when they evacuate Philadelphia—or let them remove themselves without hindrance?" He waved the paper and put it back on the table. "I have ifs—ands—buts—and shoulds, but all told, two answers: yes, and no."

"And without looking at your tally sheet, I can tell which generals answered yes and which no. The generals who are not afraid to lose a battle said yes. But this war, sir, will not be won by the generals who think only of winning battles to add to their fame—like an Indian collecting scalps for his belt. 'Twill be won by the men who believe in their souls that freedom is worth more than life. What care you—or Mad Anthony, or Greene or Knox, or I—should we lose every pitched battle, if at the end we are left with our liberty?"

"I have no quarrel with your belief, William."

"You talk of generals' opinions. Had Lee not been taken at White's Tavern in December, 1776, and had, instead, been one of your advisers at the New Town encampment, would he have advocated the crossing of the Delaware and the attack on Trent's Town?"

"I think he would have proposed against it," Washington admitted.

Stirling held out his hand, fingers spread. "But Nat, and Sullivan, and Henry Knox and Cadwalader didn't hesitate. And they'd not hesitate now were you to tell them to go fall on the English with their bare hands."

"All that you say follows my own opinion. I know that in the end, our policy of avoiding pitched battles, and wearing the enemy down as water wears a stone, would gain us the independence that is now no more than a word in the Declaration. But we cannot continue that policy."

"Why?" Stirling looked closely at the deepening furrows in Washington's face.

"Because the Congress desires—nay almost orders—a victory. And the civil populace feels as does the Congress."

Washington rose from the table in the silence that followed, and walked to the door of the hut. He dropped the bar in place and turned to face Stirling, his head to one side as if expecting an outburst.

"And because the Congress desires, nay, orders a victory, we are to fall on Philadelphia—and produce a defeat. Or will the Congress produce new generals—and new supplies—and a new army—to assure victory?" Stirling's face was red, and his lowered voice shook with restrained anger.

Very slowly Washington shook his head as he came back to the table. He picked up a map, unrolled it and spread it out, weighting it down at the edges with the sand caster and the inkwell. For once, his usually impassive face showed anxiety. The lanthorn light was reflected by the little white pits in his cheeks, a life-long reminder that he had come close to dying of the smallpox. Almost absently, he lifted a quill and snapped it between his long muscular fingers. Surprised at the betrayal of his own vehemence, he let the broken quill slide from his fingers, and clasped his hands behind his back as he spoke.

"What we face, if the truth were known, is the final test as to whether or no we are a nation. Whether or no we have a government that can govern. The Congress is our Government. The Congress demands a victory, and whether you and I agree or not, William, the Congress must be right—else we have no Government."

"But—but—'tis like ordering a farmer to get milk from a boar."

"Even so—from the Congress' view, it must be done. The Congress has made an alliance with France. Therefore, the Congress must produce victories to convince France that she is not sending her Fleet to participate in a lost cause. We need money—Congress must borrow it—who will the lender be, if we cannot produce a victory to give assurance that our Government will survive, and repay the lender? And who will tender us recognition, or recognize the Congress—and why should they, if we deliver nothing but defeat followed by defeat, even if we ourselves know it to be the best way?"

"Then a victory it must be." All trace of sarcasm and anger was gone from Stirling's voice. A victory, any kind of a victory, suddenly assumed the significance of a crusade.

"The hourglass is on its last turn, William." Washington gestured as if turning a sandglass over. "We counted on time; time to permit withdrawing actions that would cost the English more than they would us: sufficient time to engage in enough such withdrawals that the English would find themselves reduced to an attrited army. But the sands have run out on us, and we must of necessity change our plans."

"But God A'mighty, sir, that doesn't give us more men," Stirling broke in. "Nor yet make an attack on Philadelphia possible."

"Then we must fight them on ground of our own choosing," Washington said quietly.

"Where—and how?"

Washington unclasped his hands and dropped his finger on the map spread before him. "I have given this much thought. Here, in Jersey, are three places suited to our mode of fighting—and therefore not suited to the English—Brunswick, Perth Amboy, and Monmouth Court House."

"And how do you purpose, sir, to get the English out of their defensive positions in the city and at Gloucester Point?"

"By luring them out of Philadelphia—if they do not leave of their own volition." Washington sat in the chair and stared at the map. "I doubt if any of the English officers know the reason for Howe's recall. It may be, as the rumors have it, that it is the prelude to a withdrawal of all troops from the city. Again, we are agreed that the English Fleet cannot remain in the Delaware once the French vessels are sighted."

"I believe that, sir." Stirling leaned forward on the table and studied the map. "And when the English Fleet does leave, it will have to stay well at sea going north on the Jersey coast, because of the long barriers of reefs and shoals that parallel the coastline."

"Then we shall start rumors that the French Fleet has been sighted," Washington said simply. "We'll start the rumors through our agents in New York, in the Jerseys, and in Philadelphia. There is no way in which Admiral Howe can either confirm or disprove the rumors. Therefore, as a precaution, he'll move his vessels to deep water."

"Do you really believe that you can mislead the Admiral on that, sir?" Stirling was doubtful.

"It is information he expects daily, is it not?"

"Yes," Stirling agreed.

"We, as Rebels, will lend color to the rumor by showing that we believe the French Fleet is in the offing. We'll have our troops in New York State break camp and make much of a to-do about joining us for an action because the French are on the way. We'll send big detachments of our lads here out of the camp to add more color to the tale. I'll send a dispatch rider down to Commodore Barry at Middle Town, Maryland. The Commodore has captured two transport ships and a schooner besides some smaller craft. He can deck them out with French colors, and by keeping on the horizon of any craft sailing up the Delaware Bay, he'll soon have Tory fishermen reporting in Philadelphia that they have seen the French Fleet approaching."

"It might work." Stirling was still dubious.

"It will work," Washington said decisively. "Were you in Admiral Howe's place, would you ignore the warning signs?"

"No—I'd reckon it was better to protect my ships by moving out to open water, even should the rumor prove false, than to tarry and find out too late that the rumor was true."

"That is Howe's only safe answer as I see it." Washington nodded. "There is but one more thing."

"Yes?"

"You and I—and you and I alone—know that this is a rumor. We will say nothing one way or the other. I will make new disposition of various brigades—but I will give no reasons for the changes. We will let the rumors all start outside the Valley Forge encampment, but by our behavior, we will convince spies and traitors and Tory-minded that we accept the rumors as truth."

Stirling ran his thumb over the map on the table. "Of the three places you mentioned, sir, Monmouth Court House would suit our purpose best."

"How so, William?"

"The main highway, running through Monmouth and on to the Jersey seacoast, is crossed by ravines, and bordered by apple orchards. In addition there are low hills that are perfect for cannon. I've hunted red fox there—and fished in the streams that run through the marshes."

"Then if we are given the opportunity, we will force them to march by the Monmouth Court House Road." Washington picked up a quill and, dipping it in the ink, drew a circle around the forked roads that converged on the old court house. "When the time comes, we will harass them on their left flank with such force that they will be compelled to march to the coast—rather than north through the Jerseys."

"You seem confident, sir, that they will march." Stirling ran his finger along the words "Atlantic Ocean" on the map. "They may evacuate by sea."

"No, William." Washington was positive. "They may say that they will. Admiral Howe may promise them that they will—and the Admiral may mean it—but once Admiral Howe hears that the French Fleet has been sighted, he'll want no seasick soldiers aboard his fighting ships."

Stirling pulled his timepiece from his pocket. "The general officers will be here shortly, sir; is there anything else?"

"Nothing—but to repeat most forcibly what I said. We rise or fall by the next battle. Nothing could be more disastrous than to have the French envoys arriving in time to be told of another lost battle. Reading between the lines of Captain Kimball's dispatch, I find the temper of the people of Philadelphia much like the rest of the Colonies. Unless the Rebel Army gives them something to sustain them—they'll recall the English Commissioners and accept the Parliament's terms. Never forget that at least one third of our countrymen think that we are wrong. Another third believe the cause just, but that bearing arms in behalf of the cause is wrong. How long can the Rebel third stand out against the wishes of the two thirds?"

"I understand, sir."

Washington turned his head toward the back of the hut. "I hear horses, William. Be good enough to unbar the door. Remember, we give no reason for the orders I have drawn up. Write Captain Kimball to keep an ear open for our rumors, and to report their effect, successful or otherwise."

"Yes, sir," Stirling answered over his shoulder as he lifted the batten from the slab door.

There was the jangle of harness and the clumping of hooves as the officers teddered their horses to the low fence that ran along the side of the headquarters. Lights flashed in the narrow doorway as Mad Anthony, Henry Knox and John Sullivan, each carrying folding camp lanthorns, followed Nathanael Greene into the hut.

"Like waits gathering for a Yule singing," Knox boomed as he closed the door and placed his smoky light on the end of the table.

"The Baron is inspecting my guard on the other side of the Schuylkill —he begs to be excused." John Sullivan, his back straight as a fence post, and his beetling eyebrows drawn in a line across his forehead, saluted smartly.

"Of course." Washington returned the salute. "And the Marquis will not be with us. He has already taken his post on Barren Hill."

Greene, quiet, methodical and tidy, was folding his cloak and placing it on the back of a chair. His serene smile as he looked at the Commander-in-Chief was the equivalent of a shrug of the shoulders; implying almost that the boisterous entrance of the officers was something that had to be tolerated. Knox loosened his too-tight sword belt, and his sigh of relief was like the sough of the wind before a storm. Stirling, rubbing an aching shoulder against a wooden clothes peg driven into the log wall, coughed to notify the group that the Chief was waiting.

"We have had confirmation that Howe has been recalled, and that Sir Henry Clinton assumes the command."

"Oh my!" Wayne stretched himself in a chair. "Who now will take care of Mistress Loring—or does she too depart for England, leaving a sorrowing Tory husband still licking English boots?"

When the laughter subsided, Washington reached for a sheaf of papers stuck in a dispatch book. "The orders I am about to read are to be carried out at dawn tomorrow. We will dispense with any discussion of them tonight. But if you have any questions, ask them of General Stirling when he accompanies Baron—Inspector General—Steuben, tomorrow and the day following."

A chorus of "yes, sirs" followed the Commander-in-Chief's dry suggestion that they hold their peace. Stirling watched the differing degrees of surprise, anticipation and eagerness that began to build in their faces. All of them had seen Washington in this mood before, and all of them knew that it was the Chief's way of disguising his own eagerness, and that action of some sort had been determined upon.

"General Knox will send three additional cannon to the Marquis at Barren Hill. Captain McLane will take them down with him when he reports back to General La Fayette with fifty additional horse."

"Yes, sir." Henry Knox touched his forehead with his finger in acknowledgment.

"General Stirling will give you the extra cannon, Henry. William's artificers will have them ready for you by then."

"Good! Good!" Knox nodded with each boom of his cannonlike voice. "I'll not have to rob any of the redans." He turned to Stirling. "What quirk of nature made you an engineer, William, only Providence can answer. There's not another man in the encampment understands the business of working with iron, save Nat here."

"No need to go as far as Providence, Henry." Stirling chuckled at his own pun. "My mother, with three iron forges on her hands, decided they were my business."

"General Wayne." Washington looked at his dispatches.

"Yes, sir?"

"Take an additional five hundred of your lads, join them to your present strength, and move as close as you can to Fort Mifflin. 'Tis burned out, of course, and little use for defense, but you might be able to cause General Grant some trouble—if his feint the night of Howe's farewell takes him that way."

"Yes, General. I'll move my men before dawn if that meets with your approval—"

Washington's shake of the head stopped the Pennsylvanian. "I want it known that you are reinforcing that outpost, Anthony."

"Very good, sir. We'll make certain it's known."

"You, John—" Washington put his hand on Sullivan's arm—"move your bridge guard on the other side of the Schuylkill downstream about three miles."

"Yes, General."

"We'll place some of Mifflin's old command to double the guard on this side. Choose the spot you think best on the other bank—but get away three miles if you can."

"I know a spot, sir. It makes a good defense."

"Good." Washington turned to the artillery map on the wall behind him. "We don't want to weaken your redans, lunettes and forts, Henry, so we'll leave them as they are. But do hold all the cannon in the park on a twenty-four-hour alert."

"It shall be done, sir." Knox fired his usual salvo.

"And, Henry, detail Colonel Carrington to work closely with William's artificers on all repaired cannon. I want a responsible field officer to know every piece of artillery as intimately as General Stirling and Alex Hamilton do."

"He'll know them, sir, from muzzle to butt to tail spade."

"Gentlemen." Washington held up his hand. "In the past, we have been ill served by some of our sentries and our outposts, aye, and by some of our officers. Between now—and our next action—I want every doubtful man, no matter his rank, placed in a position where he can do us no harm. I want no bayonets wasted on timid men. Give the steel to those who will use it. In the past, I have cheered you when we lost battles, saying that another day would come. The battle we face will not be our last—if we win it. It will undoubtedly be our last—if we lose it."

15   AT THE PRINTER'S

Guile is a virtue when necessity knows no law.——CROMWELL

Making her way along Chestnut Street, Elizabeth was amazed at the change in the mood of the city. The Tories interpreted Howe's recall as the first step in a withdrawal of the English Army, and those Loyalists who had been most outspoken in their opposition to the Revolution were terrified at what would happen to them once the protection of the Redcoats was removed. That the Rebel citizens would take their revenge on the Tories, Elizabeth had no doubt, and she remembered her ride from the Red Lion to the Valley Forge, when Jonathan had said that he believed the Patriots would burn the Tories' houses over their heads once the English had left. At the mouth of the alley leading to the Carpenters' Hall, within view of the kilted Highlander on sentry duty, Elizabeth saw Abel Whitehead, a well-known Tory, shaking his gold-headed cane angrily and shouting threats against the English for their perfidy. On the doorsteps and at the street corners, little knots of men and women openly denounced the King for his recall of Sir William Howe.

As Elizabeth cut across Chestnut to Three Street where Scudder's gunshop straddled the corner with its half-moon doorstep, a freckle-faced urchin, thumb to nose and fingers spread at the sentry, dragged an English flag along the gutter. The sentry, red-faced with indignation, tried to pretend that he didn't see the insult. At the small, iron-gated entry to the next court, a larger group was arguing and shouting. It was made up of Tory women voicing their displeasure over the grand ball that was being readied for Howe, and demanding passionately why the Shippens and Chews and Rodmans should decide who would be invited and who would not.

In their usual manner of doing the wrong thing at the worst time, the English cheerfully went about the business of preparing for the sea-parade, the jousting tourney and the ball. They seemed oblivious of the anger of the Loyalists over Howe's departure, and besides advertising it with song and dance and women and wine, they acted as if they, too, would be leaving the city any day. Over in his quarters, Colonel Cosmo Gordon held court, and gave freely of his advice to two of his subalterns whose ladies had imparted dire intelligence to them, accompanied by threats of what would happen should the junior officers attempt to leave Philadelphia before being bound by the bonds of matrimony.

André smiled in secret at the success of his scheme, and gave full rein to his artistry. He almost forgot his duties as he worked day and night at the Wharton mansion. Squares of ships' sail were laid out on the polished floors, and André, brush in hand, painted the canvas to look like marble. Later, when the painted canvases were dry, they would be wrapped around tiers of barrels, and these imitation marble columns would decorate the ballroom on the night of the Mischianza.

The ladies' committee, hand-picked by André, pouted and puffed, and stewed and stormed over the names of the chosen ones who would display their charms in the Wharton rooms. Trivers, the printer, was having his difficulties with the design of the invitation: "A beautiful piece of design, you understand, and much to your credit," he had said to André, "but difficult to reproduce."

At the corner of Three and the new Market, Elizabeth saw moon-faced Luter Ferris wave her a greeting from his chandler shop, third down the square. The waist-high bow window with its small panes was bright with brass and sailcloth. A shiny binnacle stood like a sentry in the center, and all about were white compass cards with elaborate points and flourishing "N's" to point to the Mariner's North.

Without knowing it, Elizabeth slowed her walk the closer she came to the printer's. She felt that everybody was watching her, and she couldn't shake the guilty feeling that they knew where she was going. All her senses were sharpened this morning. She could feel the tight alertness in her step, in her hearing, and in her sight. Stray words of conversation from the groups she passed were unnaturally loud, and seemed directed at her. The trepidations that possessed her were strange as well as acute. She'd heard sailormen, who had come close to drowning, swear that their whole lives seemed to pass in review before them, and in a flash that lasted no more than a second. Hers was a similar sensation, and it made her feel as if she were seeing Philadelphia for the first time, or through new eyes.

She'd never noticed before that the gunshop had double doors, and that they were painted a sombre black. Somewhat surprised, she saw that the windows in the Christ Church tower were louvered instead of glazed. For all the times she'd been there, she had never seen that before. Most likely it was to let the sound of the bell be heard, but it also explained the gusts of wind that swirled through the church in winter, and set the candle flames to dancing in the big candelabra that hung above the center aisle.

[144]

Arch Street opened up before her, and the sight of the printer's between the tôleware shop and Mistress Betsy Ashburn's flag and upholstery shop sent spasmodic twitches up her legs, and made her throat dry and rough. It was one thing to plan the theft of an invitation, she thought, and another to carry it out. Her mind was centered on appearing natural, and she decided that she would make her visit to Printer Trivers appear a matter of chance. She would go into the tôle shop first, buy a tray, and tell Trivers her visit to him was an afterthought.

With a firm step, she turned into the alley-like space that was hung with candlesticks, snuffers and lanthorns. Spice canisters and tea caddies, painted a velvet-black, decorated with red and yellow tulips and trailing vine leaves, were stacked in piles of varying sizes. The stinging pungency of hot metal and hot pigment followed the owner from the back of his workroom as he came out of the darkness. With no word of thanks, he pocketed the shilling Elizabeth handed him for the small tray with stencilled roses running around the deep-dished edge.

Suddenly, as she left the shop, Elizabeth realized that the tôlesmith's surliness was another symptom of the English occupation. Friendliness and gaiety had been two of the city's features that impressed visitors, and now they were gone. Six months back, a shopping expedition had been a pleasure to look forward to. It had meant friendly chats with each of the merchants. An inquiry as to how the youngest son's broken leg was mending would have drawn out into a half-hour visit. This time a year ago, the tôlesmith had asked her where she had been voyaging, what new ports of the Colonies she had visited, and what strange things had she seen.

The change from friendliness to sullen disregard had been so slow that she'd not noticed it before. Wrapped up in her mother's illness and her father's imprisonment, she'd felt gloomy and isolated, but today she was seeing that these same personal moods had gripped the city. Before, a three-square walk would have seen her stopping to pass the time of day with a dozen neighbors, whereas this morning, she'd seen but three people she knew.

She was so taken up with her thoughts that she found herself in the musty-smelling print shop before she knew it. Printer Trivers looked up as her shadow fell across the bed of the press. He took an extra pull on the toggle-bar of his press, held his hand up to show that he was counting, then quickly reversed the bar and unwound the heavy wood screw that lifted the platen from the paper on the press bed. Carefully lifting the damp paper from the type form, he stuck it on a spindle to dry, and pushed his glasses up on his forehead.

"A count of six," he said solemnly, "not five—not seven—peskiest paper I ever did see. Count of five—won't take the ink. Count of seven—

ink runs. Count o' six though," he pointed to the drying sheet triumphantly, "perfect."

"Your work is always perfect, Mister Trivers." Elizabeth was surprised at the steadiness of her own voice.

"What leaves the shop is allus perfect, Mistress Ladd, but a lot of paper goes to waste to make a good print." He held up his hands. "These got to be steady. If hands shake or fingers are fumbling, paper moves on the type and—" He made the gesture of crumpling a sheet and throwing it away.

"When I was a little girl, and Father brought me to your shop, I wanted to be a printer." Elizabeth felt quite proud of her ability to speak naturally and keep a serious face as she rolled the lie off the end of her tongue.

"Honorable and ancient craft, mistress, but one that has no female journeymen, to my knowing." A quick jerk of his head brought his glasses down on his nose again, and he looked at her steadily. "You were no more than seven or eight when your father first brought you here to my shop." He waved his hand mournfully to the outside. "Sad days we fall on —with your father—"

"But you have much work to do." Irony crept into her voice despite her effort to prevent it.

"What can a printer do, lass?" He wiped his hands on his ink-stained apron. " 'Tis not like other crafts. A man in most any other can lay by a stock to sell in doleful times. If he make gloves, or shoon, or combs or pots or kettles—he can work on them at his own, and put a few away for a day of sickness or the like. But not the printer. What would he lay by? What profit for me to have the English take over my type and press— and me starve? They'd have gotten their work done anyway."

"I can see that, of course," Elizabeth agreed. " 'Tis not so much different from what I do with Father's shipping—when I can."

"Truth is, Mistress Ladd—" Trivers looked around, and a cunning smirk spread over his face—"I take their gold for what they could do theyselves for nothing—had they the wits." He bent down and pointed a bony finger at the stack of Mischianza invitations on a low bench against the wall. "Except for one thing. There, waiting for Mistress Shippen or Mistress Chew or Mistress Somebody, are the invitations for the Mischianza—and there be no other printer in town as could have done a better piece of printing on them."

"I know that," Elizabeth said, holding a tight grip on her voice to hide her satisfaction.

"André let me set my own price—if I executed his design faithfully."

"And did you?"

"They're there for you to look at, with André's design on top of them

—the exact number, and every one perfect. But I reckon there be more spoilt than good ones that I had to throw in the waste barrel."

"I had to buy a tray, and I remembered that I will need some log sheets. You might print them in a slack time." Elizabeth hoped she was showing no interest in the invitations.

"You didn't bring a log sheet with you?"

"No, I didn't expect to come here," she said innocently.

"Oh, I have a copy here—I have." He pushed his spectacles up on his brow again, and turned to a paper-littered table alongside the bench with the invitations.

Elizabeth could have bitten her tongue out. In her effort to divert the printer's attention, she had sent him closer than ever to the pile of invitations. Resolutely she moved across the shop. She'd come to steal an invitation, and she couldn't do it standing, like a statue, five feet from where they were stacked. André's design, a little larger than the full square of heavy paper on which the invitations were printed, lay on top.

"They won't smudge," Trivers said without stopping his search at the table. "Pick up André's design and look at them."

"Thank you, Mister Trivers." She lifted the original and looked at the printed copy. Frustration gripped her when she saw she couldn't steal one. These were counted, and Trivers might count them again before he delivered them to Peg Shippen or whoever came for them. Listening to the printer muttering to himself as he delved through the mass of papers, and watching him around the edge of her deep bonnet, Elizabeth replaced André's art on top of the pile. She turned her back on the bench and moved toward the press. With a twitch that sent her hand to her throat, her heart lost a beat. Hidden from her till now, under the extended end of the press bed, was the squat keg that the printer used for his rejected work. Halfway down the side, surrounded by crumpled sheets of paper, was a Mischianza invitation.

Quickly as she dared, she moved along the side of the press. Now she was between Trivers and the waste barrel. Gritting her teeth and bending quickly, she prayed that the paper wouldn't crackle as she drew it out. She gripped the invitation with fingers that shook wildly in spite of her efforts to steady them. Her neck bones snapped as she turned her head to see if Trivers was still busy searching. The pulsing blood battered at her strained eardrums, and the square of paper made a noise like a ship foundering on a rock, as it rubbed against the other papers in the keg.

She straightened her back, and by sheer will power tried to slow the beating of her heart as she folded the paper and thrust it down the opening in her bodice. A long step took her to the other side of the press and leaning over it, she forced herself to read the reversed lettering of the type set up for another printing of the English Commissioners' promises of "amnesty and redress; the removal of certain taxes: and the representation of these Colonies in the Parliament."

"Ah!" Trivers turned from the disorderly mess on the table. "Here it is." He held up a log form. "Allus find things—if you look in the right place."

Elizabeth produced a smile, and though she wanted to fly from the shop as quickly as possible, she forced herself to appear at ease, and so full of interest in printing that she was loath to hurry away.

"Your invitations are beautiful—and printing still fascinates me—" she pointed to the press—"even if I'm more of a sailor than anything else now. When do you think the log sheets will be ready?" As she spoke she wondered at the calmness of her voice, and hoped that it covered the crackling of the paper inside her bodice.

"I'll hurry it, mistress—for the sake of a visit from you again." He counted on his fingers. "I'll have them for you Wednesday a week."

"Thank you—" She bobbed her bonnet, gave him one of her most dazzling smiles, and walked out into Arch Street.

16   A PROPOSAL AND A TOAST

Honor and ease are seldom bedfellows.——JOHN CLARKE

It was four o'clock in the afternoon, and Elizabeth couldn't settle down to any one thing for more than a few minutes at a time. She had no real memory of walking home from the print shop, and never in her life had she been pulled, first one way and then the other, by so many unsettling emotions. Uselessly, she had attempted to go about the ordinary business of running the house, but Maggie's incessant chatter had driven her from the kitchen, and her mother's interminable questioning had forced her to seek quiet in her own room.

For once, even the privacy of her bedchamber failed to bring calm, and she tried to take stock of what had happened to her. It wasn't the stealing of the invitation, and yet it was, she decided. She had no regrets and no scruples over the theft, and in a moral sense she didn't regard it as a theft at all. And it wasn't real fear of detection, for that had left her so soon as she got into the house and hid the Mischianza invitation in the hollow-topped table in her father's room. Certainly, she argued with herself, Trivers wouldn't be so canny as to count the spoilt sheets he had thrown away, although for the life of her she couldn't see what was wrong with the one she'd filched from the barrel.

Coming down the stairs from Jonathan's room—it was the third time she'd looked in his room, knowing quite well that he'd not returned—she began to get some inkling of the jangled nerves that were the price of playing the part of a spy. For the first time she felt a bond between herself and the Rebel Captain; and some understanding of his impatience with her. She nodded sagely to herself at the realization that, till now, she'd only been skirting the edge of the quicksands.

Patience had never been one of her virtues, and patience was a necessity in spying, she was finding out. She was like a child with a shiny new penny burning a hole in its pocket. She'd stolen the invitation, and she couldn't contain herself till she'd told Jonathan. But there was more than that involved in her emotional excitement. Not only did she feel a bond between herself and Jonathan, she felt a strange sense of being a part of the Revolt, and in a way she had never believed possible. She'd always been a Rebel. She'd told Jonathan that and it was true. But there was a fearsome exhilaration in taking an active part in helping the Rebel Army. Once before she'd felt some of the same exciting dread, when a horse had bolted under her and she'd clung to the saddle as the crazed beast jumped fences and ditches for a mile and a half before he'd plunged them both into a millpond.

As she turned at the foot of the stairs and passed her father's room, she remembered what Jonathan had said about the difference between Patriots and Rebels. It hadn't made sense to her that night, but now it did. She saw clearly that there could be degrees of patriotism. A Patriot could be wholehearted or merely acquiescent. A Rebel was in to the death.

The jolt and rumble of wagon wheels turning into the carriageway sent her running to the dining-room window. Lieutenants Smythe and Bygrove, laughing and gesticulating, were seated on the plank seat of an old wagon urging a skin-and-bones horse to at least try the slight incline. Behind them, dismounting from a sleek, well-fed chestnut, was Major Broadmoor. They had come for the supplies she had supposedly brought up from Virginia.

Pulling aside the curtain, she caught their glances and waved them to the back of the house. Smythe and Bygrove saluted understandingly, but the Major walked up to the front door. Quickly Elizabeth recrossed the hall and opened the door before Broadmoor had time to use the heavy brass knocker that would bring Maggie, puffing and blowing, from the kitchen.

"Accept my apologies for our tardiness, Mistress Elizabeth." Broadmoor swept off his plumed helmet and bowed low. "But my 'boys' have come for your gifts," he finished, laughing.

"You are most welcome, Major. Will you come in and wait while your 'boys' transfer the load?" Elizabeth led the way to the dining room while Broadmoor closed the front door quietly.

Inside the dining room Elizabeth turned, and found herself enveloped in Broadmoor's arms. One of the gold-braid frogs across his scarlet tunic pressed into her chin and she lifted her face. Immediately he bent his head and kissed her full on the lips. Her mind flashed back to the morning in his chamber. She wondered how far he would go, and how far she could let him. To push him away was to admit that the familiarities she'd permitted that morning were for the sole purpose of obtaining the pass to see her father, and there was as much reason now as then not to offend him.

To her surprise he released her as suddenly as he had embraced her, and she watched him glance quickly behind him, step backwards and shut the dining-room door. His face was white and strained as he came back to the center of the room; and for all his six feet and more he acted like a scared boy. She looked at his widespread eyes, usually calm and clear, and saw that they were feverish with anxiety. His jaw muscles were tight, pulling the corners of his mouth into a long pinched line.

"What is it?" She asked the question in spite of herself.

"Mistress Elizabeth—would you consider marriage with me?" Having made the start, he drove ahead as though afraid to stop. "You know I've fallen in love with you, and I can state with all sincerity that I've never loved anyone else. I know, of course, that I cannot offer you the comforts you have always enjoyed, but I believe I can support you adequately and that we could be extremely happy together."

"You—you must have—must have learned that pretty speech by rote, Major," she said, groping for a chair, and lowering herself into it. "Besides the accepted answer—that, of course, I am flattered—I don't know what to say."

"Nor did I, Elizabeth." He spread his hands out. "As you surmised, I all but learned like a schoolboy what I had to say. But it was because time is short. Bygrove and Smythe will be ready any moment and—"

"But, Major, you know that marriage between us is impossible." She held her hand up as she saw he was going to talk again. "General Howe would not permit it, unless I were to take the oath of allegiance to the King—and that I will not do—any more than I would live in England."

"I am not asking you to live in England. Nor to take an oath of allegiance to—"

"Then what are you asking?" Surprised, she broke in on him.

"Only if you would consider marrying me."

"Surely, Major, you realize that with the war, the differences in our positions, you a sworn officer in the King's service, me a Rebel according to the King's edict, a simple yes or no is impossible." She tried to smile as she rose from the chair. "And even without these difficulties, you'd hardly expect the answer this afternoon?"

Broadmoor crossed the room to meet her. He gripped her wrist, and his hand was like ice. "At the moment, I am not asking you to marry me. Only if you would consider it. I know that marriage at the moment is impossible. I think—I shall not return to England myself—for I find my sympathies incline more to the Colonies with each day's stay here."

"But—but that's treasonable talk."

He smiled for the first time. "Therefore my life is in your hands. I am not alone in my feelings. Howe and Cornwallis and Monckton feel as I do. They are more guarded in their talk. Were it possible for Howe or Cornwallis to bring this war to a close with one single decisive action, then I have no doubt they would attempt it. But neither has any love for unnecessary killing, and that is what they consider these indecisive actions to be." He hitched his thumbs in his belt, and drummed his fingers against the pipe-clayed leather. "It will be a different and sadder story when Clinton takes command, and such as Grey and Grant with Tarleton and André are allowed to follow their bloodthirsty way." He stopped, swallowed hard, and went on in no more than a whisper. "I have no intention of being a party to it."

"How can you prevent that? They'll not permit you to resign your commission here?"

"No, Elizabeth. And for that reason I have made up my mind to desert. That is why I asked if you would consider marrying me."

Unbelieving, Elizabeth looked at him, trying to find an answer. Sorrowfully she shook her head. "You may be an enemy officer, but I'll not lend myself to help disgrace you. Nor will I hold myself out as a price for your desertion."

Bygrove's and Smythe's heads, bobbing past the dining-room window, stopped her. Broadmoor walked quickly to the door and threw it open. He turned in the entry. "You'll not indicate to the subalterns—that anything is amiss?"

"Of course not."

He smiled, crossed the hall, and opened the front door. Grinning from ear to ear, the two young lieutenants bowed to Elizabeth standing in the dining-room doorway.

"Your choice of delicacies, mistress, makes my teeth water." Bygrove walked across the hall holding out his hand.

"The mess can never thank you enough," Smythe said, treading on Bygrove's spurs.

"Before we bid you adieu, Mistress Elizabeth—" Broadmoor's formality was too precise—"I have been asked, somewhat impertinently I think, by Major André, to enquire as to whether or not you have a man servant?"

"Of course I do." Elizabeth looked at Broadmoor, not knowing how to take the question.

"Where is he now—in the house?"

"No, he's out marketing. I asked him to try and get some saltwater fish."

"He is a new servant?"

Elizabeth felt a tremor pass through her. She moved out into the hall to hide the shaking of her knees. "He is new to Philadelphia, but he has been one of our servants—almost as far back as I can remember. I brought him up from Virginia because Brodie, the servant who went with me, was taken with the smallpox."

"Thank you." Broadmoor unbound and a flicker of a smile passed over his face. "It was of no interest to me, mistress, but I shall report your answer to Major André."

"I have a letter from a medico—if you would like to give that to Major André," Elizabeth said contemptuously. The tremor had passed, her knees were steady again, and she could not resist the lure of carrying off the scene the way she imagined Jonathan would do it. "Major André may not be so trustful and believing as you gentlemen, he might like to see the proof of my truthfulness. I should like the letter returned, however, for I fear I might require it to show Major André's successor."

"His successor?" Bygrove stuttered.

Elizabeth turned the full battery of her gold-flecked eyes on the officers, one by one. "Surely such a brilliant young man as Major André cannot long remain in that subordinate position."

Smythe and Bygrove made no show of hiding their amusement at her sarcasm. Broadmoor hid a smile behind his hand as he bent and kissed Elizabeth's fingers in farewell.

"I shall not take the letter now, mistress. Should Major André request to see it—may I ask him to call in person?"

"You may. I shall receive him, but I would be untruthful if I were to say—with pleasure."

Not altogether certain that she had been wise in ridiculing André, Elizabeth walked slowly to the dining-room window and watched the officers ride away. It seemed to her that in showing contempt for the foppish head of Howe's Intelligence officers, she was at the same time proving that she had no reason to fear him. Broadmoor had behaved somewhat foolishly, she thought, and placed her in a difficult position, for she didn't know whether or not to tell Jonathan about the Major's talk of desertion. It might be information that Jonathan would value, but to her, it was a confidential, personal matter and she cringed at the thought of betraying it.

Watching Broadmoor ride off down Chestnut Street, she knew that this open avowal of his love for her was going to make him more difficult than ever to handle. When he had time to consider what she had said to him, he'd recognize that she had not given him a definite refusal. And so long as her father remained in prison she couldn't risk losing Broadmoor's friendship with an outright refusal. At last Broadmoor was lost to view, and as she turned from the window, she heard Maggie's voice in the kitchen.

Jonathan must have returned, she thought, and ran out of the dining room. The door to the kitchen opened and Jonathan tramped out into the hallway. He shook his head when he saw her.

"I had to hide in the stables till your guests had gone."

"Major Broadmoor asked about you—on André's orders."

"The devil he did?" Jonathan stopped short. "What did he want to know?"

"If you were new here."

Jonathan rubbed his chin thoughtfully. "I wonder if André is suspicious, or if it was an ordinary precaution? Somebody was bound to report—sooner or later—that I was a stranger."

"I'm certain Major Broadmoor and Lieutenants Smythe and Bygrove have no suspicions," Elizabeth said.

"Perhaps not," Jonathan answered dryly, "but they're not of the same suspicious bent as André. This André may be a devil and everything else to boot—but he is an artist, and there's no denying it."

"Oh?" Elizabeth was surprised. "How do you know?"

"I spent an hour watching him hard at work decorating the Wharton place."

"You—you were in the Wharton place?" She choked.

"Yes. I was determined to find out if there was any possible way to get near it—the night of the ball."

"But how did you get in?"

Jonathan laughed. "I saw a wagonload of mirrors down on Front Street, and I thought they'd be for the Wharton place. I asked the driver if he didn't need some help with them. He said he'd pay me a silver sixpence for helping carry them into the house. So I took the contract and got my sixpence."

"Did André see you? If he did—and then finds out you're my servant—"

"He didn't see *me*. He was in another room." With an air of disgust, he threw his tricorne onto the hall bench, and pushed his hands inside his breeches-band. "It's impossible for anyone to get inside the house and

[153]

learn anything. Already they have guards all about the place, and the rooms are nothing but great big barns with not a place to hide—not even a closet or a cupboard."

"I know," Elizabeth agreed. " 'Tis one of the ugliest houses in Philadelphia. A huge dining room on the right side of the entrance hall, and the withdrawing room on the left side. Both are bare plastering without a break in the walls except the windows. Then there's a music room off the withdrawing room—and a flower room beyond that."

"And no alcove or window recess where you could hide a cat—let alone a man." He pulled his hands from his breeches and pounded the heel of his right hand into the palm of his left. "Not a chance of getting into the place any way."

"I can get in," Elizabeth said as quietly as she could.

"You can what?" Jonathan stared at her incredulously.

Turning to her father's room, she beckoned Jonathan to follow her. She opened the door, and walked to the table. Leaning over, she pressed the catch and swung the top aside. With a flourish of pride, she picked up the Mischianza invitation with her thumb and forefinger, and held it up for Jonathan's inspection.

Amazement, unbelieving amazement, filled Jonathan's face. He opened his mouth, ran the tip of his tongue over his upper lip, and exhaled a long breathy sigh before he spoke. "How in the—how did you get that?"

"I stole it." Elizabeth smiled impishly.

"Stole it—stole it?" He almost shouted the question. "Where?"

"From Trivers, the printer. And don't worry," she went on quickly when she saw alarm in his face. "This is one he threw out. I took it from a pile he'd thrown into his waste barrel."

"Lass, you've taken my breath away." There was genuine admiration in his voice as he lowered himself into the captain's chair and sat staring at the invitation. "I can hardly credit it. 'Tis worth any risk if we can put it to use—"

"I'll put it to use." Elizabeth's eyes sparkled and the gold flecks glowed like flames. "I didn't steal it for somebody else to use. I'm going to the ball—and don't try to stop me."

"If—"

"Yes?" She dropped the invitation back in the hollow top of the table.

"If there's any of that Oporto we had the other night this calls for a toast—to welcome a new-found, ardent Rebel to the fold."

17   SEA STRATEGY

Rule, Britannia.——James Thomson

Not since the reading of the Declaration at the State House had Elizabeth seen so much excitement and turmoil. Looking along Chestnut from Jonathan's window, it seemed to her that everybody, Rebel, Tory, and Quaker alike, was crammed together in one jostling crowd, fighting for a closer view of the waterfront.

Long before the crack of dawn, she had heard the chattering voices of the families along Chestnut and up and down Three and Four Streets as they started down to the Delaware to make certain they'd not miss a single ship in the sea-parade. Jonathan had left the house at dawn. He'd come to her bedchamber and said that because of the press of people, he might be able to get a closer look at some of the English defensive positions without arousing suspicion.

The Delaware had undergone considerable change since the night before. The ketches, sloops and cutters had been hauled close in, leaving a clear waterway in midstream for the frigates. The frigates, thirty- and forty-gun queens of the line, were flying every yard of bunting their signal lockers could yield; everything, Elizabeth noted, except the white flag and the yellow square warning of fever. From flying jib, up to fore, main and mizzen mastheads, and down to spanker boom, multi-colored pennants and swallowtails snapped and fluttered as the wind rose and fell.

More than the Delaware had changed, she mused, placing her father's high-powered telescope on Jonathan's bed. From the moment she had shown him the stolen invitation, he had been so different that he was almost like a stranger. Of course—she leaned her elbows on the window ledge—some part of the change was of her own making, for while she couldn't explain it even to herself, her whole bearing had undergone a conversion without any seeming effort on her part.

It was odd, she thought, casting her mind back over the past few hours, that there could be such a different feeling between herself and Jonathan. She was no more of a Rebel now than she had been all along, but, because her theft of the invitation proved it to Jonathan, the bickering had suddenly come to an end, and quiet friendly debate took the place of senseless, wordy arguments.

Looking at the frigates as they sailed majestically downstream, she understood the galling despair of the Rebel Army, and why so much of Jonathan's talk had a bitter edge to it. She'd been as ready as the next Patriot to criticize the Rebel Army for its failure to recapture Philadelphia, and she'd heard more than one supporter of the Revolt ridicule Washington and his generals and the Army for sitting on their backsides at Valley Forge.

Today's sea-parade was a decisive answer to any who stopped talking long enough to think. One single frigate in the day's parade could flatten the city to fiery rubble in a matter of hours. What answer did Washington have to ten-gun broadsides belching red hot twelve-pound shot? And there were thirty such ships of destruction menacing the city from a ten-mile stretch of riverfront. Even the broad-beamed bomb ketches, ugly little monsters, that defied all the laws of good shipbuilding with their unraked masts towering high, out of all proportion to their draft, could throw fused bombs into the heart of the city and wreak havoc without fearing a single answer from anything the Rebel artillery could muster.

She picked up her father's glass again and rested the heavy brass barrel on the window sill. It must be because she was taking an active part that she felt differently. Yesterday, while Maggie fitted her into the Mary Stuart costume she was to wear at the ball, Jonathan had made clear the danger that she faced in going to the Wharton place. Instead of sweeping his warning aside, as she would have done a day or two back, she had listened carefully, but without wavering in her determination to go.

Almost unconsciously, she saw that the last frigate was passing the Market Street wharf. It was more bedecked and crowded with color than the others, for besides the full line of pennants, the shrouds were ablaze with extra bunting, and the deck was massed with the gaily dressed ladies of the Mischianza. Moving the glass from side to side, she swept the scene. Standing on the quarter-deck of the frigate, drawn sword at the salute, was a tall, blue-clad man, dripping gold and crowned by a heavily braided cocked hat.

"Admiral of the Fleet, Lord Richard Howe." Elizabeth tilted the glass and saw the big, carved lettering *Andromeda* flowing back from the bowsprit. As the frigate passed, she saw that the taffrail was lined with other women in their Sunday best. "Ladies of the committee, I have no doubt." She tried to bring their faces into focus and was certain that Peg Shippen was standing portside, and next to her, Germantown's beautiful Margaret Chew.

Suddenly the glass rolled on the sill, and Elizabeth's heart jumped. The sea-parade hadn't ended with the passing of the *Andromeda*. A schooner, small by comparison, hove in view and in the circle of the lens was a swallowtail of blue with *Sally E* standing out bold and clear in white. She raised the eyepiece of the telescope and followed the rigging down to the figurehead above the cutwater. There was no mistaking the finely carved white splash of letters on the bow: *Sally E.*

Pulling the spyglass from the window, she telescoped it with one furious slap of her hand. She needed no glass to tell her that it was her own brother Rufus who was standing motionless between the foremast and the forward hatch. There was no end to English arrogance, she thought, and threw the spyglass on the bed. Forcing the *Sally E,* and her brother, to take part in the display of might was a cruel, unnecessary turn of the screw.

Almost against her will, she watched the cutters, sloops, and barges move out from the wharves and banks, barring the channel as before. A senseless move, since the *Sally E* and other press-ganged ships and crews were to the seaward of the barrier. Certainly if any of them made a dash for freedom, it wouldn't be by sailing upstream. For all their vaunted sea power, they could commit the stupidest errors of seamanship; a carry-over, she supposed, from the days when generals commanded English ships of the line and learned their seamanship on the quarter-deck instead of the forecastle.

" 'Tis impossible they can be so stupid," she murmured on reflection. "There must be some other reason." She stood up straight and slapped the palms of her hands together. Of course there was another reason. Under the pretext of a sea-parade, the English had readied their Fleet for sailing. The ships carrying the greatest area of canvas were closest to the open sea, a certain-sure sign that! The ships were to move in line, something they'd have to do for their own protection as they sailed down to Delaware Bay.

Excited at the importance of her discovery, Elizabeth didn't hear the door open as Jonathan came in. Gripping the window ledge, she stared down at the waterfront, sorting out the vessels and making sure she was not mistaken.

"What's amiss, lass?" Jonathan hung his shapeless hat on the bedpost.

"Nothing's amiss." She twisted around to face him. "If I'm right— 'tis far from amiss. I think the English Fleet is made ready to move."

"You do?"

"Yes." She gestured eagerly out the window. "The English put on a sea-parade, but while they were doing it they moved their frigates and transports nearest to the Bay. They're in line to sail—I know it."

"You're a smart lass, and doubtless right, for there's talk along the river that the French Fleet has been sighted."

"Where—how far out at sea?"

"I have no notion," he answered. "But if you are right, and the sea-parade has served Admiral Howe as an excuse for making ready for sea, then the French are closer than we reckoned on."

"What did you learn?" Elizabeth left the window and sat in the chair by the side of the bed.

Jonathan pulled off his coat, and dropped it on the commode. "I saw a lot that puzzles me. I went down to the English encampment that you folks call Gloucester Point and watched the troops getting their inspection for the March Past—and the foray they're supposed to make."

"Yes?" Elizabeth leaned forward in the chair. "You sound as if you didn't believe they were making a foray?"

"That's what I don't know." Jonathan sat on the edge of the bed and looked at Elizabeth. "I'd have expected Grant to take his Forty-second Highlanders and Second Light Infantry—but not the Queen's Rangers—nor the Sixteenth and Seventeenth Light Dragoons—as well as the First and Second British Foot."

"It all means nothing to me," Elizabeth said, puzzled. "Grenadiers and Highlanders I can tell apart, but—"

"I wish I knew what it meant myself." He ran his fingers through his hair. " 'Tis an odd assortment of better than five thousand men—odd for a night's foray."

"Why?"

"Of what use are the Dragoons at night?" He shook his head worriedly. "Of what use are mounted troops on a diversionary foray anyway?"

There was a blare of trumpets from below.

"We can get away from the noise in my father's room," Elizabeth said, walking to the door.

"And we'd best prepare a report to Stirling about your thoughts on the movement of the Fleet—and the talk of the French being sighted."

Elizabeth smiled to herself as she ran down the stairs. At last she was going to learn the Rebel code. Jonathan had said nothing to her about it, but she'd known from his attitude that he'd avoided all mention of it because he hadn't trusted her. It was a small matter, and it made no difference who wrote their reports, but it was another indication of her acceptance as a Rebel.

Once in her father's room, she took the dictionary from the bookshelf and laid it on the table while Jonathan dipped a new-cut quill in the inkwell. Looking over his shoulder, Elizabeth watched him write.

Report French sighted
English ready for sea

"There are three things needed from the dictionary to give us our cipher. The number of the page that contains the word, whether it be in the first or second column—left or right—and the number of key words down from the top of the page."

"I understand." Elizabeth was already turning the pages. "'Report' is on page six hundred and forty-two—in the right—the second column."

"And how many words down?" Jonathan looked up from the notes he was making.

"Nine." She glanced quickly at the previous pages. "The word 'French' isn't here." She looked up in dismay. " 'French chalk' is—and 'frenchify'—"

"What number is 'French chalk'?"

"Page three hundred and sixteen, left column, one, two three—fourth word down." Quickly she riffled through the pages. " 'Sighted' isn't either but 'sight' is, on seven hundred—left column—one down. Two hundred and fifty-nine—left—twelve. Six hundred and twenty-six—left—sixteen. Three hundred and eight—right column, and ten down. And the word 'sea,' page six hundred and eighty, left column, tenth word down."

She closed the dictionary, and looked over his shoulder again.

Report	French	sighted	
642-2/9	316-1/4 . . .	700-1/1 ed	
English	ready	for	sea
259-1/12	626-1/16	308-2/10	680-1/10

"The extra dots after the cipher for French, shows that part of the word is cut off." Jonathan pointed with the point of the quill.

"And the 'ed,' of course, is obvious." Elizabeth's nod was understanding. "In the finished cipher there are only numbers, and without the knowledge of which book was used—the English would learn nothing, even if they found the message."

"They'd have more difficulty than that, lass. Remember we write it in Mister Jay's writing stain. They'd find naught but a plain square of paper."

"And General Stirling has a counter-stain which brings out the writing?"

"Yes." Jonathan laid down the quill and, reaching across the table, took hold of her hand. "There is one more thing—before we put it in our report."

"What is that?"

"You're not obligated in any way to jeopardize yourself. You agreed only to give me a haven from which to work. Should you, or your mother, have any fear about tonight—" He left the sentence incomplete.

"I'd be witless not to have some fears," she said slowly. "But you can't go—and you said it was worth any risk—and what would you say if I put my safety ahead of the intelligence we might gain?"

"I don't know that I'd say anything—nor think anything, but that you had a right to refuse."

"I'm going," she said with determination. "I know the English will undoubtedly be on guard against anyone coming unbidden to their affair —but they're not likely to suspect someone with an invitation."

"No," Jonathan agreed. "That much is true."

"Many of the ladies will be masked. So, once in the house, who can suspect me, more than anybody else?"

" 'Tis your reception by the officers at the door that gives me concern—"

"Then you'll see it—from the carriage—and either get me out, or make your own escape." She forced a laugh when she saw the look on his face. "We worry about different things. I know I'll get past the officers. Why shouldn't I? There are no marks, no ciphers, nothing on the invitations—"

Her voice was almost drowned out by the sudden crash of rolling drums. The sound came from the back of the house, and as they ran through the hall to the kitchen, they heard the brassy blare of the Hessian band playing a cavalry wheel for the prancing horses of the Dragoons.

Framed in the kitchen window, and as far as the eye could reach down Four Street, the Redcoats were on the march. At their head, gross and pudgy, and heavily squatted in the saddle, General Grant, Laird o' Ballachulish, was grim and unsmiling. A dozen side drums, tight braced and high pitched, birred and beat the left and right foot for the Light Infantry. Straight out Four Street they marched, guards and sentries snapping to the Present as they passed.

"Six thousand soldiers is a lot of men." Elizabeth was wide eyed.

"And sixteen cannon is a lot of cannon for a foray," Jonathan said speculatively.

"Seems like an odd route to take to go anywhere near the Valley Forge. The pike to the Forge lies out Chestnut, to the west—not north to the York Road as they're heading now."

"There's more than that looks odd, Elizabeth. These men are carrying bedrolls strapped to their knapsacks. Men don't burden themselves with bedrolls for a night foray."

"Not even the English sodjers?" Maggie asked from behind the curtain on the back-door window.

"Not even the English, Maggie. If these men are headed for any place near the Old Forge, they'll get there before dark—and that doesn't tally with a night foray." Jonathan turned and, placing his arm about Elizabeth's shoulders, gave her a sudden hug. "If you're determined on tonight's business—keep an ear open for some word on this." He inclined his head to the marching troops. "They look to me as if they were going to camp out all night."

"We should include this in our report—even if you already reported it to Stirling?"

"Yes, lass." He dropped his arm from her shoulder. "If camping out all night means some sort of action tomorrow, there may still be time to warn Valley Forge."

18   INTERLUDE

If you want to dance you must pay the piper.——Scots Proverb

In the tense silence of Sally Ladd's bedchamber, Elizabeth took her black silk mask from the knob that adjusted the cheval glass. There was something sombre about her reflection in the mirror as she placed the mask over her face, and even her mother withheld the criticism she was going to make about the length and width of the opening in the bodice.

Maggie was torn between pride in her needlework and fear for Elizabeth's safety, but, with Scots stubbornness, she said nothing. She'd had her say earlier, when she'd told Elizabeth that she was walkin' straight tae her doom, just as Mary o' Scotland had done when she crossed the drawbridge into Loch Leven Castle.

Jonathan's eyes searched her from velvet cap to pointed toetip, looking for any sign that would betray Elizabeth Ladd behind the disguise of Mary Stuart. Somewhat disturbed at his thoughts, however, Jonathan wondered if he'd feel as much concern if some other lass were going to the ball.

Elizabeth turned slowly before the glass. No one would recognize her, of that she was certain. From the puffed sleeves to the laced-in waist, the jet black of the bodice gave her chin and neck, and the beginning curves of her bosom, the appearance of carved ivory. The full skirt, falling in rippling folds over the ribs of the farthingale, could have hidden any pair of legs, and only the suspicion of a high instep and pointed toe could be seen peeping from the heavy brocade hem. The stiff-starched, white-ruffed collar stood up, fanlike behind her head, and the black diamond of a cap, coming well forward, created a Mary-like widow's peak.

"We'd best be starting." Jonathan's voice, strained and louder than he'd meant it to be, shattered the silence like the breaking of a window. "It might cause unnecessary suspicion were you to be tardy. There will be less scrutiny if you enter the Wharton mansion with one or two others, rather than alone."

Obediently, Elizabeth left the mirror, and crossing to the bed, kissed her mother. "Have no care," she whispered. "I'll be all right."

Jonathan picked up a voluminous cloak and threw it about Elizabeth's shoulders. "We'll keep your dress hidden from any curious eyes till we reach the grounds."

Waving to Maggie, Elizabeth followed Jonathan out onto the landing and down the stairs. She felt curiously light and free in her mind, and a vague, but nonetheless vivid, excitement mounted within her as she took each careful descending step on the wide staircase. She'd felt some of the same stirrings earlier in the day, and with a glow of pride, when Jonathan had coded the message to Stirling, ending it with the information that at the risk of her life, the lady would attend the ball.

It wasn't that she was devoid of fear, for there was no denying that she was taut as a fiddlestring at the nearness of the adventure; but a pose of unruffled composure was what she had to display when she presented the Mischianza invitation, and she had to set about achieving it.

A blast of night air swirled through the kitchen as Jonathan opened the back door. Elizabeth stood hidden in the entry while Jonathan looked about the back yard and down the carriageway. When he came back and opened the carriage door, the signal that the way was clear, she ran out to the yard.

"You don't look afraid, lass," he whispered softly over his shoulder as he mounted to the driver's seat.

"I don't rightly know whether I am afraid or not." She settled back in the leather seat, sitting bolt upright to keep from crushing her ruffled collar. "But I'm no cozey to play only the safe wagers. If I'm to gamble—I'll gamble all the way."

She sounded braver than she felt, but took secret delight in the result of her answers, for Jonathan waited no longer and the carriage rolled away at his slap of the reins. Watching his back, she was amazed to see how much the coachman he looked with his double-caped cloak and broad-brimmed, Quaker-like hat. Late that afternoon Maggie had dug around in the upstairs clothes press, and as she said, "In the hindmost corner of the press—there was the old cloak and bonnet."

Certainly Jonathan looked less a Rebel captain than ever, sitting hunched up on the driver's seat. He belied his six feet, and could pass for an old man huddled and bundled against the night. The lank Virginian possessed the uncanny ability to lose himself in his surroundings or to become whatever he chose for the moment, servant or coachman, and doubtless if he wished could wear an English uniform with all the necessary insolence, if it weren't that his South talk would betray him. That he had made good use of his journeying about the city was evidenced by the route he was following. She'd not have picked a better herself for the avoidance of patrols and sentries, and he had tacked his way left and right southward from Two Street to Lombard down King to South, and was swinging onto Front without passing a lighted tavern or a lantern-topped watchbox.

Fog was crowding in on the riverfront, swirling down from White-marsh and deadening sight and sound as it rolled in banks of dripping smokelike wreaths across the low-lying ground. Port, starboard and running lights of the vessels in the river were dull and blurred. The never-ending creaking of ropes and spars combined with the racking of timbers to fill the air with a tremulous cacophony that vibrated up and down the scale as ships pitched and rolled with the current.

These were the sounds that put a sailor to sleep, but were more like to set a landsman's teeth on edge, she thought as a blare of lights from the Wharton mansion jumped suddenly from the surrounding dark. Spluttering torches, stuck in the crevices of the wall, outlined the gardens; beyond them, the windows of the house reflected the candle flames dancing like fireflies on a mist-shrouded summer's night.

The carriage stopped at a low side gate. Jonathan leaned back over the driver's seat and spoke in a whisper.

"Do you know where you are?"

"Of course! What do you mean?"

"We're on a direct line with the withdrawing room—"

"I know." She felt faintly irritated. "I've been here half a hundred times."

"Then you'll know, lass, that the flower house is on the end of this wing."

"I do. What has—"

"Hear me out. The only door open to the outside, except the big double doors of the entrance hall, is the door to the flower room. All the others are covered with sailcloth and mirrors except the entry to the flower room—"

"Because it leads to the necessary house?"

"Your reckoning is right, lass, even the English have need of them. Should you feel you're under suspicion, don't waste time and don't go out the front door—get to the side door and run out here, I'll be waiting."

"I'll remember." She was anxious to get on with the matter. "I'll remain in the background till things are moving well."

"Good luck, Elizabeth. I'll drive you to the front and come back here, soon as you've 'lighted." He picked up the reins again and the carriage moved along the side of the gardens. Strains of music came from the house, lights shone down on the honor guard standing at stiff attention along the front wall. A six-foot-six sergeant major Guardsman assisted the ladies from the carriages then they stopped momentarily at the front gate.

"Four, three, two—" she counted to herself as the carriages rolled to a stop, then moved on to make way for the next. Though she'd braced herself for it, she held her breath as the sergeant major, his towering fur busby bending down like a funeral plume, opened the door when Jonathan pulled the carriage to a stop.

"Good evening, Milady!"

His white-gauntleted hand was steady as a stair rail. She leaned confidently on it, and stepped down from the carriage, letting the cloak fall to the floor behind her. There was an approving gleam in his eye, when he saw her in the light, and the steady hand shook slightly at her huskily whispered, "Thank you, Sergeant Major."

Carelessly holding the Mischianza invitation in the same hand that held her skirt clear of her toes, she walked with regal tread up the path and mounted the three marble steps at the front door. A bead-bedecked and feathered Indian princess, and a too-plump Anne Boleyn were handing their invitations to a pink-cheeked subaltern with a tired smile. The smile was revitalized when Elizabeth held out her ticket and she noted, happily, that he paid more heed to the open neck of her bodice than he did to the invitation.

Her elation was cut short when she saw a second subaltern write "Anne Boleyn" on the invitation of the guest ahead of her, and then hand the invitation to a captain who stood to the rear with a guest list in his hand. Here, she thought, was the unknown factor Jonathan had warned of, but she walked on into the house with a steady step and her head held high. Even though they were checking the costumes of the masked guests, they couldn't be certain of anything till the last guest had arrived and they found an extra invitation. And how could they be certain that one of those who had declined to attend, hadn't had a change of mind and decided to come.

The two rooms opening off the center hall were bright as day in contrast to the dark outdoors, and wherever she looked, costume after costume was reflected over and over in the eighty-five mirrors André had borrowed for the occasion. She had to admit that Sir William Howe's Chief of Intelligence had proved his artistic ability. What small wall space wasn't covered by mirrors was panelled in a pale blue with the narrowest of gold beading, and one of the ugliest features of the Wharton house, the square plastered pillars that framed the entrances to the rooms, had been disguised by André's sailcloth-marble columns.

On a draped platform in the corner of the large room, a Hessian band, puffing and blowing, wrestled with an English Morris dance. To her relief, Elizabeth saw that recognition of anyone masked was nigh to impossible. What with the candle-filled chandeliers hoisted as high as possible and the dozens of reflections in the mirrors, the rooms were dizzy gluts of color, and even the officers' faces were flat and featureless if they were more than a dozen paces across the room.

An excited murmur on her left caused Elizabeth to turn toward the door in time to see a bronzed colonel of the Forty-second make an impressive entry. His bonnet was perched on top of a hayrick-shaped shock of red hair. The tartan of his plaid flowed from under an enormous cairngorm mounted between silver stag antlers on his shoulder, and his kilt swung from his hips, showing a weathered tan that extended well above his knees.

He marched into the room, staring haughtily from right to left till his eyes caught Elizabeth. With a steady step that shook fire from his feet every time the candlelight struck the glittering buckles on his brogues, he advanced to her side. Bowing low, a mildly mocking smile on his craggy features, he took her hand and kissed it.

"Mary o' Scotland—a Montrose at yer-r ser-r-vice."

"Thank you m'Lord." She tried to combine some of Maggie's burr with her husky whisper. "The gatherin' o' the clans I trow," and inclined her head to the door where the Royal Highlander's drum and pipe majors all but filled the opening.

"Aye, your Highlan' Majesty. Now you'll hear music!"

The drum major stepped into the room. A protective leopard skin, covering his velvet tunic with its silver clasps, fell to the edge of his kilt in front, while the beast's head and dangling forelegs draped his shoulders like a collar. Two drummer boys lifted the bass drum to the crossed leather straps on his chest, and handed him the drumsticks. Beside him the pipe major blew the bag o'pipes full, and all eyes were on the slowly disappearing creases and folds in the green and black tartan of the Royal Highlanders that covered the bag. The bag was full, held tightly under the piper's arm, and the drone pipes spread fanlike on his shoulder. His fingers were pressed on the holes in the chanter pipe, and his eyes waited the first twirl of the drum major's sticks.

Sticks whirled in the air and fell crashing on the drum. The first snap note of "Over the Water" skirled through the room, and the officers stood at stiff attention as the ladies curtsied to the pipe toast to the King. In two lines, other pipers filed into the room, each piper joining in as he took his place in the circle forming around the pipe major until Elizabeth knew the wail and skirl must be heard over in Scotland itself. Without a pause or break, the tune changed from the toast to a wild Highland reel, and Elizabeth found herself being alternately whirled and dragged around the room by the kilted Colonel.

In moments the maple-block floor—pride of the Whartons' house—was a sea of chattering dancers. Thanks to God, she thought, the Scots took their pleasures seriously, and the Colonel, as intent on his dancing as he would be on fighting, said nothing and didn't want her to say anything either.

Instinctively it would seem, the Colonel knew when the dance would change, for he released her to a slim major of Dragoons on the beat that ended the reel and started "Bonnie Dundee."

"A brave scene of revelry, Milady." He held her more tightly than had the Colonel.

"Yes, Major. We've seen many brave scenes today." She was afraid her voice was too low, but his bent head brought her lips close to his ear.

"An' which would you say, Milady, was the bravest?"

"Truth is, and with no offense, Major, I have little liking for ships," she lied. "Nor am I too fond of horses. For my own I thought the troops marching off for Valley Forge were the brave sight. A matter of sympathy, doubtless," she said after a few dance steps—and prodded by the discovery that the Major's breath was loaded with liquor.

"Grant would laugh at your sympathy, fair lady. He's a lucky dog."

She made no answer, but allowed herself to yield more and more to his tightening arm. Closing her eyes, she returned the tentative squeeze of his left hand.

"You prefer military parading to dancing?" he asked when they had danced around the room.

"Oh, 'tis not that, Major!" She whispered, "But we are all looking for the war to end—and troops on the march seem to bring the end nearer."

"Grant's march will bring the end nearer, never fear." He dug his chin into her shoulder in what she supposed was a confidential move. "But like you, I prefer military action—and, no offense, Milady, I wish I were joining him now."

The music ended with a crash, and she took his proffered arm as he guided her to the opposite side of the room. Halfway there, a subaltern approached the Major and discreetly signalled him. Bowing an apology, the Major hurried away and Elizabeth, feigning indifference, watched him go to the door and talk hurriedly with a Grenadier officer in field dress. For a moment, her heart leapt to her mouth. Had they discovered some mistake in her invitation? How could they? It was now with all the others, and in the earnest confab at the door, neither the Major nor the Guardsman had glanced her way.

Caution was strong, and she continued her walk so that it would bring her near the entrance to the flower room. In spite of the pipe band, or because she was becoming used to it, her ears picked up stray snatches of talk from the groups scattered about the room. A brawny-armed and pigeon-breasted Boadicea, big even for that Druid queen, was holding forth to Cleopatra—whose nose may have been the same length as that of the Serpent of the Nile, but who lacked all other voluptuous attributes of Antony's mistress.

"I'm told," Boadicea whispered in a foggy roar, "that their fathers forbid them any more dancing."

"No one can tell," simpered Cleopatra, "since so many are masked."

"The fathers Chew and Shippen alike can be quite forceful." Boadicea bobbed her brass helmet sagely. "If they said no I doubt if the daughters are here."

From their glances, Elizabeth gathered that the Shippen girls and Peggy Chew—if indeed they were at the ball—must be in the dining room on the other side of the main hall. So she'd avoid that room. Gradually it dawned on her that other little groups of officers were forming in corners, around the floor, and in the flower room. The word "Frenchie" caught her ear, followed by a cautionary "hush." As she turned her head slowly, the band piped a new dance, and a shy subaltern, in a very new uniform, stood bowing before her.

"The honor, Mary of Scotland?"

She accepted his arm and he spun her away in a dance she didn't know, but which seemed to consist mainly of linking arms, spinning twice, then linking opposite arms and going through the giddying spin again, but in the opposite direction.

"I've not seen Sir William this evening," she spoke airily as if the thing were of no consequence, "but I was tardy in arriving—he may have been present earlier."

"The General is here," the subaltern said politely, as they changed arms. "He's in council in one of the rooms above."

He showed no more disposition to talk than the Highland Colonel, and Elizabeth, remembering Jonathan's warnings to ask no questions, finished the dance in silence, and smiled sweetly on the baby-faced subaltern as he bowed his thanks.

Finding herself at the flower-room doorway again, she was about to enter when the words "capture" and "Broadaxe" stood out clear and unmistakable from the jumble of conversation inside the room. Pretending to adjust her mask, she turned slowly from the doorway, straining every nerve to hear what was being said. All she could see beyond André's imitation marble column were the draped folds of an officer's field cloak. "Shorter by six miles on the ridge—" the man in the cloak said, and then she caught the words "*Andromeda*" and "Schuylkill," before the rumble of voices buried the rest of the sentence.

Certain that she had stood in one place long enough, and fearful lest she become noticeable, she moved slowly along the edge of the floor. Suddenly she recalled what the Major had said. Not so much what he had said, as how he had said it. "I wish I were joining him now." That could mean that he, the Major, was joining Grant at some other time—later tonight perhaps? She gritted her teeth and turned about. What had she come to the ball for, to walk away from a confab between officers, or to learn what they said?

The group was larger than when she had walked away. Someone was talking in a tone that tokened instructions of some sort, for she heard, "Bide your time till Grant comes over Cold Point to Plymouth—"; another voice cut in—"I'll leave afore midnight—"

In one sudden rush, the picture was clear to her. Broadaxe—Cold Point—Plymouth—Ridge—Frenchie, and *Andromeda*. They were preparing more than an attack on La Fayette. They were going to capture him! That's what was meant by *Andromeda*; Howe's flagship was anchored at the mouth of the Schuylkill awaiting the Marquis. Grant's march out the York Road was a trick. For one horrible second her feet stuck to the floor. She felt if she tried to move she'd keel over. Venturing a look around to see if anyone had been witness to her momentary panic, she saw the kilted Colonel walking deliberately toward her. Doubtless, he wanted another dance; she groaned inwardly, but forced a smile of recognition to her face. He stared straight at her, unsmiling, and too late, she saw he was carrying a Mischianza invitation in his clenched fist.

There was nothing for it but flight—instant flight. She turned toward the flower room and walked as quickly as she could. The Colonel must be at the entry by now, she thought, but daren't look behind to see. Once in the flower room she'd move even more quickly, and she almost commanded her feet not to run.

"Mary o' Scotland!"

She pretended not to hear, and hoped that the other guests between her and the outside door would assume that she was hurrying to the necessary house. Somehow, the officers had checked the invitations more quickly than she'd believed possible. Perhaps they only wanted to ask a question, but she wasn't going to wait and see. In the flower room, officers and ladies alike smiled and tried to draw her attention to the pursuing Colonel. She smiled inanely in return and pointed to the garden. Knowing winks and laughs greeted her gesture, and one guest in a Quaker costume no Quaker would ever wear, said in most un-Quakerish humor, "Go it, lass, a' hope thee makes it."

"Stop her! Stop her!"

Smiles faded at the Colonel's shouted order. Caution was useless now, and she flung herself past a restraining arm, through the flower-room doorway, and out into the garden. Now more voices were raised in clamor and she felt, rather than heard, the pursuit behind her. The white-ruffed collar was a splash of light in the darkness, and tearing it from her neck she held it in front of her as she pulled her skirts to her knees and ran for her life across the uneven grass.

Back at the house, someone was shouting for torches, and above the general babel she could hear the Colonel's Scots brogue damning the sentries for not barring her way. The distance across the garden had seemed short when Jonathan pointed it out to her, but now it taxed her breath and her knees were shaking as though they'd let her down at each succeeding step. What had gone wrong? The thought kept pounding in spite of danger threatening her. And where was Jonathan? He must have heard the furor.

She risked a glance over her shoulder, and saw torches dotting the garden. But they were spread out, and indicated that the searchers couldn't see her. Thanks to God her dress and hair were black, and except for her collar and hands which she held firmly in front of her—

"Beth?"

"Yes!" she gasped.

"This way, lass." His arm was about her almost before the words were out. She felt her feet leave the ground as he lifted her bodily across the ditch and onto the hard road. The carriage loomed up, and seeing that the door was open, she threw herself inside. In one gesture, it seemed, Jonathan slammed the door, climbed up the wheel, shook the reins, and the carriage rolled off, leaving the river and the Wharton house shrouded in mist behind them.

As the carriage gathered speed, she leaned over the top of the door and looked back at the Wharton place. The moving torches seemed to be confined to the one short strip of riverfront, so the sentries must still be searching the grounds for her. Letting the horse have its head, Jonathan leaned back over the seat.

"What happened, lass? Or do you know?"

"Not for certain-sure." She was still panting for breath. "A young officer wrote the names of the costumes on the invitations as we went in—and then passed them to a captain who had what I think was a guest list."

"Ah," Jonathan said grimly, "I'll wager that André had a list of the guests' costumes—even if certain ladies' identities were supposed to be secret. What warned you to run?"

"A colonel—walking toward me—carrying an invitation. And when I started out into the flower room he called after me, 'Mary o' Scotland.'"

"When you get your breath, lass, tell me if you learned anything."

"I learned much." She stood up in the carriage and spoke loudly to make herself heard over the rumble of the carriage wheels. "There's a plot to capture La Fayette."

Jonathan almost pulled the horse out of the traces as he leaned back. "A—a plot to capture La Fayette— How do you know?"

"I heard enough. Some officers were in field dress, and they were passing orders to the other officers there. From snatches of conversation in different groups—I heard 'Frenchie,' and 'Cold Point,' 'Ridge' and 'Broad-axe'—as well as '*Andromeda*' and 'Schuylkill.' "

"The *Andromeda* is anchored at the mouth of the Schuylkill, I saw that myself," Jonathan called back to her.

"Ridge is the main pike to Barren Hill. Cold Point is a hill over-looking the crossroads at Plymouth Meeting just beyond Barren Hill. And Broadaxe Tavern is just beyond Cold Point. An army coming down that road would come between Barren Hill and Matsons Ford across the Schuyl-kill."

"Cutting La Fayette off from Valley Forge." Jonathan's voice was hoarse. "I'll have to warn them."

"Go yourself?" Elizabeth stuttered as the carriage bounced over a rutted spot in the road.

"What else? Stirling and the Valley Forge lads aren't looking for anything like that—nor is the Marquis. We sent them wrong information, lass. 'Tis no fault of ours—but I'll have to warn them."

"If we get home—" Elizabeth clung to the rail behind the driver's seat—"I'll show you a quick way to Barren Hill, on Father's map."

"We'll get home." Jonathan slapped the reins and urged the horse to greater speed. "Or we'll hang."

"You have a plan?"

"I have, lass, but this is no place to stop and try to put it into effect. We'll put a mile more distance between us and Wharton's."

"Where are you going?" she asked as Jonathan wheeled the carriage to the left.

"A roundabout way that will take us in from the top end of the city, the west, in the stead of driving in from the south. There is a deal of shouting and noise back there behind us, but I doubt if any of it will be heard up and around the State House. We'll go out a bit yet, then turn west—"

"But we'll meet patrols and pass sentries on this road, same as any other."

"True—but I doubt me if they're looking for a carriage. Most like they're falling over their own big feet looking for a Mary Queen of Scots on Shank's mare."

"I'd not thought on that."

From behind them, a deafening roar split the air. Flashes of light leaped across the dark sky, followed immediately by more thunderous crashes. There were shrill whistles and bellowed orders, faint and indistinguishable in the distance, with musket shots following on the heels of the orders, and the whole drowned out by another reverberating crash.

"That's gunpowder," Jonathan said decisively.

"It came from the Wharton place—I saw the house in the flashes."

"It was near there. But that was no part of the hunt for Mary. They'd not be blowing up the waterfront for that."

"It might be a powder magazine on one of the frigates."

"Nay, lass." Jonathan turned his head. "Look again—no sign of fire there. It sounded to me like powder that was loose packed—powder that had been spilled somewhere. Whatever it be—" he whipped the horse up —"'twill serve us in good stead. Hearing that how-de-do, no one about the State House or Chestnut is going to bother much about a carriage with a drink-fuddled groom in it."

"The rest of your plan?"

"Can you get out of your Mary clothes while the carriage moves?"

"I can. But I'll be left sitting here all but naked."

"All but naked, lass, is better than being all dead—as you would be— were the English to find the clothes in your house. We've got to bury them, or sink them in the duck marsh as we pass by." He turned and laughed at her in the dark. "You'll not be naked. You'll put on my cloak, and take the reins. I'll lie down on the carriage floor. And if we're stopped—you had to get the carriage out to carry your bibulous servant home from a tavern."

"I'll do it—" She started taking off her velvet cap. "I saw most everything at the ball, but no Godiva."

The carriage rumbled along as she held on with one hand, untying the tapes of her Queen Mary costume with the other. From the talk she'd overheard between the officers the attack on La Fayette couldn't begin before daybreak. Grant's men, on their roundabout route, couldn't be expected to march over twenty miles and fight a battle without some rest. She remembered that Jonathan had remarked on their bedrolls, so most likely they were camping for the night at some hidden spot. If Jonathan could get home quickly enough he'd be in time to warn La Fayette, since the route she could show him on the map would take but twelve miles, and whatever English troops were leaving Philadelphia to join Grant couldn't march along the trail she knew.

Letting her costume fall about her feet, she sat down and started unlacing the clumsy farthingale and uncomfortable stomacher. "I'll need that cloak in a minute, Jonathan." Her teeth were chattering and the cool air was turning her skin to gooseflesh. "Why can't I keep the stays?" she demanded, scrambling to her feet. "Other women wear them. They can't be linked to my Scots dress."

"You know best." He slipped the cloak from his shoulders, and dropped it back into the carriage. "Put on this cloak, and climb up here."

He pulled the horse to a stop and jumped down from the seat. Gathering her clothes together he placed them in her cloak on the carriage floor. "I'll get me a good-sized stone," he said, and went to the edge of the road.

Warmer now, with his cloak wrapped about her, she got up on the seat. With the warmth came added courage, and she contemplated the next moves with some of the enthusiasm she had enjoyed when she started out. Except for the foulest luck, they should be able to get back to the house. Sentries or no sentries, it was unthinkable that, having come this far, they should be caught in the remaining nine squares.

"This should serve." Jonathan dumped a heavy stone on the carriage floor. "Does the duck blind ever dry up?"

"It hasn't since I can remember." She leaned from the seat and watched him tie her clothes around the stone. "In the winter, I've seen this road flooded till you could scarce use it—and betimes the water has lapped at the back door of the hospital."

"Good." He grunted, tying the last knot. "I'll feel safer when these are under water." He picked up the bundle and carried it out into the reeds that grew shoulder-high. With a mighty effort he threw the incriminating clothes far out into the water.

"I hope that ends Mary o' Scotland," Elizabeth said when he got back to the carriage. "We were witless, now that I think on it, to believe we could do it."

"You believed you could—and you did, lass." He lay down on the floor and lolled into the position of a man deep in his cups. "If I forget to say it later, I'll tell you now, you deserve a deal of credit for this night's business—but you'll not get it. Drive on, lass."

Tingling with pride, Elizabeth slapped the reins and turned the carriage up the narrow dirt road that became Eight Street after it passed the hospital. Jonathan's casualness didn't mislead her for an instant, and she knew that he was more than pleased with the outcome, and filled with admiration for her part in it. She was beginning to understand him better, and one thing she had learned was, the tighter the fix, the more cool and unhurried he became, and the less he said, the more approving he was.

Despite all the noise there had been at the waterfront, the outskirts of the city were as quiet as ever. A few lights shone in the hospital windows, but Eight Street stretched ahead black and empty-looking. She had no notion of the time, and any attempt to guess was useless, for what had happened within minutes had seemed to last for hours. Not a single bell chimed the hour any more, since the City Fathers had spirited away the State House bell, and most of the churches had followed their lead, to prevent the English melting them down for cannon. When the wind was out of the west the ships' bells along the river couldn't be heard this far inland.

One single light burned in the Logan house, and she braced herself as she turned onto Walnut knowing that she'd have to pass the guard at the State House. Slowly the light in the Logan window passed over her left shoulder, and the campfire glow above the State House wall bloomed up in the fog. Now she could see the sentry on the corner, a tall Guardsman, smartly walking his post. He stopped when he heard the carriage, turned around, and walked to meet her.

She slowed the horse as he came near, and with an off-hand wave, she invited him to look into the carriage.

"Sick or drunk?" The sentry walked alongside.

"Drunk—disorderly—and abusive. So the tavernkeeper said." She put all the bitterness she could into her voice.

Grinning widely, the sentry looked at her. "Put the old bastard under the pump when you get him home. 'Tis no way to treat a fine-set-up lady."

It was all she could do to keep from speeding the horse when she left the sentry behind, but she let the beast take his own slow pace along the square, and left the reins slack as he turned up Four Street on his own. She felt limp and weak as a rundown clock spring now that lights of her mother's room hove in view. The strain had been more than she'd felt at the time, and now that it was past, she'd like nothing better than to sit down and cry.

"Sick?" Jonathan was kneeling back of the seat.

"No," she managed to get out.

"You should be—I am. I was never so scared in my life."

"I—I'm weak—"

"Weak?" He cut her off. "Been me, I'd a-had the horse galloping ere now."

She knew he wouldn't, and she knew he wasn't sick. Scared he might have been, but she recognized it was his way of calming her down, and making her feel good by pretending that he was in worse fettle than she. The horse speeded up as it walked into the driveway, and Jonathan was out of the carriage and unhitching the harness before the wheels had stopped. To show she was still capable of action, she slid from the seat and started loosening the off-side traces. In moments, the horse had walked from between the shafts, trotted to his stall at the other end of the carriage house, and started munching oats as Jonathan closed the stable door.

With the closing of the door, the last stretched thread of her nerves gave way. Stables, garden, house and darkened sky spun around her in a dizzy arc, and her knees lost all sense of supporting her body. In an effort to steady herself, she put one hand to her head, and the other reached out blindly toward Jonathan. The cloak fell from her shoulders. In the strangely turbid darkness she saw the Captain's face swimming closer to her, and as her senses left her, she felt Jonathan's arm about her waist.

She had no measure of how long her swoon lasted, but as she came back out of the blackness her first consciousness was of Jonathan's lips pressed tightly on her own. Under his arm, the bent bones of her stays poked her in every direction, and she almost laughed as she thought of the picture she must make. She kept her eyes shut, and her body limp as she pondered this new turn that affairs had taken. This was no comradely salute born of the adventure they had been through, nor was it an effort to bring her back to her senses. This embrace had more fire to it than even Broadmoor had engendered.

Slowly, still keeping her eyes closed, she made a show of coming out of her swoon. Immediately, Jonathan withdrew his lips and moved his arm up from her waist to her shoulders. Gradually she straightened, taking her weight on her own legs till she stood erect and opened her eyes.

"Are you all right, lass?" He spoke as if nothing had happened. "You must show me the map—and the short road to Barren Hill."

"I'm all right—now."

He dropped his arm from about her shoulders, and started up the path to the kitchen door. Following him, she looked at his tall, gangling frame, and smiled to herself in the darkness. Most odd behavior, she thought, and much in contrast with his avowal on the road to the Red Lion when he had said, "Mistress, we can share the bed—it's that little interest to me."

19 AT BARREN HILL

So comes a reck'ning when the banquet's o'er. The dreadful reck'ning,
and men smile no more.——JOHN GAY

"The fork in the trail, Elizabeth pointed out on the map," Jonathan murmured and bore to the left, looking over the rim of the ravine for the little tavern in the Valley Green. So far, he'd found her directions most accurate, doubtless because she was a sailor's daughter and used to maps and the like. It had been rough and tiresome, following the foot trail along the steep side of the Wissahickon Creek, but again, in that, Elizabeth had been right, for more than once he'd heard the clatter of a mounted patrol on the Germantown Pike over to his right.

It irked him that he had to travel without a timepiece, but servants who had timepieces were scarcer than gooseberries on a currant bush. He judged it to be nearing four of the clock, considering the distance and the ruggedness of the old Indian footpath. "Ah!" he grunted with satisfaction as he saw through a break in the trees. There, down below him was the peak roof and double-porch of the Valley Green Inn. It was here that he'd find the easiest place to cross the Wissahickon—so Elizabeth had said—and, following her advice, he broke through the underbrush and started carefully down the rocky side of the Wissahickon Valley.

Somehow, the English must have learned of La Fayette's outpost on Barren Hill. There was no doubt in his mind that Elizabeth's assessing of the talk she had overheard was correct, and that La Fayette was in danger of being unmercifully whipped, if not captured. Pushing aside branches and shrubs, and testing every rock before he trusted his weight on it, he lowered himself cautiously, from one irregular ledge to the next. It was nigh to foolproof, this plan the English had worked out, for it cut off every escape route, and hemmed the Marquis in between the hills to the right and the swiftly flowing Schuylkill on the left.

Grant, with his five or six thousand, must have marched out Old York Road as a bluff, and was to veer to the left over the Skippack Pike till he came to the Broadaxe Tavern. There he would turn to the left almost at right angle, come down over Cold Point Hill and march to the Ridge Pike, some three miles beyond Barren Hill, and between Barren Hill and the Old Forge. "Thus," Jonathan thought to himself as he dropped another six feet nearer to the creek, "the bottom of the sack was stitched up tight." For even if the Frenchman were warned, the Scotsman Grant would reach the one place where the Schuylkill could be crossed before La Fayette could, since Grant was closer to Matsons Ford by three miles.

Nor could help be expected from the Valley Forge. No matter what warning, or how soon Washington received it, the Rebels had a nine-mile march before they came to Matsons Ford, and in that length of time the skirmish—or massacre—would be over. He gritted his teeth and swore.

Just what good could come of this lone march of his along an abandoned Indian trail, he didn't know. Even when warned of Grant's circling move to cut him off, La Fayette couldn't escape through the neck of the sack. Once again he felt that Elizabeth was correct in her assumption. The officers in field dress at the ball, and the talk of the "Ridge," could mean only that La Fayette's attempt to seek escape by retreating toward Philadelphia would be blocked by fresh English troops marching out the Ridge and Germantown Pikes.

It was the devil's own fix they were in; once again, it was due to some spy at the Old Forge selling the whereabouts of La Fayette's position for a pocketful of English gold. He turned and saw the tavern on his left. If he could only find the big rocks Elizabeth had spoken of, he thought,

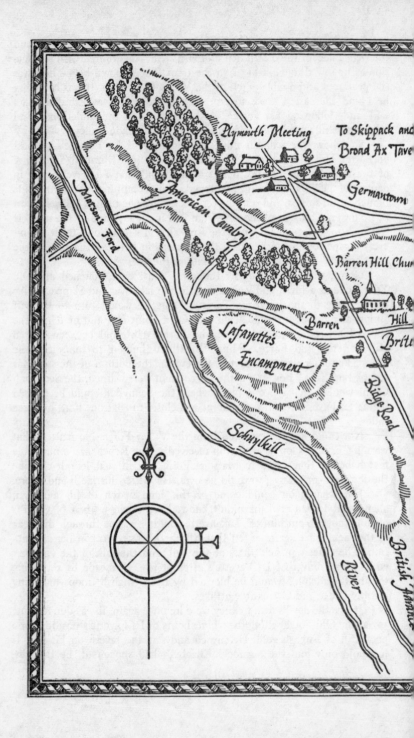

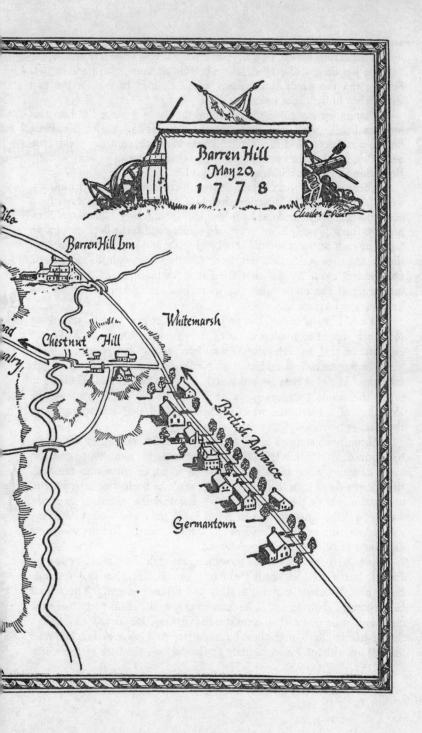

Barren Hill
May 20,
1778

Charles E. Pait

Pike

Barren Hill Inn

Whitemarsh

oad

Chestnut Hill

alry

British Advance

Germantown

and worked his way up the tumbling creek. No matter what opinion he'd held of Elizabeth before, he'd have to change it now. The lass had guts to back up her fiery, stiff-necked, let-me-be turn of mind, and he as well as Stirling and the whole Rebel Army were beholden to her for the part she'd taken in the night's affairs.

Despite the danger of the situation, the thought nagged at him that he, Jonathan Kimball, was somewhat of a fool. Not for kissing Elizabeth, for she was delectable and provoked a man to kissing, but the tricky business of spying shouldn't be mingled with women, especially pretty women. But damn it, that was Stirling's fault, not his.

There were the rocks. The first leap, Elizabeth had warned him, was wide. In the dark, the glittering stretch of creek looked wide even for a good jumper, but he reckoned his long legs should carry him across. Running, he threw himself over the gap and skidded across the flat, moss-grown top. The rushing water sounded cool and fresh, and kneeling he bent over the sloping edge and sucked refreshing mouthfuls through his pursed lips. On his feet again he saw that the flat rocks made a well-defined step bridge across the creek, with the water frothing and bubbling its way between the jagged edges.

It could be, he thought as he leaped a wider gap, that he was giving too much weight to his few minutes' dallying with Elizabeth. She'd not even known of it, and after she'd shown him the map and pointed out how to get to Barren Hill, she'd bade him goodbye without showing the slightest sign of knowing that he had kissed her when she fainted. He tried to brush the whole thing away as he landed on the right bank of the Wissahickon, and started west on the foot trail that was spongy with the spring's new growth.

Abruptly he stopped in his headlong pace. Something, or somebody, had moved over to his left. The sound was slight, almost like the soft rustle of leaves when birds settle down at night, or when they stir with the first streaks of light. But the rustlings made by birds were intermittent, not continuous as these were. Neither was this the sound of one man walking quietly. This was the sound of many men who were wise to the ways of walking quietly. This was the sound made by Indians who were not afraid of being spied on or followed.

As to why Indians should be walking through the Valley, he had no answer, but if he had heard them over on his left—they had certainly heard him. He stood without moving and listened intently. The sounds had separated slightly, and if he guessed aright, the main party had gone on ahead while one or two were coming his way. He looked about for a sizable tree to climb, one where he could leap to a lower branch and haul himself up without leaving telltale scuff marks on the bark of the trunk.

Such a one, gnarled and twisted and full of leaf, was ten feet away. Cautiously he moved toward it.

"Kimball!"

Jonathan spun on his heel, and found himself staring into the blackened but wide-grinning face of Captain Allan McLane.

"What make you here?" Jonathan spluttered.

"I might ask the same of you—" McLane held out his hand—"but instead I'll tell you. Every night, since we brought you and Mistress Ladd down from the Forge, I've gone out with a patrol of Oneidas, and we've probed as close to the city as we dared—testing the defenses. Last night we went right through the sentries to the Wharton place—just to let the English know we were on the alert—something to offset Grant's foray and maybe make the English think twice before they tried anything big."

"They're trying something big," Jonathan said. "How did you get down to the Wharton place?"

"Over the ferry. The Indians swam out and slit the throats of the guards on the ferryboat. Then we crossed. We had old kettles and pots filled with stones and gunpowder, and we set them off within a hundred yards of the Wharton gardens—" McLane stopped. "But you said they were attempting something big?"

"Mistress Ladd went to the ball. She overheard talk that leads us to believe that Grant is marching from Broadaxe to get between La Fayette and the Schuylkill—Howe and the others are marching out Germantown and Ridge Pikes—most likely Bethlehem, too. The *Andromeda* is anchored in the Schuylkill to take La Fayette aboard when the English capture him."

"Then we'd best move." McLane started running up the trail, Jonathan after him.

"I've been working my brains as to how we can get the Marquis out of his trap."

"We can't," McLane snapped over his shoulder. "We'll have to fight our way out. How many men does Grant have?"

"Five to six thousand—and sixteen cannon I saw. How many are marching from the city, I have no way of knowing."

McLane said nothing. Both men were in need of all their breath as the Delaware Captain led the way up a steep incline between two slanting faces of rock that showed where the spring rains had started a landslide. Jonathan had no idea where he was until the small spire, with the crowing-cock weather vane, of Saint Peter's rose above the brow of the hill. The square tower, like four dormers fitted together, making a roof for the four squat tower sides, followed into view.

Jonathan panted, following the deer-footed McLane across the dirt road and over the graveyard wall. For the first time he saw the Massachusetts Oneidas, and waved as he darted between the headstones of the old Barren Hill graveyard.

Ahead of him, McLane thundered up the steep stairway of the church tower, and he could hear La Fayette's excited voice from above greeting the Delaware Captain. Once in the belfry, Jonathan could see the situation plainly. Over the hill at Cold Point, a steady stream of Redcoats poured down on Plymouth Meeting. The first Light Infantry companies had already reached the road that continued on till it joined Spring Mill Road. And Spring Mill Road, running along the bank of the Schuylkill, was the only road by which La Fayette's troops could reach Matsons Ford to cross the river.

"General." Jonathan pulled La Fayette's sleeve. "Grant has close to six thousand men there—and sixteen cannon—but Howe is marching out from Philadelphia with twice that number for all that we know."

"Then there is no retreat that way?" La Fayette waved toward Philadelphia.

"None, sir," Jonathan answered quickly.

The Marquis turned to McLane. "General Grant must be halted. He must not attain the Spring Mill Road."

"Yes, sir?"

"Order four columns to advance on the corner made by the Germantown Pike and the road that joins the Ridge Pike—you follow?"

"Yes, General. The juncture of Germantown and the north end of the crossroad."

"You are perfection, mon ami. Then you order four more columns to advance on the corner at the other end of that short road—for which we know not the name."

"Yes, General, the south end."

"Tell the columns to let themselves be seen—not too clearly you understand—and do not push beyond the edge of the wood. Have the columns, all of them, do much activity that can be seen by Grant's men, but not distinguished."

"Feint?"

"The perfect word, mon ami. Do as I say, quickly. Tell the men to be cool and do no firing till I give the order. And you, Captain McLane, will return here."

"Yes, sir."

There was profound admiration in McLane's voice as he saluted and disappeared down the church-tower stairs. Jonathan watched the Marquis coolly survey the battlefield before him. Around the church was the graveyard, surrounded in turn by a low stone fence. Beyond that, the trees extended almost to the road that Grant's men were about to occupy. To the left, Spring Mill Road ran between the trees and the river, and on to Matsons Ford.

Jonathan fidgeted from one foot to the other. It was not his business to advise a general how to conduct either an attack or a retreat, but the Marquis was French, and it could be that he had misunderstood the warning. At the speed with which Grant's men were marching they would have the two-and-a-half-mile-long crossroad occupied in less than half an hour.

"You will see—you will see." La Fayette was nodding confidently, apparently talking to himself.

"What was that, sir?" Jonathan seized the opportunity to break in on the Frenchman's thoughts.

"Pardon, Capitaine Kimball, but I was—how do you say it?—talking with myself. Tell me, if you were Monsieur Général Grant, what would you do if you saw eight columns peeping at you from the trees?"

"Why, sir—" Jonathan hesitated. "I suppose I'd deploy and get set for an attack—but, sir, since Grant knows you're here at all, he must have been informed by a traitor in our own camp—and the traitor will have informed the English of the small force you have."

"No doubt of that, mon Capitaine. But traitors have been wrong before—and Grant's news is a night old. I might have been reinforced during the night."

"Yes, sir."

"And were you Monsieur Général Grant, you might think this was a trap—the more so since I advance to the attack—rather than making the retreat."

"Yes, General. I agree with all you say, but the bloody situation remains the same. You have twenty-two hundred—"

"Watch, mon Capitaine. You shall see."

Jonathan leaned on the narrow ledge of the tower opening and looked across the fields toward the mass of Redcoats running at the double along the crossroad. The battleground was ideal for the English forces. Only one advantage, perhaps two, lay with the Rebels. The Rebels were screened by the woods, and Grant would have to advance over the open roads; also the Rebels were on a hilltop. The advantage of a hilltop, however, Jonathan discarded, since prolonged defense was impossible. A hilltop was of no advantage in executing a retreat, and besides that, he estimated that five minutes must have elapsed; five minutes that brought Grant's men a full half mile along the crossroad.

Until overlooking the countryside from this height he'd had only the sketchiest notion of how it lay. At this point, on his left, the Ridge Pike ran well nigh north and south before it turned on its westerly course. On his right, the Germantown Pike ran almost parallel to the Ridge, until it veered to the left and joined the Ridge about a mile beyond the hamlet at Plymouth Meeting—and the Meeting House itself was due north of him—not more than two miles away. Farther to the right where he could not see it, the Skippack Pike also ran parallel with the Germantown Pike, and it was north on this that Grant had marched till he reached the Broadaxe Tavern. Turning left at Broadaxe, the English had marched on a cart road that ran westerly to Plymouth Meeting.

It was the continuation of that Broadaxe-Plymouth Road that gave Jonathan concern. The crossroad did not continue its westerly direction, which would have ended it at Matsons Ford. Instead, it curved south and joined the Spring Mill Road, effectively cutting off La Fayette's route of retreat. Down in that little triangular patch of green where the Spring Mill had been grinding meal for more than fifty years was where the clash was due to come. Another five or six minutes would see the Laird of Ballachulish closer to the mill than La Fayette, and ready to pull the drawstring that would close the sack.

"General Grant is a good general." La Fayette nudged Jonathan's elbow. "He has stopped his march."

"By God, General, you're right." Jonathan leaned out from the tower and peered through the leafy trees. Grant had seen the column spearheads feinting along the edge of the woods, had stopped his march and was deploying his men for battle. The long column of red-coated English and green-clad Hessians had wheeled by twos from their column of fours into the two ranks so typical of the British line of action. Less than thirty minutes had gone by since Jonathan had pounded up the church stairs, and already La Fayette had improved his position.

Up the tower steps, McLane came running. "They're stopping," he said breathlessly.

"But yes, of course," La Fayette agreed quietly. "What else is there for them to do—they are at the disadvantage."

"They—are at a disadvantage?" McLane was incredulous.

"But of a certainty!" The Frenchman waved his arm at the road the English were spread out on. "Their whole flank is exposed—while all we present are our spearheads, hidden among the trees." Standing on tiptoe, he gave the area of battle a quick birdlike glance, dropped back on his heels, and turned quickly to McLane. "Now, mon Capitaine, it is time!"

"Yes, sir."

"Take your cavalry, small as it is, and gallop left oblique. You understand?"

"Make a charge—from where they are at the corner of the graveyard—diagonally to the left."

"Exactly. Direct your charge to the exposed right flank of the General Grant. Having turned his flank—which you will do—wheel about and return to the cover of the woods at the left of our spearheads—where our six cannon are."

"I understand, General."

La Fayette held out his hand. "Give my horse to one of your officers, I will be on foot—with the columns."

McLane shook the General's hand, and ran down the stairs. La Fayette gave a quick salute to Jonathan, and followed McLane. It was full daylight now and a curious stillness hung over the woods. The whole scene was one of unreality, and Jonathan felt his heart pounding as he watched McLane climb into his saddle, while the little Marquis ran across the graveyard and into the woods.

For his life, Jonathan couldn't understand why Grant didn't open fire, unless it was that he was wholly unprepared for the Rebel attack that seemed in the making. Of course, Grant's muskets were completely out of range, but the Scots General might have made some use of his cannon. Again, Grant might have given orders to hold musket fire—just as La Fayette had done—to make certain that the fire, when it did come, was effective. But it was the quiet that was unnerving, and Jonathan felt the sweat beginning to gather in the hollows between his neck and shoulders. At Brandywine, the air had been filled with shrieks and yells, as well as the roar of cannon and the sharp crack and ping of muskets and bullets. Here, in a lazy spring morning-quiet, an army was drawn up facing an outpost in a coming struggle as unequal as the silence was unnatural.

Down below, he saw McLane look up at him, then draw his sabre. The cavalry, pitifully few, sixty at the most, waited the order to charge. La Fayette, at the edge of the woods now, looked behind and raised his arm above his head. Up flashed McLane's sabre, and the cavalry started as though thrown by a giant catapult. Down the western slope of Barren Hill they went, their horses' hooves throwing sod, but making little noise above a hollow drumming. Their sabres flashed in the morning light, and keeping order as well as they would have on the parade ground, they crossed the open space between the gravestones and the woods that all but hid La Fayette's spearheads.

A thousand puffs of white hid the British front line for a moment. The sharp crackle of the muskets was distant enough to sound more like the snapping of twigs trodden underfoot, and the brown spurts of dust on the hillside showed that the musket balls had fallen far, far short of doing damage to either McLane's horsemen or La Fayette's infantry. Certain it was, Jonathan saw, that the Frenchman's strategy had worked so far. The Redcoats hadn't advanced a foot farther on the curved road that led to the Spring Mill Road, but more than that, the Redcoat rear was forced to march past the vital road and take positions along the Germantown Pike, east of the juncture.

Jonathan felt the excitement of possible success replacing his convictions of disaster. Never had the truth of Washington's simple assertion on warfare been more truthfully borne out: "To act safely, a general must know what is happening on the opposite side of the hill." Grant didn't know, couldn't guess, what was happening on Barren Hill, and, being uncertain of La Fayette's strength, the Scotsman had done the right thing. He'd moved his rear down the pike so they'd not choke up his own retreat should retreat become necessary. But, by doing so, he'd cut his superiority of numbers in half, and all but eliminated his advantage in position.

"Damnedest battle I've ever seen," Jonathan spoke aloud, and was startled at his own voice as he leaned farther out the small opening of the tower. Everything was quiet again. McLane's cavalry were a mile away by now, completely hidden from him by the slope of the hill, and hidden from the English by the trees that grew right up to the edge of the disputed road. The whole picture was one of time standing still, and yet it couldn't have taken McLane's horsemen above six or seven minutes to reach the small triangle of trees where Jonathan could see the glint of their sabres as they wheeled onto the crossroad.

Not a sign of life had come from the hamlet of Barren Hill, but he had no doubt the windows of the hostelry nestled at the foot of the incline were filled with faces hidden behind the blue and white checked curtains. He'd noted the likeness of the inn to that of Elizabeth's house when he first climbed into the tower; and was a little surprised that the details of the mansard roof and its inevitable dormers with the slate guard running beneath them should impress themselves on him at a time like this. A little to his left, the Schuylkill hurried along to meet the Delaware, splashing and gurgling over the lowered bed where softer rock had been worn away to a deeper channel. It was this distinct drop, Jonathan noticed, that shallowed the water above, making the fording of the stream possible at Matsons Ford. It was such a short distance away. But in that short distance, the Spring Mill Road leading to it would be in full view of Grant and his Redcoats; and the first Rebel who tried to escape by it would be a mark for fusillade of English lead.

A distant yell was the signal for clamor that shattered the morning calm. Dimly, through the leafy tops of the trees, he could see McLane's riders galloping along a short strip of road between the woods and the right of Grant's line. Muskets flashed and cracked. The white puffs held to the still air for a moment, then were gone in trailing wisps of bluish gray. When they cleared, Jonathan could see no gaps in the charging cavalry riding breakneck, within yards now of the red British line.

Far to his right, Jonathan saw the first smoke of cannon fire, and on the instant, the deep boom of a British brassbound six-pounder rolled across the woods like summer thunder. The ball was short of its mark, as it was bound to be at that range, and was intended to frighten or impress rather than to hit. The early sun picked out the sabres as Mc-Lane's men slashed and cut and jabbed their way in a wheeling turn right through the red-coated ranks. No infantry could stand their ground under such an onslaught, and the forefront of the English line faltered, broke, and was turned back on itself.

McLane completed the wheeling movement and thundered back over the road. La Fayette's men raked the English with an enfilade of musket fire. The Rebel fire started on their right, and one after another the Rebels fired in turn till the enfilade finished on their left. Each man as he fired dropped to the rear and reloaded as La Fayette's second rank moved into their places and repeated the enfilade, raking Grant's men again before they had recovered from the first scythelike stream of bullets.

But the first-rank men, reloading as they ran, and crouching low, were tearing helter-skelter down the hill. Each rank of the Frenchman's columns did the same in turn. Thunderstruck, Jonathan realized that in but a few moments La Fayette had moved more than half his men to within yards of Spring Mill, and Grant was unaware of any change. Like peeling cards from the top of a deck, La Fayette's men fired their muskets, filed out of the way of the next rank, and ran for the tree-filled triangle where the crossroad joined the Spring Mill Road.

In the thick stand of trees, they were so completely hidden that McLane, pounding along the road, didn't see them till he'd swept around the point and brought his cavalry to a halt in the same shelter. Over on the extreme right, new action was shaping up. A troop of English Dragoons had moved east on the Germantown Pike and were going to copy Mc-Lane's manoeuvre on La Fayette's right flank. They drove their horses across the fields beyond the Barren Hill Tavern and, opening out in line, charged up the slope toward the graveyard.

"Slim pickings they'll find there," Jonathan thought, and then suddenly realized that the Indian troops were lying motionless and almost invisible behind the far wall of the graveyard. In their dirt-brown cotton, shirtlike coats, and their bronzed skin, he'd not seen them till the charging Dragoons had forced his attention their way. On came the pounding horsemen, riding in their stirrups and readied for the jump over the low wall. Still the guides showed no sign of movement, and Jonathan marvelled at the nerves that could keep men motionless while cavalry drove straight at them.

The first horses were at the wall. Nostrils flaring and hooves pawing air, they sailed over. With blood-curdling war whoops, the Indians leaped to their feet, almost under the bellies of the horses. The animals, terrified and thrown off balance, rolled sidewise, throwing the Dragoons in a tangled pile. Screaming and jabbing with knife and bayonet, the Oneidas fell on the luckless English and dispatched those who had not already taken to their heels and retreated back down the hill. The remaining Dragoons couldn't handle the mounts that reared and plunged at the sound of the Indian war whoops, and the demoralized troops fled to the safety of the tavern yard and the Germantown Pike.

Turning back to look at La Fayette's infantrymen, Jonathan saw that nothing but a thin straggled line of Rebels along the fringe of the woods faced Grant's troops. Of the others, there was not a sign. It was as if they'd dropped into some hidden hole in the ground. Even the six four-pound cannon had disappeared into that triangular patch of woodland no bigger than a city plat. Desultory as the Rebel fire was now, it still held Grant's men pinned down on the same stretch of road. The situation of the English was becoming ridiculous. They'd marched out from Philadelphia, spent a night in the woods, and now they were immoblized by a force they couldn't see and whose strength they didn't know. Some time, and soon, Grant would have to make a move. He couldn't stand there forever firing uselessly at an enemy hopelessly out of range—and himself afraid to advance in the face of musket fire that didn't come within a furlong of him.

Grant could have heard his thoughts, for at that moment the British line started to advance. Far away as he was, Jonathan could see that it was a cautious feeling of their way, more than an aggressive attack, for they paused on each step and held their heads at a wary angle, as if wondering where the next fusillade would come from. Halfway to the woods, they were stopped by a long roll on the order drums. Grant, waving his sword and riding as though the devil were on his tail, charged along the line and down toward the Spring Mill.

But the Redcoats were too late.

Jonathan could hardly believe his eyes when he saw Rebels on the Schuylkill bank. There was no mistake. They were La Fayette's lads. And they were well beyond any possibility of capture by the baffled and be-wildered Grant, whose roaring could be heard as he lashed his horse to-ward the mill. What was more, the few scattered Rebels who had stayed behind to play out La Fayette's bluff stood more than a chance to make good their escape, and it was their final dash that showed how the Frenchman had outwitted the English.

With the need for secrecy gone, La Fayette's rear guard tore through the woods, and without bothering to hide their actions, threw themselves into the creek that ran the Spring Mill. Winding through rushes and tall grass, the millstream was as effectively hidden from Jonathan as it had been from Grant. All eyes had been fixed on the escape road, but La Fayette had ignored the road, and used the bed of the millstream. Even as he watched, Jonathan could barely see the heads of the rear guard as they waded along the creek and down to the mill. He didn't understand why he hadn't seen their escape when they climbed from the creek at the mill, and he was puzzled now, when the read guard failed to show on the open road.

He shaded his eyes and looked at the mill, then burst out laughing. The Rebels had never left the stream. With the connivance of the miller, La Fayette and his men had gone through the inside of the mill, out the other side, and remained hidden in the tailrace until they reached the end where it poured out into the Schuylkill.

Jonathan all but danced up and down, watching the Rebels pull themselves out of the tailrace and onto the riverbank. As close as he could guess, the whole action had lasted less than half an hour, and already the first Rebels were forming in line, and waving insolently at Grant to follow them. It was a hopeless chase, and the General recognized it before he reached the mill. Bobbing up and down like floats on a fishing net, their muskets held high above their heads, some of the Rebels were well out into the water. McLane, his horsemen, and the cannon went all the way to the ford where the shallower water wouldn't get into the gun barrels. But to follow them was futile, and the enraged Grant, spluttering and fuming, waved his discomfited Redcoats back into line while the jeering Rebels shouted and hooted in oath-spiced derision.

The rattle of side drums, and the deeper booming of a bass drum, sent Jonathan to the opposite side of the tower. Marching up the Ridge Pike, colors flying, red and gilded generals leading on horseback, came the troops from Philadelphia. Over on the Germantown Pike, the picture was duplicated as General No-Flint Grey led the Guards, two troops of Dragoons and the hated Rangers—the Colonials who had enlisted to fight against their brothers.

Jonathan wasted no time in making for the stairs that twisted inside the tower. This was no place for him to be caught by the English. Climbing down the stairs, he had visions of standing in front of a court-martial, trying to explain how he, a Philadelphia Patriot's servant, happened to be in the middle of La Fayette's encampment. Running from the church, he took cover behind the graveyard wall, and worked his way to the brow of the slope he had climbed with McLane less than half an hour before.

Securely hidden by the heavy brush, he waited long enough to watch the first of the English march past on the Ridge Pike. There would be drinking, and cursing, and sad singing in the taverns tonight, he thought. And reprisals on the morrow, for not only was General Sir William Howe leading the parade, but Admiral Lord Howe was there, giving proof that La Fayette's capture was the prime reason for the attack, and that

H.M.S. *Andromeda* had indeed expected to receive the "boy" aboard that night.

Shaking his head, Jonathan slipped down the hillside and left the English to their chagrin. What a tale for future campfires! Well nigh fourteen thousand of England's best, and Generals to spare, Howe, Clinton, Grant and Grey, with the Admiral of the Fleet for witness, had been outwitted by the twenty-year-old La Fayette with but twenty-two hundred men. The tale would be long a-dying—Jonathan grinned, as he struck out for Philadelphia—of how the Marquis won his golden spurs.

20 SLIP OF THE TONGUE

A word and a stone let go cannot be called back.——OLD ENGLISH PROVERB

Stirling and Von Steuben, making their inspection rounds of the sprawling Valley Forge encampment, could scarcely believe that this was the same Rebel Army they had inspected the week before. The Marquis de La Fayette's successful escape, and the resultant ridiculing of the English generals, had raised the spirits of the men even more than Washington's reading of the signing of the French alliance on the Grand Parade three weeks before.

The day following the battle La Fayette had reoccupied his Barren Hill post with an additional five hundred men and two more cannon, but during his one day's return to Valley Forge he had been feted and congratulated and patted on the back by every man who could get near him. There was no question about it, Stirling thought as he and the Baron rode past the Forge, the Frenchman had infused the Rebel ranks with a spirit that had been lacking for too long. It was a fighting spirit, and it was born of a realization that Rebel troops could outwit the English if competent Rebel officers were in command.

The men had the same sort of feeling for their Commander-in-Chief, and for Von Steuben, Greene, Knox, Wayne, and, he hoped, himself. Even if La Fayette had been driven from his post, the men regarded the escape as a victory, and after Brandywine, Germantown and Paoli, any kind of victory was strong wine.

Only one thing had marred the day following Barren Hill, and it still hung like a depressing cloud over Stirling, although he did his best to hide his feelings. General Charles Lee had returned from York, and bitter chagrin was marked in every line of the undersized General's face when he saw what should have been a grand welcome back, ignored because of the wholehearted admiration being heaped on La Fayette.

It was almost second nature for Stirling to watch Lee's face. He wondered how the other officers could fail to read treason in the man's cruel, tight-pressed lips that seemed set in a fixed sardonic grimace. To Stirling, Lee's deep, close-set eyes, refusing to look anyone in the face, gave proof enough of dishonesty and double-dealing. Lee's arrogance and refusal to brook anyone's opinion but his own, Stirling was willing to ascribe to the exchanged General's short stature and lack of proportion. Seated on a horse, Lee looked as tall as Greene or Knox, but his legs weren't long enough for his body, and out of the saddle he was distinctly odd with an oversized head and an elongated nose that split his face in two.

Stirling reined in his horse as he saw Von Steuben stop and point to the forge. The artificers had one of the heavy cannon suspended by ropes and propped up with shoring blocks so that one wheel overhung the sluiceway.

"What are they doing?" The Baron rested his hands on his saddle and watched.

"They are going to put a new iron rim on that wheel, Baron, to tighten up the spokes."

As Stirling spoke, three men, well-nigh naked, ran out from the forge carrying a circle of dazzling white iron. The long tongs by which they held the ring were invisible in the glaring light, and it looked almost as though the white hot circle floated onto the wooden rim of the gun wheel. From the edge of the wheel, tiny spirals and spurts of smoke shot up and out as the glowing iron slid over the wood. At a shout from one of the artificers, the other kicked the supporting blocks from under the carriage and, lowering the ropes, allowed the wheel to dip into the sluiceway.

"When the iron is white hot it is expanded and slips easily over the wheel. They'll turn the wheel to cool the iron," Stirling explained. "Then when the iron is cold it will grip that wheel so tight that blows from a sledge couldn't knock it off."

The Baron nodded, understanding. "Our cannon will be in good trim." He shook the reins and the horse moved up the road. "As our men are—if we that way can keep them."

"We will, Baron, the drill and discipline you have hammered into them will not be lost. It is a far better army than we have had since this war started." Stirling turned and looked back at the men lowering the cannon to stand on its own wheels. "The men are like that iron rim, Baron, they have to go through the forge and be hammered into shape, before they can stand up."

They cantered up the Valley Road and wheeled to the left as they came opposite the covered bridge that crossed the stream on their right and carried the road that led to Stirling's quarters. As they rounded Mount Joy they could see the entire camp stretched out below them. Caleb Gibbs and the Life Guard were drilling in front of Washington's headquarters while two companies of Rhode Islanders stood at attention along the stream bank, watching and learning.

As the two generals rode east along the outer line of defense, they saw Knox's artillery manhandling four- and six-pounders with ease and confidence. They trundled the pieces over the log-strewn ground, swung the muzzles around and trained them on make-believe targets while the swabbers and loaders followed them with ramrods, powder and ball.

North of the artillery park, on Gulph Road, was Letitia Penn's small one-room schoolhouse. Built of stone, with a sound roof and wood floor, it was more fitted for use as a hospital than the stables or the log huts with their hardpan floors, and here the camp's most desperately ill were cupped and bled and physicked in the hope that the drastic treatment would rid them of camp fever.

Stirling's eyes swept on to the Grand Parade where North Carolinians and Virginians sweated at bayonet practice, but abruptly he turned his head and looked at the schoolhouse hospital again. A horse was teddered at the side of the open door, and unless he was mistaken it was the horse Lee had been riding when he came back to camp.

Immediately, all his suspicions were aroused. He turned to Von Steuben. "I'm going down to the hospital, Baron. I'll join you at the commissary in a few minutes."

The Inspector General nodded, and Stirling galloped off across the artillery park. Before he'd reached Knox's guns, he saw Lee come out of the schoolhouse, mount his horse and ride off in the opposite direction along Gulph Road. Clutching his reins till the oil ran from the leather between his fingers, Stirling felt his suspicion and anger mount with every stride of his horse. Never before had Lee shown the slightest interest in the sick or wounded. The sergeant who had been wounded at Barren Hill was the only man in the hospital who could have any information that would be of interest to Lee.

Stirling knew that he was building a case against Lee on personal suspicion. But someone had advised the English that La Fayette was posted at Barren Hill, and Lee had been corresponding with Howe and André. If that assumption were correct, Stirling thought, as he pulled up and dismounted at the schoolhouse, then it was a logical move on Lee's part to find out why his treachery had failed.

Even with the door and windows open, the combined smell of simples, pitch and black powder, was enough to make a man's stomach revolt. Stirling held no belief in the efficacy of pitch and powder for the eruptive itch that plagued the camp, but he was no medico and said nothing. The tiered bunks with their thin straw mattresses were filled, and on the surgeon's table, set against the back wall, lay the sergeant.

"How are you making out, Sergeant?" Stirling dropped his tricorne on the end of the bench and leaned over the wounded man.

The sergeant forced a wan grin. "I'll get me well, sir. But that musket ball made a bigger hole and gave me more hell coming out than going in."

"They do," Stirling agreed. "But a man can't get well till they're out. You'll soon be well enough to join the Marquis again."

"A good soldier is the Marquis—for all that he's but a boy." The sergeant moved his bandaged arm to a more comfortable position.

"Was I mistaken, Sergeant, or did I see General Lee down here?" Stirling moved to pick up his tricorne, and turned as if he were leaving.

"He was here, General. Said as how he wanted to hear all about the battle from someone as was there. You know—wanted to hear about the escape through the stream—but mostly why the Marquis didn't retreat down the Ridge Pike and cross over to the Skippack Pike and escape that way."

"What explanation do you have, Sergeant?"

"Why, sir, I thought you knowed that. One of our lads came out from Philadelphia and warned the Marquis."

"One of our lads?" Stirling asked, pretending surprise.

"Yes, sir." The sergeant screwed up his face as if trying to remember. "I can't tell him by rank or name—but I seen him running across the churchyard—he was out of uniform but he was one of our officers, I can swear to that."

"Thank you, Sergeant. Get well in a hurry, we need you."

"I will that, General."

His mind on what he had learned, Stirling waved to the other men in the bunks, and walked to the door. Tonight, he'd send a message to Dan Jarrett. He'd have Jarrett warn Jonathan to be on the sharpest lookout for the slightest hint of treachery. He hoped he was being overcautious, that his suspicions were unfounded, and that the warning was unnecessary. He hoped so, but he was going to send the warning just the same.

21   WALNUT STREET PRISON

For depriving us . . . of the benefits of Trial by Jury.——Declaration of Independence

Since the debacle of Barren Hill, Philadelphia had taken on the aspects of a city struck by the black pox. The fury of the English was without restraint. They had been made to look ludicrous by a handful of Rebels under the command of a "boy," and the Redcoats had marched back into Philadelphia to find the streets empty; a gesture of contempt that, for once, was common to Rebel and Tory.

That night drunken Lobsterbacks roamed the streets, and neither the Provost's guard nor the commanding officers made any effort to stop looting or street brawls. Women's screams went unheeded, and even the Tory wenches crouched panic-stricken in the cellars every time a fresh band of liquor-laden soldiers came down a street. Musket shots could be heard all over the town, and houses that had been fired were left to burn to the ground. Broken glass littered the streets, and by morning there was scarcely a court or alley that didn't have smashed windows or splintered doors to show for the night's atrocity.

As the days passed, discipline was slowly restored, but the gaiety was gone from Philadelphia. Officers drank alone in the Indian Queen and City taverns, or had to be satisfied with the company of the guest wenches instead of the Loyalist ladies who had considered entertaining the officers a matter of patriotic duty. Howe sailed for England on the *Andromeda*, and the last sounds he heard were the jeers of Rebels shouting, "Where's the Marquis?"

Before the *Andromeda*'s sails had disappeared over the horizon, Sir Henry Clinton's heavy-handed discipline was laid on soldier and civilian alike. Officers were forbidden to visit any house unless accompanied by another officer. The press-ganged crews were cut off from the news on shore, and death was the penalty for flying a pennant not ordered by the English officer aboard. Curfew was strictly enforced, the night patrols were doubled, and "search and seizure" followed a misspoken word or a suspicious movement.

English nerves were frayed to the breaking point, Jonathan realized, as he looked out the Ladd dining-room window at the rain-drenched street. Every day brought more reports of vessels flying the French flag, and raiding patrols were met with Rebel fire when they ventured more than ten miles beyond the city's boundaries. In spite of Clinton's show of discipline, each new report of the sighting of the French brought a corresponding outbreak of defiance from the Rebels. Redcoats who were foolish enough to go out alone after dark were beaten and had their uniforms stripped from their backs. Von Knyphausen's Hessians, lured down side streets, found themselves blindfolded and gagged, and given a choice of desertion or having their throats cut before being dropped into the swift-flowing Delaware.

It was not only the Redcoats' nerves that were reaching the snapping point. Since the Mischianza and Barren Hill, Jonathan had experienced all the emotions of a man caught in some sort of invisible trap. Elizabeth, too, seemed aware of the dangers that surrounded them, and her concern and co-operation were as wholehearted now as her disdain and self-will had been before.

Once again it was visitors' day at the Walnut Street Prison, and this time he was going to accompany Elizabeth. They had done their best to follow Von Steuben's advice about not making unnecessary changes in their daily habits, and Maggie had continued to go to the prison with Elizabeth. On the last visit, Jailor Cunningham's advances to Elizabeth had been so openly suggestive and insulting that she had returned in tears and Maggie had refused even to tell Jonathan what had happened.

When he had told Elizabeth that he would go with her on the next visit, her lips had trembled and she'd come close to crying with gratitude and relief. When she'd recovered herself she tried to dissuade him from taking the extra risk. She knew now that the house was being watched, for she'd seen the red-haired man; and holding her quivering chin up she had said that it was foolish for Jonathan to risk himself for the sake of keeping the brutal Cunningham's hands away from her.

The stair clock chimed the quarter hour as Elizabeth came into the room.

"He's at the back—watching—the red-haired man." She placed the basket of foodstuffs on the table and joined Jonathan at the window. "You still think you should go, Jonathan? Maggie will get herself ready in a minute if you—"

"I'll go, lass. This rain is excuse enough for you to take me in place of Maggie. So Redhead is at the back?"

"Yes. Most likely he thinks he's hidden by the stables but I could see him from upstairs. This makes the third time I think I've seen him."

"I've seen him twice, Elizabeth, so there's no doubt but that he's watching."

"Then you shouldn't go to the prison—"

"That's where you're wrong." He put his arm through the handle of the basket and lifted it from the table. "Going to the prison is one way of convincing him that I'm not aware that he's watching. And that we're not doing anything against the English—else I'd not go with you to the prison."

Saying no more, Elizabeth led the way to the front door. Outside, the gutters were running over, and the rain rushed down the roofs like streams over a dam. Despite the downpour, which was in its fourth day, the air was warm, and a clinging mizzle rose from the marshes and hung low over the houses. As they reached the corner of Four and Walnut, and turned right along Walnut, Jonathan twisted his head and looked back. A bulky, sopping-wet figure, wearing a broad-brimmed hat that shed water in every direction, emerged from the court between Chestnut and Walnut.

"He's following us," Jonathan spoke in Elizabeth's ear. "He's a damn poor spy if he doesn't know we're making for the prison."

"He may think we're going somewhere afterward," Elizabeth answered. "Or we may find ourselves in the prison—unable to get out again."

Across the State House Yard, the long ugly block of the Walnut Street Prison stood in bleak contrast to the beauty of the State House. The pouring rain made the red brick of the Independence Chamber and its council halls and banquet room clean and shining, but the massive gray stone oblong, with its barred windows, and its grim-faced sentries eternally pacing, was more dismal and forbiding than ever in the pounding downpour.

Both the State House and the prison had cupolas overlooking their roofs and yards, but for somewhat different and ironical reasons, Jonathan thought, as he sloshed along, following Elizabeth west on Walnut Street. Until the threatened occupation of the city, the cupola on the State House had housed the big bell with its "Proclaim Liberty" inscription around the crown, whereas the cupola on the prison housed two sentries with loaded muskets whose aim was to bring death to any who sought liberty beyond the walls of the dread prison. No better reason existed for this war of revolt than the very prison toward which they were ploughing their way, and he must remember to tell Elizabeth so.

The flight of stone steps that led up to the massive door piercing the front wall had been mounted by hundreds who, once inside the maw, were never seen or heard of again. This was no prison filled with convicted felons, for the prisoners had never been tried. Truth was, Jonathan clenched his fingers angrily around the basket he was carrying, hundreds of the men and women in Walnut Street had never been charged with anything. He remembered Lord Stirling saying that because of prisons like Walnut Street, Doctor Franklin had insisted on including in the Declaration the charge that the Colonials had been deprived of trial by jury.

It was all he could do to keep from whispering encouragement to Elizabeth as they climbed the prison steps. The thirty-three barred windows glowered down like malevolent eyes, and the moatlike space between the prison and the outside wall was wide and impassable when seen from the top of the steps. Few, except visitors, came down these steps. If they did, it was to a tenuous freedom made well nigh unendurable by the heavy footfalls of Redcoat feet, the knock on the door, the nightmarish memory, and the appalling fear of returning to the place.

The big door opened, creaking harshly, and clanged shut behind them. The Redcoat sergeant barely glanced at Elizabeth's writ, and thumbed them into a tunnel-like passage that divided the long building in two. In a room to the left, its doorless opening flanked by two wooden-looking Hessian Yagers, the Governor of the prison, ill-famed Captain Cunningham, sat at a table. His eyes were rheumy from the smoke of the puffing fireplace. His blotched face and succession of loose-skinned chins gave him a hideousness that fitted his surroundings and matched his repute.

The foul air that seeped into the vaulted passage burst into a stupefying stench as they entered the prison keep. Rotted straw, broken down to filthy wisps, drifted across the flagged floor at the slightest movement, and every step brought a new and more malodorous stinging of the nostrils. High in the walls, the barred openings let down meagre shafts of light that quivered and broke as they reached the thick dank layer of heat rising endlessly from the human wreckage that covered the floor.

Picking their way over arms and legs and between bodies that Jonathan would have left for dead on a battlefield, they reached the west wall of the long continuous cell. A stone fence, with iron bars jutting up from its top, made the private quarters for the political prisoners. Running across one corner, with an iron gate in the middle, the wall left a triangular space with benches and chests for the half-dozen hostages who, like Enoch Ladd, were kept on a day-to-day lease of life. Jonathan looked at the group, wondering which was Shipmaster Ladd. With their prison pallor, and in the dull light, their looks had much of a sameness. They were better dressed and better fed than the wretched devils lying on the floor of the main keep, and while the iron-spiked fence gave them protection from the starved horde, it in no way lessened the putrid miasma that filled the hellish place from wall to wall.

This prison within a prison had windows, but the outlook was nothing but a grisly reminder of the fate that waited them should their relatives on the outside fail to live in accordance with the English orders. Outside, in the yard, a heavy wooden "T" with cross braces to give it strength towered above a pair of two-wheeled carts. Two noosed and knotted ropes hung from the two ends of the top bar, and the rutted ground showed how often the carts had been moved from under the gallows, leaving their victims to dangle in full view of the gaping crowd.

Holding the basket in his hand, Jonathan stood in miserable silence as Enoch Ladd stretched his hands between the bars to pat Elizabeth's cheeks and stroke her wet hair. He looked tired and sick and almost doddering, Jonathan thought desperately, a far cry from the vigorous shipmaster he had been a few months back, according to Elizabeth. The overpowering horror of the place had already sickened Jonathan; five months' imprisonment in this pesthouse-dungeon was enough to send a strong man mad, he knew, but for all of that there was something unreal in Shipmaster Ladd's senile affection.

"This is Jonathan, Father. Our new servant."

Jonathan jumped at the sound of Elizabeth's voice. Its very naturalness was shocking, and he had to force himself to look at Enoch Ladd's face. All he got was a glassy stare from pale blue, empty eyes. Enoch Ladd's lips moved, but no sound came, and Jonathan gripped the basket handle tighter than before, for as sure as he stood there, the shipmaster's lips had carefully formed the words, "Be careful."

A burly Redcoat, ambling like a bear, pulled back the iron bolt that unfastened the cell door. Looking over his shoulder, he mumbled to Elizabeth through the side of his mouth, "Don't linger, mistress, the Gov'ner will be 'ere in a moment." He gave an almost imperceptible twist of his head toward the yard. "An 'angin', mistress, which a noice lidy loike you shouldn't ought to see."

"Thank you," Elizabeth whispered softly.

"You won't say nothin', mistress, but Captain Cunningham—'e'd mike you stiy—for the moral effect you might siy."

Elizabeth nodded, and Jonathan carried the basket into the cell. He emptied the contents onto a bench against the wall, and gave the Redcoat guard a close look as he went out the gate. If ever he chanced to meet him again, he'd remember this one courtesy to his credit. The gate clanged to, and the bolt scraped as the guard pushed it home.

There was a sound of tramping feet from the main passageway. The guard sprang to attention, and whispered to Elizabeth, "Get in the shadow, mistress, till he gets outside."

Stepping backward, she was almost invisible in the gloom. Jonathan moved slowly in front of her till he felt she was completely hidden. Except for the louder tramping of the marching feet, a deep, chill silence fell over the square-long prison. Four Redcoats with lowered bayonets marched out of the passageway, crossed the keep and out into the yard by the back door which a Hessian guard unbarred. Striding along, his sabre held point upward, the broad back of the blade pressed against his shoulder, Cunningham followed close behind them. Two double ranks, formed in a hollow square, hid the prisoner behind a hedge of bayonets as they trod their way out to the muddy yard.

The Redcoat, stepping in front of Elizabeth and Jonathan, signalled to them with the palm of his hand. Elizabeth flew to give her father a last embrace through the bars, and Jonathan looked at the shipmaster, wondering if he had any other wordless message. Enoch rolled his eyes back, and inclined his head toward the execution squad. Slowly and clearly his lips moved:

"Dan Jarrett."

Gripping Elizabeth by the elbow, Jonathan pushed her through the mazelike space between the prisoners. She started to speak, but the look he gave her silenced her before she opened her lips. He all but pushed her into the vaulted passage that led to the front of the prison, and seeing that the corridor was empty, he bent down and whispered in her ear. "That was Dan Jarrett they took out to hang. God alone knows how many messages from Stirling to us they found—or how many of ours they may have seized."

They reached the guardrooms. Jonathan shot her a sidewise glance and squeezed her elbow encouragingly as she smiled at the sergeant and showed her pass. The sentry opened the big door, and the fresh air was like a blow in the face. Jonathan could see that Elizabeth's lips were pressed tight against her teeth, and that she was holding on to herself by the slenderest of threads. They walked down the steps onto Walnut Street and as the prison receded behind them, he felt the knots in his own stomach start to loosen.

"What do we do—now that we can't get word to Stirling?" Her arm was shaking but she held her voice steady.

"We'll get word to him, lass, but we'll have to do it by regular post rider."

"But the English examine every letter and package that goes out of the city," Elizabeth interrupted. "It makes no difference what part of the country the letters are sent to, Boston—New York—Reading—the post rider has to take them to the English post, and if they're suspicious, the letters won't go out."

"That I know. Now listen carefully. We go home first—to show that we have no interest in Jarrett's hanging."

"Yes."

"I'll slip out and go back to Potter's Field and see if I can learn anything about Jarrett's friends, but you'll have to go to some printer's and buy fifty squares of writing paper. Tell the printer to wrap the squares and address the package to James Vaux—"

"James Vaux?"

"Yes, lass, he's the Quaker who owns the land just beyond Sullivan's bridge. You take the package of writing paper home—open it carefully and count down five squares. On the sixth square—using the secret stain —tell Stirling what befell. Put the papers back as they were, close the package making certain-sure that it looks exactly as it did when it left the printer's. Then post it at Postmaster Bache's house in the regular way."

"It will reach Stirling?" Elizabeth voiced surprise.

"Yes, it will. He knows how many squares to count."

"But can we depend on the English letting the package go through?"

"They have before," he cut in quickly. "They're not likely to suspect a package that's been wrapped and addressed by the printer himself. If they do open it—they find nothing but plain paper."

They turned into the carriageway and Jonathan looked along the street. "I see no signs of Redhead."

"But the package, Jonathan. Suppose the English write or ask Quaker Vaux about it?"

"Our lads are just as careful about searching the post as the English are," Jonathan answered. "Any inspecting officer who comes across the package to Quaker Vaux knows it is intended for Stirling. It will be sent by dispatch rider to Stirling. He'll extract the sixth page and send the package on to Mister Vaux, who, being a good Quaker, can honestly attest that he received it."

Jonathan opened the back door as he finished, and they went into the house. He left the empty basket in the kitchen and followed Elizabeth into the front hall. She untied the tapes of her wet cape, and as Jonathan lifted it from her shoulders, she turned and gripped him fiercely.

"What is going to happen to us, Jonathan?" Her fingers clutched his arms as she looked up at him. "I can't pretend any longer. I'm afraid—afraid for my father—everyone—myself—you."

"Easy, lass, easy." Jonathan placed his arm about her trembling shoulders. "You're overwrought, and I don't blame you. But things are not as bad as they seem." Steadying Elizabeth with his arm, he guided her into her father's room. "Sit down and listen to me." He lowered her gently to a chair. "Your father is not as sick as he pretends to be. And his mind was clear enough to warn me to be careful—and to tell me that it was Jarrett they were readying to hang. Somehow, your father must have learned who I am. He's playing sick, lass, just as your mother is."

"You're—you're not saying that—just to cheer me?"

"I'd not try to deceive you about your father, Elizabeth."

"Oh, Jonathan—" Her voice choked. She jumped from the chair. Her eyes filled with tears of relief.

With his own thoughts drumming in his ears, telling him not to be a fool, Jonathan swept Elizabeth to him in a tight embrace. He kissed the tears from her eyes, and when she offered no protest, he fastened his lips on her mouth. All the time, he was waiting for her to come to her senses, and when she stirred, he braced himself for the explosion that was bound to follow. Instead, he felt her arms move up around his neck, and when he was about to take his lips away, Elizabeth's were returning his kisses with an ardor as great as his own.

He tried to tell himself that this surrender to their emotions was absolute insanity, but every sense of danger, every rational thought was swept away in the sudden astounding discovery that he was in love with

Elizabeth, and the more astonishing awareness that she loved him. War, Redcoats and spying were all forgotten in this tumultuous elation that left no room for rival emotions.

Feeling Elizabeth move, he took his arm from behind her back, and ran his fingers lovingly through her hair. He was conscious that she was standing on tiptoe, that her back was being crushed by his other arm, but he couldn't let her go. Against the palm of his hand, he felt the rapid beating of the pulse in her neck, and was surprised to find that his whole body was shaken by the pounding of his own heart.

Ordinary sound sense, and the world of reality, were slow in returning to him. More astonishing than the fervor of his love for Elizabeth was her surrender to her emotions. The wealth of passion she displayed overwhelmed him, and she, as much as he, had forgotten all their quarrels and outbursts of sarcasm and mutual scorn. It was almost as if the love they had tried to fight off with angry contention had flared up to defy them. And Jonathan was the more surprised at the responsive abandon of Elizabeth's caresses, for he would have staked his life that this self-willed lass would never love to the extent of casting off every curb on her emotions.

At last he forced himself to take his lips from hers. "We're witless," he whispered shakily. "The house watched—both of us under suspicion—I should be on my way to the Potter's Field."

Her finger-tips brushed across his mouth, silencing him. Throwing her arms about his neck again, she pulled his head down and pressed her lips to his. He found himself incapable of fighting the intoxication, and his arms held her more tightly than before. At last Elizabeth unlaced her fingers and took her hands from behind his neck. She pressed her palms against his chest and pulled her lips away. "How long have you loved me, Jonathan?" She leaned back and looked in his face.

"Forever it seems, Elizabeth, although I didn't know it." He loosed her, and placed his hands on her cheeks, tilting her chin with his thumbs. "To be truthful, I'd not given the matter of love much thought, but I scarce expected it to hit like a lightning bolt."

"Then you weren't sure the night of the Mischianza? When you kissed me—thinking I was in a swoon?" She laughed outright at the embarrassed look on his face.

"I suppose, Beth, if the truth were known, I've loved you since I watched you from the window of the Silver Dolphin." A grin crept slowly across his face. "And I doubt if that first glimmer was lessened any at the Red Lion."

"If you ever tell anybody about that—ever at any time—even after we're married—"

"Married!" He looked at her as if he'd never heard the word before.

"Married," she said firmly. "I know all the excuses as well as you do."

She counted them off on the fingers of her right hand: "The war—you're out of uniform—we're both living under the shadow of the gallows—you don't know how you'll support me after the war." Her fingers closed one by one and she shook the lightly closed fist at him, laughing. "You can't kiss a maid the way you did, Jonathan Kimball, and not follow it with a wedding. Not in Philadelphia."

He took her hand and clasped it between his own, covering it with kisses. "Excuses they may be, darling, but they are truths that can't be ignored. For myself, I'd not have ordered things this way, but needs must when the devil holds the reins. Like it or not, lass, I must be off to see what I can learn of Jarrett's arrest, and you must purchase that package of paper." He pulled her to him and kissed her goodbye. "I'll leave first. That way, Redhead will most likely follow me, if he's watching."

"Goodbye, Jonathan, my dear." She clung to him a moment. "I'll be waiting for you—no matter how late it is when you get back."

22   REVENGE

. . . And though we benefited from his [Lee's] *treason, we loathed him for it.*——George Crabbe's Diary

In shirt, drawers, and stockinged feet, André stood at the upstairs window of his quarters, trying to cool himself in the faint breeze off the river. The castle of dreams he had built so carefully had turned out to be a castle of cards that had collapsed with the blight of Barren Hill. All the success of the Mischianza and the credit it had earned him in Sir William's eyes had been wiped out by the inglorious aftermath. André was too tired and heartsick to indulge himself in any impassioned outbursts. For the time being, the bottom had dropped out of his world, and he needed patience and a clear head to put it together again.

He turned from the window with a sigh and, sitting down on a small bench, dropped his arms on the table top and buried his face in his cupped hands. Whoever said that fortune was a fickle whore, was right, he thought, in a burst of self-pity. Only an hour before he had experienced a bitter foretaste of his changed fortune. He had been closeted with Sir Henry when the military secretary announced the arrival of Admiral Lord Richard Howe. Very properly, when the announcement was made, he had risen from his chair, excused himself to Sir Henry and walked into the adjoining room. Where in the old days General Howe would have said, "Sit still, John," General Clinton had let him go without a word.

And the talk between the Admiral and the General had been loud and angry, and distressing. The Admiral had wasted no words, nor had he bothered to be polite or diplomatic in his ultimatum. Although he hadn't been able to see him, André could visualize the tall, lean, hawk-faced Lord Richard standing there with his cocked hat in the crook of his arm, and his elbow resting on his sword hilt.

"By God, sir," the Admiral's voice was harsh and penetrating. "I'll not hold the Fleet at anchor much longer. The French Fleet, General, is reported a dozen times a day. The time has passed when I could have taken the major part of your Army aboard. 'Tis useless, sir, to tell me that you cannot evacuate thirty thousand men in a night, for I will answer by saying that I will not—will not, sir—risk an action against the French with my decks awash with seasick soldiers. Even the Parliament, sir, cannot—cannot, mark you—order me to sacrifice the Fleet."

André raised his head and rubbed his closed eyes with his knuckles. He had heard more of the same, but the General had waged a losing battle. No one, not even himself, had ever thought in terms of evacuating Philadelphia, or the problems such a move would present. The Fleet couldn't carry both the men and the supplies it would require to feed them for a week or more. And the horses, carriages, wagons and all the rest of the loot they had gathered in Philadelphia would have to be abandoned.

Immersed in his own thoughts, he didn't hear the knocker on the front door, and Mistress Darragh had to call him for the third time before he realized there was a message for him. Heedless, for once, of his appearance, he went to the head of the stairs.

"What is it?" he called down into the hall lighted only by the single taper Mistress Darragh held in her hand.

A bearded face was pushed into the door opening, and a hoarse voice answered, "A message, sir. The gentleman as give it me said you'd pay a gold crown for it."

"A gold crown for delivering a message?" André shouted. "Where in God's name did you walk from—London?"

"No, sir." The voice from the darkness was aggrieved. "I brought it from the Valley Forge."

André dashed into his bedchamber, pulled a crown from the pocket of his breeches hanging over the end of the bed, and ran downstairs. The messenger took the crown, examined it in the light of Lydia's taper, and disappeared into the darkness. There was no name or address on the outside fold of the paper, and there was no signature, André noted as he broke the seal and unfolded the message. But there was no mistaking Lee's firm small handwriting, nor the importance of what he had written.

Finished reading it for the second time, André took Mistress Darragh's taper and touched it to the letter. He held it, fluttering and burning, till the black ash crumpled and fell to the bricked floor of the entryway. Handing the taper back to Lydia, he turned and walked slowly up the stairs.

So their plans to capture La Fayette had been frustrated by a Rebel officer hiding in Philadelphia. And Lee didn't know who. André clenched his fists and struck the stair rail in fury. Maybe Lee didn't know, but John André could put two and two together. What had only been a suspicion till now was confirmed. The uninvited Mary of Scotland had been the Ladd wench after all, or Broadmoor had been seduced into talking. In either case, and it made little difference, the unknown Rebel officer was playing the part of servant in her house.

He reached out for his breeches and started to pull them over his foot. Discovery of who had thwarted their plans might not restore him to favor, but he would have his revenge. He'd do three things. He'd have that wench-struck fool Broadmoor brought to his quarters. He'd have the Provost Marshal arrest the Ladd woman and her Rebel servant. Then he'd bring Broadmoor and the treacherous wench face to face.

23   SEARCH AND SEIZURE

Fear itself made her daring.——Ovid

Elizabeth decided it was too dark to see whether or not anyone was watching the house. She moved away from the side of the window in the upstairs back bedchamber, and walked along the hallway to Jonathan's room.

For days, she had worried about the red-haired man's spying on the house. Now, after going from window to window all day and seeing nothing, she was more worried than ever. Following her visit to the prison yesterday, she had bought the squares of paper, written the report to Stirling, and taken the package to the English post. No one had even glanced at it. So far as she could tell, no one had followed her, and yet she was filled with a depressing, heart-pounding feeling that she was under constant observation.

When Jonathan had kissed her goodbye that morning he'd warned her that she must fight off the feeling. He'd explained that many a spy had been caught, not because they were suspected, but because they couldn't hide their apprehension. In spite of her worry, she smiled when she thought of Jonathan's goodbye. He had been in a hurry to get down to the waterfront, but his lingering farewell showed that he hated to leave her. He had explained over and over that it was of the direst necessity that he learn if anyone besides Jarrett were suspected. She had agreed with him, kissed him soundly, and taken her arms from about his neck. Still he hadn't left, and it was only when he heard Maggie coming toward the kitchen that he gave her a final quick kiss, and ran down the back steps.

Going into Jonathan's bedchamber, she saw his timepiece lying on the commode. It was after eight. He should have been back by now, she thought, and once again felt the fluttering, palpitating anxiety that she didn't have the power to control. Since yesterday, she had been forced to hide more emotions than she had ever known in her life before.

Till almost dawn, she and Jonathan had talked the night away in her father's room. Sitting on Jonathan's lap, she had tried to persuade him to tell her mother that they were in love, but his better judgment had won her over when he pointed out that having to hide their love from both her mother and Maggie compelled them to be circumspect, and added to their safety. Jonathan had argued that, should they disclose their love, they might become careless in hiding it from others, and an embrace, a kiss, or a meaningful look between mistress and servant could start gossip that would soon reach English ears.

Now as she left Jonathan's room she heard him greet Maggie in the kitchen. For the moment, her fears left her. They met in the dimly lighted hallway and he swept her into his arms. Each was hungry for the other's kisses, and while Jonathan forgot that he was rain soaked, Elizabeth didn't notice it. At last Jonathan loosed his embrace, and putting his fingers under her chin he looked into her eyes.

"You've been afraid, Beth?"

"Yes," she whispered. "Every minute you were gone."

"I had to force myself to stay away," Jonathan admitted, placing his arm about her shoulder, and holding her to him. "And when I saw the sentry at the back—"

"A sentry?" she cried out. "I was watching. I didn't see anyone."

"There's a sentry behind the stables." He took his arm from around her shoulder, and started pacing the floor. "I watched him go the length of the alley and back. Then I slipped into the garden at the side of the stable wall when his back was turned."

"He wasn't there at dusk—I know." There was a frightened catch in her voice. "And the redheaded man hasn't been there all day."

Jonathan stopped his pacing and faced her squarely. "I must go out again. At once!"

"Oh, no." Elizabeth reached out and gripped his arms.

"But I must, Beth, I must." He crushed her to him and spoke quickly. "I told you last night that I'd found Jarrett's house. And that his widow wasn't there—the place was tight shuttered."

"You mean she's returned?"

"I can't tell. But there was smoke coming from the chimney as I looked again before I came back just now. Don't you see, sweetheart, I have to find out what she knows?"

"I—I suppose you must, Jonathan dear." She tried to stiffen her shaking knees, and force a smile to her face. "It's just that having found that I love you—I can't bear not knowing what may have happened when hours go by without seeing you."

"I know, darling, for I have the same fears about you. But if we are suspected—then we can't sit here waiting to be caught."

"What can we do anyway?" Elizabeth asked suddenly. "We can't run off and leave my mother and father. Even if we could get Mother out of the city—"

"I don't know, Elizabeth darling, and it's useless trying to plan till I do know." He smoothed the hair away from her face, and kissed her roughly. "I daren't wait longer. Don't come to the back door, and don't look out any of the windows."

He was gone before she could force out a goodbye. She stood listening and trembling for the sound of the back-door latch, but the only noises she heard came from Maggie's clattering pots and kettles as the old Scotswoman cleaned up her kitchen. Holding her breath till her eardrums throbbed, she waited for the shout of the sentry, and when there was no challenge, her relief was so great she could scarcely walk to her father's room.

Exhausted, she was about to lower herself into the captain's chair when the tinkle of a pebble striking the thick glass of the back window held her transfixed. A few seconds passed, and a whole rain of carriage-drive chips hit the window.

"Rufus," she gasped, and sped to the back hall. Many a time she'd heard the same signal, and crept downstairs after her father was asleep, to let Rufus into the house. He was always being locked out for coming home late. She opened the small door that led to the cellar, ran down the rough steps, and pushed up the slanting doors that opened into the back yard.

Her brother slipped into the cellar and lowered the double doors behind him.

"I'm soaked," he whispered. "I had to swim ashore, and I've got little time. I have to be back before the watch changes. The English swine who stands guard over me is aboard the *Cadiz*, drinking, but he ordered the small boat for five bells. So while they're rowing out to get him, I must slip aboard and get into my bunk."

"What did you swim ashore for?" Elizabeth guided him up the steps in the dark.

"The English skippers have their orders to sail." He stopped at the top of the stairs and pointed up. "How's Mother?"

"Better. And Father, too—I saw him yesterday."

"Good. Now listen to me, Beth." He followed her into their father's room. "The English ships are preparing to sail. When they will sail, or where to, I know not. But if I can find out, you must take the word to Dan Jarrett. He's a friend of—"

"Dan Jarrett is dead," Elizabeth said bluntly. "Hanged by the English yesterday."

"Then you must find other means to send word to Valley Forge. I'm sorry about Dan—" Rufus shook his head—"but the information must be sent—I don't care how."

"We'll send it." Elizabeth put more confidence into her voice than she felt. "A Rebel captain is staying here at the house—pretending to be our servant."

A raising of his eyebrows was the extent to which Rufus ever showed surprise, and Elizabeth smiled slightly when her brother continued, as though a Rebel spy in the house were a most ordinary affair.

"One thing I do know, Elizabeth. The English are going to scuttle the Sally E."

"Oh—" Elizabeth bit her lips. "But I thought they would."

"They told me they would. We're to sail her to the sandbar above Port Chester. The crew will get onto the sandbar, and the English will sink her between the bar and the Penn shore. 'Tis my reckoning, they'll do the same with the other pressed ships, and try to block the narrow channel." He stopped and shook his fist. "But I'm not going to play it their way. If the Sally E has to go down—she'll go down fighting."

"Without guns?" Elizabeth asked sorrowfully.

"Without guns," Rufus repeated. "The Fleet can only sail at the turn of the tide. Now I'll know when they're going to hoist anchor, at least one tide ahead of sailing time. Somehow—I don't rightly know how— I'm going to cut the Sally E's hawsers and let her batter her way through the English Fleet as she runs wild with the tide."

"You think you can?" Elizabeth was doubtful.

"The Sally E draws little water compared with the frigates and the transports. With the force of the river and the outgoing tide—she'll be like a battering-ram. One thing more, and I must run or I'll never get back aboard."

"I'm listening," Elizabeth said.

"I'll do my damnedest to find out the English port of call. If I do, I'll fly a signal flag just before I turn her loose."

Elizabeth nodded, reached under the table and pressed the catch. Swinging the table top aside, she took a square of paper. "I'll write it down, Rufus."

"For 'Boston,' I'll fly the straight Blue."

"Boston—Blue," Elizabeth wrote quickly.

"For New York—the Blue Peter. For Amboy—the Black Triangle. For Sandy Hook—the Blue and White Swallowtail, the *Sally E*'s house flag. And for Cape Cod—the Red Pennant."

"I've got them." She laid aside the quill and closed the table top. "What's afoot here?"

Elizabeth and Rufus turned at the sound of their mother's voice. In her night robe, she stood framed in the doorway.

Rufus ran to her side. "Mother—you shouldn't be about."

"Fiddlesticks." She snapped her fingers, and waited while Rufus kissed her. "I'm as well as ever I was. Didn't Beth tell you?"

"There's been no time, Mother. For once, ask no questions and say nothing. I must be off or I'll get shot climbing aboard my own ship—"

"You're leaving—now?"

"Yes, Mother."

"But, son—"

She got no farther. The front door knocker sounded, loud and threatening.

"Upstairs, Mother, fast." Elizabeth leaped to life. "It may be some of the English officers—calling on me." She went out the door.

"More likely to be some who followed me here." Rufus swore under his breath and ground his teeth.

"Down to the cellar as quick as you can," Elizabeth whispered, halfway to the front door.

Again the knocker crashed, and a voice from outside shouted loudly, "In the name of the King—open!"

Elizabeth saw Rufus disappear into the darkness of the back hall. Her mother was turning the landing on the stairs. Drawing herself up, she pressed her lips together for a second before she opened the door.

Two Redcoats with fixed bayonets forced their way past her, and a captain she had never met, but who wore the green tabs of a provost marshal on his stand-up collar, stood facing her. Behind the Captain stood Lieutenant Smythe, very stiff and ill at ease. Even in the poor light, she could see Lieutenant Bygrove wringing his hands as though he would twist a finger off.

"Good evening, gentlemen." She curtsied. "I've not had a visit from you, Lieutenant Smythe, or from you, Lieutenant Bygrove, since you came to gather your presents from Virginia."

"No, Mistress Ladd, and—and I wish—" Smythe choked, coughed, and stumbled on, "I wish to introduce Captain Mosgrave, Provost Marshal."

"I'm sorry, Mistress Ladd, to meet you—under these circumstances." The Provost Marshal bowed.

"Won't you come in?" Elizabeth fought desperately to put irony into her voice. "Your two sentries needed no invitation."

"I should like to warn you that you need make no statements if you do not so desire—but if you do, they may be used against you. Is that clear?"

"Not at all, Captain." She forced a laugh. "Why should I worry about —making statements, did you say? I have nothing to hide." At the same instant she was praying that Rufus was out of the cellar, and her mother in bed.

"I wish I could believe you." The Captain bowed again and walked into the hall. "Search the house!" he ordered the Redcoats. "No, madame, I am afraid that at the moment I do not believe you."

"Oh, come, Captain." She waved him to the hall seat. "Nothing could be as serious as to call for searching the house."

"Were you at the Mischianza Ball—costumed as Mary of Scotland?" He ignored the invitation to sit, and fired the question point-blank.

"Certainly not." She smiled. "As my mother and servants will tell you."

"The truth will make matters much simpler—I assure you. Did you send a cipher message, disguised as a package of paper—"

Elizabeth burst out laughing. "Do you not think, Captain, that some little proof of your first charge would be in order—before you saddle me with a second crime?"

Abruptly the Captain turned to Smythe. "Bring them here, Lieutenant."

Elizabeth felt a cold, hard lump in her throat when she saw Smythe turn to someone behind him. Could they possibly have proof? Her mind raced back over every detail. How could they, and what could it be? She'd made no blunders, and neither had Jonathan, of that she was certain.

"Is this the woman?"

She found herself facing a colonel, a colonel in kilts, and beside him, a horrible-looking beefy man in black, with a fringe of red hair that she would have recognized anywhere. The kilted Colonel took his time. His eyes searched her face, and she knew he was staring at her chin and throat. She could feel, as well as see his eyes take in every detail of her hands. In spite of every effort, a slow flush rose to her cheeks when he searched out the curves of her bodice, and she sensed his calculations as to whether they matched what had been more visible in the low-cut Mary costume.

"This is the same woman." The Colonel's voice was incisive.

"Did I not tell you so?" The man with the odd hair pulled a dispatch case from under his arm. "Trivers was right, as I knew he would be," he mumbled, opening the case and drawing out a batch of papers. "You recognize these?" he asked triumphantly, holding the Mischianza invitations before her.

"Certainly I do." Elizabeth controlled her voice. "Printer Trivers showed them to me—"

"He did—indeed he did." The hateful man leered. "And especially this one." He held it up and waved it. "One that Trivers did not think perfect, and which he discarded—but one which you, mistress, used to gain entry to the Wharton house."

"Nonsense—"

"Nay 'tis not," André's informer threw at her. "For I took all—all the invitations back to Trivers, and he picked this one from all of them—and swore that no one—no one but you, mistress, ever laid hand on it."

"Printer Trivers is mistaken."

"Is the Colonel mistaken?"

"Yes." She managed a smile to the Colonel as she turned. "The Colonel is in truth mistaken."

"Not so, mistress. The mask could no' hide those eyes, nor the chin. The hands I paid much heed to—as I always do—being somewhat proud o' ma own." He held out his well-formed hands. "And I will add, lass, that all the hoops and farthingales will no' hide a fine figure any more than they can hide a bad one."

"And what of this?" The man with the odd hair drew the package of writing squares from his dispatch case.

"What of it, as you say?" Elizabeth felt on more secure ground and allowed her contempt to show. " 'Tis a packet of writing squares for Friend Vaux—as it says."

" 'Tis a cipher message."

"Then show it me—and the Colonel—and the lieutenants."

" 'Tis skillfully hidden, and—"

"If it be skillful, mister," her voice was ridiculing, " 'tis more than you make out to be." Angrily she stepped forward and struck the package from his hand, scattering the paper over the floor. "There be no cipher there, Mister Informant, unless you forged one."

The shot went home, and the man's face burned red. "I removed the page."

"You are a liar to boot," she snapped. "Count the pages, Provost. You'll find fifty to bear witness that this—this—whatever you call him

—lies." She stopped and her eyes ranged from one to the other. "And being gentleman, some of whom have enjoyed my hospitality, you'll see that these blank sheets are not changed—to count against me."

The Provost Marshal nodded. "We will be fair, mistress. You have at least four here who will bear witness that there are fifty pages—all clean and bare of marks. I counted them—and I will keep them."

"But I must have—"

"You must have much to do." The Provost interrupted the red-haired man brusquely. "I will see that the papers are not lost or interfered with." Holding the writing squares in his hand, the Provost signalled two more Redcoats into the house. "You may fetch your cloak and bonnet, mistress. Speak to no one."

"I may speak to my mother." She threw her head back defiantly.

"You may speak to no one. You will go with the soldiers." The Provost was grim.

Inwardly raging, and clenching her hands in chagrin as she suddenly remembered that her mother did not know of the signal Rufus was to fly, she walked slowly to the hall closet. And, she thought savagely, she had no way to let Jonathan know.

"There is no male servant in the house, sir." It was one of the Redcoats who had been searching.

So they were after Jonathan, too. Elizabeth stiffened her shoulders, and waited for the question she knew would come next.

"Where is this Kimball fellow of yours?" The Provost's voice was harsh.

"Out drinking, I would suppose." She turned with her cape and bonnet in her hand, and stared the Provost from head to foot. "Truly, Captain, you'd not expect me to know which taverns my servant favors with his patronage?" she asked contemptuously.

"Truly, Mistress Ladd, I'd not." He turned to the two Redcoats who had searched the house. "Wait here and arrest the servant Kimball when he returns. You, Smythe, order the town searched. Come, mistress. We must not keep Major André waiting."

Elizabeth walked out the door, flanked by the two Redcoat sentries. Smythe ran on ahead, and the Provost Marshal followed her, with Bygrove, the kilted Colonel and the red-haired man bringing up the rear. She had heard no outcry from her mother or Maggie, and she was suddenly proud of them; and she'd heard no sentry's challenge that would indicate that Rufus had been caught. Lifting her skirts clear of her toes, she stepped out onto Chestnut. Turning right, she strode out briskly, forcing the sentries to march quickly. Fear had passed. Her brother had escaped. Her mother and Maggie had played their parts, and she could do no less. "If only they don't catch Jonathan," Elizabeth promised herself proudly, "I'll face this corseted and perfumed André—and outwit him."

24   COOPER'S ALLEY

Danger itself is the best remedy for danger.——HERBERT

Try as he might, Jonathan could not blot out from his memory the dismal sight of Dan Jarrett's hanging squad tramping across the prison yard. Even now, as he plunged through the ankle-deep puddles in Cooper's Alley, the immediate danger that overhung Elizabeth and himself seemed remote. It was almost as though the danger affected two other people, two people who were at least still alive, while Dan Jarrett was dead. Not only dead, but already buried, if such a ceremony as he had witnessed yesterday at the Potter's Field could be called burial.

It was no matter for wonder that superstitious folk gave the unhallowed acre a wide berth when the nights were dark. If there were such things as ghosts, Jonathan thought, running his forefinger along the rim of his hat in a useless effort to train the water in some other direction, then the field that lay cater-corner from the State House Yard and just west of the Walnut Street Prison must have more than its share of restless spirits. The penniless, the unknown, the suicides, the blasphemers—and now the victims of the English hangman—were lost forever in hastily dug, unmarked holes in the water-logged soil.

The drainage gutter running down the center of Cooper's had long since filled to overflowing, and now miniature waves were lapping at the flights of two and three steps that led up to the front doors. The steps were more numerous as the alley sloped down to Front, and the water was deeper where the flagstone footwalk was broken away by the cart wheels that had turned too sharply from Front into the cobbled alley with its brick houses and their white-pedimented door frames. The light wasn't bright enough for Jonathan again to see the chimney on Jarrett's house, but, smoke or not, he was going to see if the widow had returned. The weather and curfew together had driven most everybody indoors except down here by the waterfront, where sailors and dock rats worked as noisily by night as they did by day. The constant squeaking of ropes running through sheave blocks was followed by the creaking thud of chests and boxes being landed on deck or dock, and the clicking of pawls snapping into ratchet wheels was sharp and explosive when the capstans were turned to draw or slacken mooring ropes as the ships were loaded or unloaded.

The shutters on Mistress Jarrett's house were closed and hooked, but Jonathan stooped close to the ground and looked up through the down-tilted louvers. A light burned in that room, he saw, and, holding his breath, he ran his finger-tips over the loose slats of the shutter. He heard the window catch being turned, heard the sash lift, and then the clink of the hook as it was lifted from the staple.

"Who is it?"

A low, steady voice; unafraid, Jonathan decided as he answered, "A friend—if you are Mistress Jarrett."

"I am."

"I have to talk to you, mistress. 'Tis most important. I'm—I was—a friend of Dan's."

There was no tremor in the answering voice. "Go to the door. I'll douse the lamp afore I open it."

Reassuring himself that he'd neither been seen nor heard, Jonathan slipped round to the door and climbed the stone steps. He felt, rather than heard, the door open. A hand was laid on his arm, and he was drawn inside as the door closed softly behind him. His left elbow rubbed against what he thought must be the railing of the stairs to the upper story when, without a sound of warning, he felt himself seized from behind. His arms were pinned tight to his sides, and the cold edge against the side of his neck could be nothing other than a sailor's clasp-knife. Two men, he reckoned; one couldn't do it. And he made no effort to struggle.

"So, mister—whatever your name may be—you want to talk with me?"

The same voice, unafraid, level, hardly raised above a whisper, which had spoken to him through the shutter, sounded now behind him. "If you are Mistress Jarrett—as I said outside," Jonathan answered, keeping his own voice low, and being careful not to move his head. "I watched Dan's burying yesterday—and learned that his widow lived here. I came to find if Mistress Jarrett knew why the English hanged Dan?"

"And if she did—for why should she tell you?"

There was still no tremor in the woman's voice. Jonathan's wits worked fast. Neither was there a trace of hatred or venom, as there would have been, had she been for the King's men—and a party to her husband's betrayal. In the blackness, he tried to assess the two men. The one holding his arms was less than six feet, with hands that held his elbows in an iron grip. No soldier, Jonathan decided, else the man would have twisted his arms instead of pinioning them. A sailor's clasp-knife! A soldier would have used a bayonet. Quickly he made up his mind. If he had to guess whether they were Tory or Rebel, then he'd guess Rebel; and if he guessed wrong, his muscles were taut and he was ready for the fight. He picked his words carefully. "I was a friend to Dan as he was to me. He had other friends. We knew of nothing that he did, for which the English should hang him."

"Nor did I," Mistress Jarrett answered.

"From your voice, mistress, 'twould seem that I—and certain of Dan's other friends—are more grieved than his widow."

For the first time, there was a catch to her breathing, and Jonathan spoke quickly. "Had I but known—in time—I'd ha' done something to save him."

"Nobody could ha' saved him." Her voice was not so steady now.

"Had I been told in time, I could," Jonathan said quietly but with cruel goading. "When they marched him out of the prison to the yard—and to the gallows—a few determined men would have pulled down the gallows, and a few more would have started a riot to keep the English bastards busy." He drew a long suggestive breath. "Leastwise, he'd not be lying in the Potter's Field now."

"His friends will get him out of the field," Jarrett's widow blurted out, her voice rising.

"I'm glad they have the bowels to do that much," Jonathan said sarcastically. " 'Tis too bad they're tardy with their aid."

"You talk out of a big mouth, mister. Now that the thing be over."

It was the man holding his elbows who spoke angrily in his ear, and Jonathan knew which way his captors leaned. " 'Tis true I do," Jonathan admitted, "but I'm angered that naught was done. Dan was already out in the prison yard before I knew who 'twas they were hanging."

"Then you knew afore we did," the man spoke again. "We had no knowledge of it—till 'twas all done. How did you know?" he finished with threat and suspicion in his voice.

"I was in the prison," Jonathan retorted. "A prisoner told me it was Dan."

The man holding the knife took it from Jonathan's throat. "For God's sake let's an end to this chatter and see what the hell he looks like. Open the shutter, Abbie."

A sickly yellow beam of light shot into the hall as Abbie Jarrett slid aside the shutter on a dark lanthorn. Jonathan found himself looking into a small parlor with a Franklin stove set on the hearth in front of a green marble fireplace in the wall opposite the door. In the center of the room, the dark lanthorn sat on a small round table, and standing behind it, Abbie Jarrett, dainty and prim in a high-necked black linsey-woolsey dress, stood looking at Jonathan with big, wide-open eyes.

"I'm truly sorry, Mistress Jarrett, that I spoke as I did, but my own neck is forfeit if the English know that I had dealings with Dan."

"Could you have saved Dan?" She smoothed her almost white hair with a hand no larger than a little girl's.

"Had there been warning enough, I'd have made the try."

"Had there been any warning—" the bigger of the two men spoke, "we'd have tried too."

"It could be, mister," the man who had held Jonathan by the elbows broke in, "that you can help us free the other prisoners—iffen you know how to get into that prison."

Jonathan shook his head. "No—not that way. To try and free them all would only result in a lot being killed who'd not be killed if you leave things as they are. The English will leave soon, and they can't take all the prisoners with them—leastwise not far. They'll be too busy fending off the Rebel troops once they set foot out of the city."

"In the meantime," Abbie spoke up, "some more will be hanged—like my Dan."

"Do you know of any who are in danger of hanging—right now?" Jonathan asked.

"No," the big man answered. "But we didn't know of Dan's danger either."

"But Dan wasn't a prisoner for any length of time," Jonathan pointed out. "If he had been—I'd have known."

"That's true." It was the big man who spoke again. "The English swine picked him up at noontime—and 'twas all over afore eight bells."

"But why?" Jonathan asked. "That's what I must know, else some of the others—including me—will be stretching English rope next."

"That's not like to be the case, young man." Abbie shook her head decisively. "I see no reason for not telling why they hanged Dan. The English accused him of playing post carrier between the New Jersey Militia and the camp at Valley Forge."

"But that couldn't be." Jonathan looked from one to the other.

"Oh, but it was," Abbie said, proudly raising her head. "I've known my Dan was carrying messages from Governor Livingston to Mister George and the others at the Forge—ever since the English took the city. Not always did I know what they were—but I know that this last was word that Governor Livingston was raising as many militia as he could—to harass the English when they leave Philadelphia."

"How did you know that?"

"The paper was on him when the English took him at noontide." Abbie's shoulders drooped, and she shrugged despairingly. "Of what use was there to dispute it—when they took the paper out of his boot?"

"Damn!" Jonathan exploded. "Wasn't it in cipher?"

Abbie nodded and bit her lip. "Yes, lad, but somewhat must have gone amiss. 'Twas an ordinary letter—from one friend to another—and in between the lines of writing the message was written in stain."

"Yes—I know," Jonathan prodded her.

"The English officer took the letter, held it to the heat of the stove, and in a few seconds—no more—the second dispatch was there to read."

Jonathan nodded grimly. "Something was amiss. Governor Livingston doesn't use that system of writing. But the English do. The bastards had their suspicions of Dan—but no proof—so they made proof, the damn butchers."

"You're certain-sure on what you say?"

"I am that." Jonathan turned to the big man. "The Rebel officers use a cipher the English couldn't read even if the message were painted on the side of a barn."

The big man thought for a moment, looking Jonathan up and down. "You made no fight when we grappled with you when you was let in here by Abbie. Why so?"

"Why would I?" Jonathan looked at him. "I came for information. I'd not be like to get it by fighting. I had to find out who besides Dan Jarrett was suspected."

"I believe you." The big man shook Jonathan's hand. "My name is Aaron Cults. I was a master mariner—till the English took my ship."

"I believe him," Abbie said quietly.

The other man reached out his hand to Jonathan. "Name's Parson Poole." He shook Jonathan's hand vigorously. " 'Parson' because I quote scripture and only swear when it's needful."

"It could be that we can help each other," Jonathan said.

"Well, lad, I don't rightly know." Parson Poole scratched his head. "A lot of us here on the waterfront has had to live close-like since the English took our ships and trade. Aaron here works at anything, him as has captained his own ships out and in Delaware Bay for nigh to twenty year."

"And Parson—" Aaron Cults pointed with his thumb—"though he pretends to being rough, could stow cargo so that a ship would sail through China waters and never spring a seam or rack a rib, even in the wussest storm. Now he scrubs decks and the like."

"I had fair fortune today, Aaron," Parson Poole said solemnly when Cults had finished his say. "I polished brass on H.M.S. *Alert* today. The mate said I did my chore well. I did too—I dropped a magnet in the binnacle housing. Wait till he finds Magnetic North has moved somewhat."

"I'd not be much of a help to you on such chores." Jonathan grinned.

"We do other things," Aaron said grimly. "We dispose of known traitors—and we give warnings to some of the Tory brothers—which they ignore but once."

"In that, you might help me," Jonathan said, thinking of the man with the odd hair. "I'd like to find out somewhat about a man who has red hair that sticks out like a brim on a hat—"

"We'd like to put a halter about the traitor's neck—could we lay hold on him." Aaron grunted. "We suspicion it was him as betrayed Dan. He's André's private civil spy."

"Then your suspicion is most like to be correct. You know his name?" Jonathan asked.

"Name's Quimby," Aaron said. "Tracy Quimby, a lickspittle of Royal Governor Will Franklin's. A bastardly, miserable, viperish Tory from New York who was—and mayhap still is—an informant for the Pine Tree Robbers over in Jersey, as well as for the English here."

"Governor Livingston had him put in the stocks and whipped for trying to prevent enlistments in the Jersey Militia," Abbie Jarrett interjected. "That's why we suspicioned him in connection with my Dan."

"Then he's one lad I will work on—with vigor," Jonathan said. He paused a moment, then included the three with a wave of his arm. "How many men could you muster if it came about that we could act with profit to the lads at Valley Forge?"

Poole spoke up. "A hundred—given the time. Fifty on short time—say two hours."

Jonathan held out his hand. "I'm beholden to you more than I can say. And you, Mistress Jarrett, should you have a fear that the English will try to punish you—say so and we'll get you to a safe place."

"They can do no more to me than they've done to Dan. I'm gray-headed and not so well formed as once I was—so my hanging will come as quick as his. I'll stay, lad, till the matter be ended—one way or t'other, but I give you my thanks."

Jonathan held up his hand, stopped her, and bent his head, listening. From outside came the sound of marching feet and the clatter of arms.

"They're on both sides of the house," Cults whispered.

"Douse the light again, Abbie." Poole leaped for the window. "They're on Front Street—a big patrol. And there's somebody at the front door."

"Who?" Cults ran and looked over Poole's shoulder. "It's John Norris, by God!"

In a swirl of skirts, Abbie Jarrett flew to the front door. She pulled the bolt, and Jonathan heard a man's footsteps in the narrow hallway.

"Norris is one of our lads," Cults said throatily to Jonathan. "He watches André's quarters."

"They've arrested Elizabeth Ladd," Norris spoke to the room. "She's at André's quarters now. And the Provost's patrols are looking for her servant."

"They're looking for the lad from Virginia?" Cults asked.

"Yes."

"Then it's me they're after." Jonathan looked about. "Where's the back door?"

"House don't have one. 'Twas bricked up to make a back window." Poole pointed to the recess made by the fireplace. "If the Redcoats followed either of you here, we go out that window, but don't get panicky—they mayn't be comin' here. It's a fairish drop to the yard, but it's dark, and our best chance for escape if they're after us."

A musket butt crashed against the street door, splintering the panel. It was followed by a second crash, metal on metal this time, as a second gun butt hit the iron bolt. Shouts and threats were bellowed through the shattered panel, and in the background an officer's voice ordered the Redcoats to fire into the house.

"Oh, Jehovah! Jehovah!" Parson Poole chanted as he swept everything from the table. "Look after Abbie, Aaron." He picked up the table and hurled it through the back window.

Jonathan watched Aaron Cults seize Abbie Jarrett in his arms and leap out into the blackness. Jonathan followed, and he felt Poole's hands in his back pushing him down into the shadows that filled the small yard between the back of the house and the next street.

"Know the ropewalk at Rodman Alley?" Poole's breath was hot on the back of Jonathan's neck.

"Yes."

"Then make for it."

"I must go to Elizabeth."

A fusillade of shots drowned Poole's reply. Stabs of orange flame leaped from everywhere. The angry voices of the Redcoats were drawing closer. Abruptly, for Jonathan, the voices stopped. The scattered shots merged into a deafening roar. Darkness changed into one searing flash of brilliant white, and Jonathan pitched headlong, hands clawing the air, and blood gushing from a bullet wound in his shoulder.

"Take his feet, Norris, and keep your head down." Poole bent low and slid his hands under Jonathan's shoulders. "We'll take him to the ropewalk—if we can—and, if the Lord don't claim him, come midnight we'll move him to the old ferryhouse by the floating bridge."

25   TEMPORARY REPRIEVE

I say, hang every Rebel—two to a tree.——ANDRÉ

In the ground floor parlor of André's quarters, Colonel Monckton and Major Broadmoor listened in amazement and disgust to the stream of foul-mouthed abuse that poured from the sensuous lips of the Chief of Military Intelligence. Both Monckton and Broadmoor were thinking that here was a far different André from the quick-quipping bon vivant of the officers' mess, or the dashing gallant who had charmed the Tory ladies with his elegant manners and witty tongue.

Monckton was somewhat amused and a little sickened at the display, but Broadmoor, arms stiff by his side, was controlling his own temper, mostly for the reason that Mistress Darragh in her kitchen could scarcely avoid hearing André's insulting remarks about Elizabeth. Dislike, even hatred of the Colonies, both officers understood, but André's fury was close to insanity, Monckton believed, and the Grenadier Colonel made a mental note, as André crashed his white-knuckled fist on the table, that John André would frequent no more London clubs on a Monckton guest card.

At last, purple-faced, out of breath, and with a thin edge of foam lining his gleaming teeth, André threw a shaking pointing finger at Broadmoor. "And you, Broadmoor, you swore she was to be trusted. You argued and pleaded and convinced me—against my will and my judgment—when I knew, I tell you, that the wench was leading you like a stupid fish after bait."

Broadmoor opened his mouth, caught his Colonel's eye and closed his mouth again as he read Monckton's unspoken warning.

"Are you dumb, Broadmoor, as well as a fool?" André's voice was rising higher. Globules of sweat broke out at the bridge of his nose and trickled unnoticed down to his twisted mouth. Enraged at Broadmoor's silence, he pounded the table again, bouncing the quills out of the holder that sat like a paperweight on top of his spies' reports. "Are you too stupid to understand that this wench of yours and her servant fouled Sir William's plans to capture l'enfant La Fayette? You know right well," he shouted, "we've been held to blame for overwenching, and if it ever leaks out that a major in the Royal Grenadiers put his whoring ahead of his duty—"

"You go too far, André!" Broadmoor turned on his heel.

"Be damned, sir, I do not." André shot from behind the table and gripped Broadmoor's arm. "She'll hang—hang! Do you hear me—as will her Rebel bastard of a servant when we catch him—and I'd court-martial you were it not for the stink it would make. Damn it to hell, Broadmoor, were there not Tory wenches enough who were willing without your getting entrapped with a Rebel?"

Slowly and deliberately, Broadmoor turned his head to look at Monckton. Certain of his Colonel's attention, Broadmoor's glance travelled from his own shoulder, down his arm to where André's fingers still gripped it. Without a word, Broadmoor raised his hand and brought his white gauntlets against André's face with a stinging slap. Unbelieving,

André stepped back. His eyes were staring, glazed and unseeing, and his hand guided by sheer instinct had half drawn his sword from its scabbard.

"Don't draw it, Captain André." There was such coolness in Monckton's voice, such emphasis on the word "Captain" that André's hand froze inside the basket hilt of the glittering sword.

"Push it back in the scabbard, Captain."

The room was so deadly quiet that the sound of the sliding blade was like the warning hiss of a snake. André's knees were trembling. When he tried to lift his hand to wipe the slaver from his mouth he missed his face and his gesture ended in empty air. He looked from Monckton to Broadmoor and found the Major's back turned to him. His breathing was rattled and heavy, and choked him when he spoke.

"I'll kill you on the dueling field for that, Broadmoor."

"Major Broadmoor, from you, Captain. If you please." Ice could not have been colder than Monckton's order. Without haste, the Colonel walked to André's side. "Much may be forgiven for statements made in the heat of anger—but you, Captain, descend to limits beyond those of an officer. I must remind you, sir, that you are in fact, and in rank, only a captain. Your field rank of Major is by courtesy. You can in no way, sir, demand satisfaction of Major Broadmoor on the field of honor, for you, sir, were guilty of flagrant insubordination by laying your hand upon a superior officer. I suggest, Captain André, that you apologize to Major Broadmoor—and that you calm yourself." He stopped and glanced out the window as he heard the tramp of marching feet. "And I suggest, too, that you call the prisoner who is being brought in, by her name and nothing else."

In the silence of the room, the tramping of the soldiers, and an occasional burst of voices from the tavern across Two Street, could easily be heard. Broadmoor, standing rigid as a tent pole, kept his back to André and watched Elizabeth, heavily guarded, being brought across the street.

"My apologies, Major Broadmoor." The words broke from André in much the same tone as a tortured prisoner might use before the last turn of the rack.

"Accepted." Broadmoor's stiff shoulders eased, and he turned to the door as Elizabeth and her escort filed in.

Elizabeth, pushed forward by one of the sentries, found herself staring into the face of the dreaded André. Somewhat to her surprise, she felt no fear. In her forced walk from home, she'd had a chance to sort out her mind. "If," she'd argued with herself, "they have no proof in the matter of the squares of paper—most like they are playing a like game in the affair of the ball." Not that they'd need proof, she realized, but try as she might she couldn't quite bring herself to accept the fact that she'd been caught. 'Twas strange indeed; after all the countless hours of fearing this very thing, now that she had been caught she couldn't believe it.

"Well, mistress?" André fought to control himself. "This is the end of your spying."

"Spying, Major?" She forced a smile and waved at Broadmoor and the two lieutenants who stood just inside the door. " 'Tis hard to spy within one's own home, and if you make reference to these officers who visited me, I neither asked them questions, nor did I hear a word that was not already common talk."

"I speak, mistress, of your communications with the enemy."

"Doubtless you refer, Major—" she looked him straight in the face with all the confidence she could muster—"to the fifty squares of blank paper your red-haired servant has not had time—nor enough wits—to forge a cipher on."

"They contain a cipher—" André clenched his hand—"and we'll find it."

"Not in these fifty squares!" She laughed out loud. "Your red-haired friend has already confessed, in the hearing of the Provost Marshal and the Highland Colonel—and Lieutenants Smythe and Bygrove—that he extracted the cipher page."

"That much is true," the Provost Marshal spoke up. "I have all fifty in my possession."

"Bring them." André pointed to the table.

"I think not." Monckton interposed softly. "Serious charges have been levelled against Major Broadmoor—which I do not propose to ignore. I hold no brief for this young woman—but the cases are somewhat tied together. Be so kind, Provost, to keep these squares of paper in your possession until they are called for at the court-martial. I will see that justice is done."

"Justice!" André fired the word like a shot from a gun. "Court-martial!" He all but screamed the words. "She'll be tried by summary court— and hanged. And so will her servant, Kimball, when we catch him."

"That—she most certainly will not." Grenadier Monckton seemed to stretch himself to his full six feet two. "You have levelled charges at Major Broadmoor, and I intend to give Major Broadmoor opportunity to clear himself. To that end, this young woman's testimony is necessary. After that, she will be tried by a properly constituted court-martial."

"One of two things is true, Colonel." André kept his hands by his side. "Either she attended the Mischianza and learned of our plans. Or —she was told of them by Major Broadmoor."

In the silence that followed, André walked around the table and stood toe to toe with Monckton. He'd been humbled in front of Broadmoor. He'd had his orders countermanded in front of all these officers.

Now he would have his revenge. He looked up in Monckton's face, and a deliberate sneer twisted his lips. "I have not been guessing, Colonel. I know that she is a spy, and that she has been sheltering a spy. Her so-called servant from Virginia is an officer in the Rebel Army." André raised his hand and waved down the murmur that followed his disclosure. "And that information, Colonel, comes from no paid informer—but from a high-ranking officer at Valley Forge—one of their generals, no less."

André waited in vain for the explosion he had expected. Monckton smiled faintly, then slowly pulled his white gauntlets from his sword-belt and started fitting them over his fingers. "At the court-martial, Captain André, you will have every opportunity for presenting evidence from all the Rebel generals with whom you correspond. In the meantime—" he turned to Elizabeth—"the charge is serious, and you will be placed under arrest. Lieutenants Smythe and Bygrove will be your guards. Remove her, gentlemen, to my quarters and place her under constant guard."

As the soldiers marched Elizabeth out, the kilted Colonel followed. Quimby, furious that Elizabeth should escape immediate hanging, was all but tearing his broad-brimmed hat to shreds. Broadmoor walked slowly to the door but Monckton's voice stopped him.

"I am calling on Major Broadmoor to witness that I have given an order, Captain André. There will be no summary court. Disobey me, and it will be disobedience in the theatre of war."

In amazement, André looked at the Colonel. For the moment he was speechless. The flush that had ebbed from his neck and face started to rise again. Baffled, he watched Bygrove, Smythe and Elizabeth walk past the window. The Highlander, swinging his kilts, marched behind them, followed by the Provost Marshal. When they had disappeared, André touched the hilt of his sword suggestively. "You have reminded me," he said bitterly, "that my inferior rank prevents me from seeking satisfaction. That will change. I shall renew my demand—in London."

"Much will change," Monckton said quietly. "I shall make it a point —so help me God—to blackball you in every London club and see you for-bidden every Mayfair home." The Grenadier pulled his gauntlets over the cuffs of his tunic. "Come, Broadmoor, I'll treat you to a nightcap at the Indian Queen."

26   MENTAL RESERVATIONS

It will not out of the flesh that is bred in the bone.——John Heywood

The rains that had changed Philadelphia's gutters into streams had made of the Valley Forge an enormous quagmire. The Valley Creek had overflowed its banks and the muddy water was lapping at the fringe of the grass plot in front of the Commander-in-Chief's headquarters.

In the upstairs bedchamber, Martha Washington and Lucy Knox were gathering together the little odds and ends that had to be packed for the journey to Mount Vernon. Downstairs, in the front parlor that served as the orderly room, Stirling looked up as the women crossed and re-crossed the floor above.

"The prelude to action." The General stuck his hands in his breeches-belt and walked to the rain-splashed window. "Send the women home when it comes time for fighting."

"Yes, William." Washington laid aside his quill, poured sand over the report he had been writing, and lifting the paper, tilted it to let the sand run back into the caster. "'Tis harder on the ladies than on us. Though Patsy wouldn't say so, she dreaded going back to Mount Vernon alone. I'm more indebted than I can say to Lucy Knox for accompanying her."

Stirling nodded agreement. "I'm thankful to God that only one of my daughters is married at the moment. I'd not let Sarah stay at Baskingridge if Kitty weren't there for company."

"Lady Sarah and Kitty, together or singly, are welcome at Mount Vernon." Washington pushed his chair back from the drop-leaf desk and rose to his feet. "You know that, William, without my saying so."

"I do, sir. And if there's to be any serious fighting near Baskingridge, I'll send them to Mistress Washington's."

"Excellent." The Commander-in-Chief walked toward the door. "I think most of the general officers are in the council room." He paused by the table and lifted a small Bible. "I'll need this for the oath," he said, and went out into the hall.

The rumble of voices died away as Washington entered the log hut. Stirling's eyes flashed quickly over the group, searching out General Lee. The Commander-in-Chief was going to divulge his plans, and Stirling wanted to be certain he could watch Lee's face. Lee, and the possibility of his downright treachery, had been on Stirling's mind for days. Not one scrap of information had he received from Jonathan or Elizabeth since he'd sent them his warning note. Nor had he heard anything from Jarrett, and that was unusual, for Jarrett reported once a week even if there was nothing of importance to relay.

The general officers were ranged round the table that all but filled the middle of the council hut. Their position had nothing to do with rank. They were grouped where they could avoid the drops of water that leaked through the shake roof and keep up an incessant plopping as they dripped on the papers and maps spread on the council table.

Stirling noted that Lee, as usual, was by himself, standing against the log wall where it butted against the back of the house proper. In the corner, on Lee's right, was Henry Knox, who had never dreamed, when he studied artillery from the books in his own store, that he would one day put his theories to the test of practice. Next to Knox, caring nothing for the raindrops that fell on his shoulders, Wayne, the farmer, leaned against the wall, impatiently biting his fingernails. Nathanael Greene, Quaker Quartermaster, with a wide grin on his placid face, held up ten fingers to let Washington know that ten more of the Leman brothers' rifles that could outshoot the muskets by a hundred yards had arrived from the gun-works at Lancaster. Cadwalader and Dan Morgan were on the other side of the hut, leaning over Benedict Arnold, who sat in a chair, his wounded leg propped up on a milking stool.

"Gentlemen." Washington held up his hand. "Several days ago I said that if we won our next battle we would go on to fight others. But should we lose—it would be our last. I am more than ever of that opinion. Our next engagement will be with the main force of the British Army and our fortunes rise or fall on the outcome. The English Commissioners with their promises gained more adherents than we like to think on. 'Tis true that the Congress has spurned the offer, but to the English, and those of our weaker Patriots who would temporize, the refusal is in words only. The Army must give those words meaning, and truth and determination. The Army must follow words with deeds. We must establish for all time that we will accept nothing but independence."

Watching the nods of approval, the Commander-in-Chief picked up a square of paper. "Reports from Philadelphia leave no doubt that the English Fleet is preparing to move. The English Army must follow. We are helping them to make up their minds, and I propose additional efforts to that end. General Morgan will take twenty-five hundred men into the Jerseys and ride the countryside spreading the word that we are going to attack. When the English leave the city—you, General, will harass them as time and the situation dictate."

"Yes, sir." General Morgan stood straight up and saluted with his scarred right hand. "When do I leave?"

"Tomorrow," Washington answered. "And starting when this council is over—the entire camp will be placed on a two-hour marching alert. I desire all the troops out of huts and under canvas. Within two hours of the order to march, I want to see the first units crossing Sullivan's bridge."

There was a shuffling of feet, and the smiles of the officers reminded Stirling of other times when Washington's flat simple issuance of orders had worked miracles of regeneration. He looked at Lee, but found no smile lighting that contemptuous face.

Washington waited for a few seconds, and again raised his hand for silence. "Governor Livingston is busily engaged in recruiting a large Jersey Militia. General Dickinson will be their commander and he will work hand in glove with you, General Morgan."

"A pleasure, sir." Morgan bowed.

"There are several courses open to us. But I am resolved that one, and only one can be pursued if we are to do our duty. We could permit the English to withdraw from Philadelphia unmolested. That is unthinkable! We could harass their flanks as they move. That is not enough! We could engage their rear. But that is foolhardy! It would be likely to cost us as many men as a full engagement. Therefore, gentlemen, I am determined upon a full engagement and have prepared three plans. Colonel Alex Hamilton has the plans—in detail—for each officer. You will be given them at the exact moment they are required. You will study all three. At the appropriate time you will put into effect the designated plan. The three are called—Perth Amboy—Monmouth—Brunswick."

Washington returned the square of paper to the pile of dispatches on the table. He folded his arms, and the tips of his fingers beat a noiseless rhythm against the sleeves of his coat. "We are not going to wait for the English to evacuate Philadelphia in their own time. We are going to drive them out. Since we admittedly cannot do that by force of arms, we will do it by guile and strategy—rumor and false reports. But drive them out we shall, onto a battlefield of our own choosing. I await your comments."

"I'll welcome the action," Wayne spoke up. "Any time, anywhere, and under any conditions."

"Agreed!" Knox rattled the shakes overhead.

"I have served in the English Army."

All heads turned as Lee spoke. But Lee himself looked at no one. His eyes were fixed on an invisible spot on the opposite wall, and his voice was directed at the room. "I know how the English fight—tenaciously. They will not give up. They will stand and be shot down before they will retreat."

"And our lads have turned tail?" Washington asked without expecting an answer. "We know that. But mostly that was because the thirty-, sixty- and ninety-day militia fled—breaking our front and leaving our flanks exposed."

"And with all respect for General Knox," Lee went on as though Washington hadn't spoken, "you will be facing the Royal Regiment of Artillery—men who have spent years becoming gunners, not men thrown in at the last moment, trained only to load and fire. These are not the Hessians you faced at Trent's Town. These are the Royal Regiment."

"If General Knox will permit me—" Stirling stepped forward and nodded to Knox. "'Tis the use to which cannon are put by commanding officers that counts. The English use massed cannon as they use massed infantry. I will pit Henry Knox and Alex Hamilton against the Royal Regiment on any field."

Lee's face flushed and his lips curled. "I maintain, General Washington, that you are weighing expectations against experience—promises of what can happen against what has happened. You cannot, without more experience, take to the field and expect to face the full might of the English Army officered by Grey, Clinton, Grant, Cornwallis, Von Knyphausen, Leslie and Erskine."

"Half of whom—with more than ten thousand of these same efficient British—couldn't capture La Fayette." Wayne laughed outright as he finished.

Lee's lips parted defiantly, and Wayne's laughter drove him to step forward. "I am doing my duty, by expressing my opinions. They were asked for by the Commander-in-Chief."

"They were indeed, and taken note of, General Lee," Washington said soothingly.

"But one more opinion, and I have said all on the matter." Lee threw an angry look around the hut. "I do not believe the English will leave Philadelphia to go to New York—as the three plans imply. I believe their eventual goal will be the head of Chesapeake Bay where they will establish a base of operation, then drive inland to separate the South States from the North."

"A situation we shall meet—if it arises," Washington said briefly.

"Unfortunately I shall not be able to take part in the coming battle." Benedict Arnold raised himself in his chair, and grimaced with pain as his shattered leg rubbed on the milking stool. "But I do believe that much of General Lee's criticism belongs to the past. I, too—" he attempted a laugh —"have had some experience with the English. While they do not break and run, they do surrender. Incapacitated as I have been, I have had leisure to watch the Drillmaster at work on the Grand Parade. These men out there—" he waved to the out of doors—"will match the English, bayonet for bayonet, and outmatch the English, shot for shot. As the Baron has explained, it is difficult enough for a Rebel to kill a Redcoat, even with a good aim. How much more difficult for a Redcoat, firing blindly from the hip as they do, to kill a Rebel." He gasped and gripped the arms of the chair. "The Baron has removed fear—which is the single reason for running away."

Washington looked slowly from face to face. "Unless we have more dissenting voices, or an opinion on more desirable plans, we shall continue."

Taking silence for consent, the Commander-in-Chief lifted the Bible from the table. "Some of you were not in camp on May twelfth. That was the day the officers signed the Oath of Allegiance that the Congress requested. There are copies of the oath on the table. It is the oath we have all taken before, but it is printed and requires a signature."

The officers waited while Lee, who had been visiting the Congress May twelfth, moved out from his place by the wall and picked up a copy of the oath. Lee's face was almost lost in shadow as he bent over the table, but Stirling kept a close watch on the man he distrusted.

After a quick glance at the paper, Lee reached out and placed his hand on the Bible Washington held before him.

"I, Charles Lee, Major General, do acknowledge the United States of America, to be Free, Independent and Sovereign States, and declare that the people thereof owe no allegiance or obedience to George the Third, King of Great Britain; and I renounce, refuse and abjure any allegiance or obedience to him; and I do swear that I will to the utmost of my power support, maintain and defend the said United States, against the said King George the Third, his heirs and—and—"

In tensed, shocked silence, the generals watched Lee withdraw his hand from the Bible. He looked at no one and kept his eyes on the printed paper. Stirling glanced sideways at Washington, and saw what he remembered seeing only once before—the same baffled, pained look in the Chief's face the night Washington had looked at him after reading the proof of the cabal against him.

"May I inquire, sir, the reason for this singular act?"

Washington's question, asked in a flat emotionless voice, increased the mounting pressure of discomfort in the room.

"As to King George—" Lee gave an oddly hollow laugh—"I am ready enough to absolve myself from all allegiance to him, but I have some scruples about the Prince of Wales."

A burst of laughter broke the tension. It was as though the group wanted to mark the "singular act" as one more example of Lee's droll wit. Anger boiled within Stirling. He felt his neck and face flushing hot, and he was furious that the group should be misled into thinking that this was anything else but proof of Lee's mental reservations, anything other than weakly disguised mental treachery. His fury must have shown in his face, for when he looked across the room he saw Mad Anthony hold a warning finger to his lips. Like him, Anthony wasn't smiling, and there was a cold hard look in the Pennsylvanian's eyes as General Charles Lee placed his hand once more on the Bible, and finished reading the oath.

27   ALTUM SILENTIUM

They did not go away, they vanished.——CONTEMPORARY LETTER,
June 18, 1778

Jonathan turned his head slowly. The effort opened every pore in his body and the sweat ran out of him like water from a squeezed sponge. Except for a purplish curtain that seemed to press heavily on his eyes he could see nothing, and he was about to raise his hand to pull the purple veil away when it came to him that his eyes were closed. Waves of hot and cold pain surged through him as his eyelids grated over the eyeballs, and when he tried to find relief in crying out, he found his throat hard and dry, and his tongue so heavy in his mouth that he couldn't move it.

Even with his eyes open he could see little. He seemed to be lying in some sort of vaulted chamber. The walls were far away, and the domed roof was held up by adzed beams that rested on nothing but the blackness beyond his vision. Gradually it dawned on him that he was actually looking at a light. It was limitless miles away, at the far end of a succession of yawning caverns, and it had an up and down movement to it, almost as if it were beckoning to him.

With a tremendous summoning of strength, he raised his right hand. The light responded, and with incredible speed it rushed toward him. He gasped, drew his head back, and found himself staring into the face of a man who had a guttering candle in his hand.

"Thought I heard you moving." The man leaned down and placed a cool hand on Jonathan's forehead.

"Where am I?" The words dragged slowly.

"In the old ferry that used to be a mill." The candle moved in a semicircle. "This used to be the storage bin."

"What happened to me?"

The instant the question was completed in his mind, Jonathan's thoughts started to arrange themselves in order. He remembered falling, the shot in his shoulder, the leap through the window, the Redcoat patrol—"My God!" He sat upright, almost knocking the candle from the man's hand. "Elizabeth?"

"A prisoner, but still alive," the man said, placing his arm about Jonathan's shoulders. "Parson Poole did some asking around. Mistress Elizabeth is in Monckton's care. Lie down again, lad, I'll tell you what I know, so save your questions."

Jonathan leaned back and felt himself lowered gently to the straw pallet. He recognized the old ferryman, and recalled the day when he had spoken to him about the contrary weather vane. He sighed with relief as his head dropped level with his body, and the pounding jabs in his shoulder eased off to a dull throbbing.

"Monckton took Mistress Elizabeth out of André's hands. She's well treated, and Monckton's landlady has told her that you're alive." The ferryman moved the candle so that the light didn't fall on Jonathan's face. "The English scoured the city for you day after day—they still are—but they'll not find you here. We sent word to the Valley Forge that we got a good medico to patch you up. The bullet's out o' your shoulder and it looks like the fever's broke."

"What day is it?" Jonathan whispered.

"Thursday—eighteenth o' June. Now lie quiet. You've been out of your head with the fevers and 'tis only by the will of God you're alive. Best you go back to sleep. Medico says it's the best medicine for you."

"The eighteenth of June—" Jonathan found the problem of the last days too difficult for his mind to grasp. He closed his eyes, and drifted back into forgetfulness.

Outside, the rain that had deluged Philadelphia had finally stopped. It changed to a thick fog that coiled its way around the houses and through the alleys and lanes, all the way from the river to the State House and beyond. Although the city had been quiet since General Clinton's orders had ended the nights of love and joy, this night's quiet was filled with stealthy movement that the English generals hoped was hidden, as well as silenced, by the muffling blanket of white marsh mist.

Admiral Howe had issued one last ultimatum giving Clinton twenty-four hours' notice that he was removing the protection of the Fleet. The General, swayed by rumors of preparations for battle at Valley Forge and convinced by reports of Rebel troops massing in the Jerseys, capitulated and ordered the withdrawal. Prominent Tories, frightened at the revenge the Rebels would be certain to exact once the English were gone, descended on Lord Howe pleading for sanctuary aboard the transports. Reluctantly, the Admiral agreed, and seven hundred Tories, clutching what gold and jewels they could carry, went below into the stinking holds to share space with the hundreds of Hessians Von Knyphausen was afraid would desert on a march across the Jerseys.

Long lines of sullen figures, English red and Hessian green, all reduced to a gray sameness, marched silently to the ferries. They would have been silent without Clinton's orders, for despite all the fine brave words mouthed by Clinton to his staff, it was a retreat. The officers knew it, and the men knew it, and both were glad of the fog that hid their slinking, silent, stealing-away in the dark of the moon.

Up at Cooper's Ferry, the cannon wheels, covered and deadened with muffling, were eased over the wharf planking, and slid down chutes onto the rocking boats. Baggage wagons, piled high with supplies both bought and stolen, were floated out into the Delaware and towed by barges and ferries, while the bat horses, with hooded heads and muffled hooves, were floated across in the flat-bottomed scows.

One ferryboat crossing to the Jersey shore was closely guarded. Lieutenants Bygrove and Smythe stood in the prow, while the Provost Marshal and a guard of six Redcoats stood in the stern. The guards had their bayonets fixed and their muskets loaded, and they were under orders to shoot to kill. Huddled amidships in the ferry were the prisoners against whom specific charges had been brought. And seated next the rail, wondering how much chance she had of slipping over the side, was Elizabeth.

In the taverns, the lights were low and officers who had no special duties risked a last chance at the tables or a last visit with the guest wenches. A few Tory tailors, cobblers and hatters, with bills clutched in their hands, and fast-dwindling hopes in their breasts, were scurrying from wharf to wharf—looking for payments that were long overdue. At the Walnut Street Prison, Captain Cunningham left one lanthorn glimmering in the guardroom, as he followed his guards out to the stone steps. Viciously, he turned the big iron key in the massive spring lock, pulled it from the keyhole, and flung it into the yawning blackness between the prison and the wall. He cursed silently as he stepped down to the street. He'd plead ignorance of Clinton's orders to free the prisoners who had not already been taken, under escort, with the retreating columns. "Let them rot till someone discovers they are no longer guarded!"

From eleven o'clock it had been going on, this exodus from the Colonies' biggest city, and only a handful of the citizens were aware of the evacuation. For the first time in six months the two lights outside the Provost Guard at Dock and Pear guttered and went out, and no one noticed. Hour after hour the silent parade marched to the waterfront till fifteen thousand of England's pride had tiptoed out of the houses, out of the huts along Callowhill, and out of the tents that dotted the mud island opposite Gloucester on the Jersey bank.

They left their litter and garbage behind them, and looted everything of value that they could conveniently stow in their baggage. Their flight was speeded by the frightening possibility that Washington might learn of the evacuation, and send the Rebel Army pouring down on them before they had completed their crossing to the Jersey side of the Delaware. At four of the morning, an elderly lady, up all night with an aching tooth, looked between her shutters and murmured:

"They did not go away, they vanished."

Down where the Schuylkill ran into the Delaware, a hollow, drumming noise penetrated Jonathan's consciousness. The familiar sound of troops on the march roused him as no other sound could have, and setting his jaw he struggled to his feet. Groping his way out of the disused grain bin, he stumbled into the open and saw the old ferryman peering across the water.

"What is it?" Jonathan dropped to his knees beside the drum that ran the ferry.

"The whole guard—marching across the floating bridge." The old man jerked his thumb over his shoulder. "The guards has left the boat, too. 'Tis my belief—" He stopped as a figure loomed out of the darkness. "Who's there?" He pushed Jonathan flat with the ground as he called out.

"Parson Poole." Poole's voice was filled with excitement. "The Lobsterbacks are gone—they're marching—most of them are across the river already."

Jonathan flattened his hands in the damp grass and pushed himself to his knees. With deliberate, conscious intent he forced his heavy tongue to move mechanically.

"Send a rider to Captain McLane. Tell him to pass the word to Valley Forge."

28   DOWN TO THE SEA

Who goes to sea, is but four inches from death.——Anacharsis

It was barely light when the first of the British line of ships started moving down the Delaware toward the bay. Directly aft the *Sally E*, the frigate *Phoenix*, and the ship-rigged war sloops *Isis*, *Alert*, *Somerset* and *Active*, had cast off their hawse lines, and the frothy bubbles streaming out from their rudders showed that they already had some way on.

Standing by the *Sally E*'s taffrail, Rufus watched the barefooted midshipmites coiling the hawse lines on the decks of the English ships. Already the bow of the *Somerset* was passing the *Sally E*'s portside, and the *Alert* was fast coming abaft to starboard.

Knowing that the insufferable Redcoat officer Benbow was watching him closely, Rufus left the rail and walked along the deck. He ran his hand over the broad mahogany rail, but his eyes were on the lower rail that held the belaying pins; especially the pins that had no lines or falls belayed to them. One of these pins, at an exact moment, was going to stretch the Redcoat officer flat on his back on the *Sally E*'s holystoned deck.

The night before, at the change of the midnight watch, Benbow had come alongside deep in his cups. For ten minutes he and the drunken officers who had brought him back from the *Cadiz* bobbed up and down in their longboat, talking about the evacuation, and Rufus had heard enough to convince him that the Fleet was sailing for Sandy Hook.

Now, as Rufus came abreast the *Sally E*'s wheel, he prayed for two things: that Elizabeth was watching, and that he'd have one full minute to break out the *Sally E*'s house flag. For an hour, the tide had been on the turn, and the swift flow of the river, added to the peak of the outgoing tide, was what Rufus needed to send his ship crashing through the English line.

With a surge of water that rocked the *Sally E* and set her lines to creaking in the blocks, the frigate *Phoenix* sailed by majestically. Her white canvas, towering overhead, was beginning to fill, and her shrouds moaned with the thrust against her masts. As Rufus watched, he saw her signal board blink. White squares changed to black and back to white again. Redcoat Benbow was also watching, and he threw a hand signal, acknowledging the order to cast off.

"Now or never!" Rufus thought. With his left hand he jerked the boatswain's pipe from his pocket. His right hand shot out, and his fingers gripped a belaying pin. Both hands came up together. The pipe was at his lips, and the shrill "All Hands" whistled through the rigging. Benbow turned and Rufus brought the upraised belaying pin crashing down on the red-clad shoulder. Out shot Rufus' left fist and Benbow fell to the deck, his jaw twisted to one side. Bending down, Rufus gripped Benbow by the heels, dragged him to the scuppers, and rolled him into the Delaware.

At the first shrill whistle of the pipe, the crew had jumped over the rail and struck out for the shore. Too late, the Royal Marines on the decks of the war sloops saw what was afoot, and before they could ram shot home in the barrels of their stub-nosed muskets, the crew was out of range. Tumbling down the open companionway, Rufus raced along the lower deck to the forecastle. The ports were closed and the gloom was like that of night, but he knew every rib, bulkhead and stanchion between decks. He made for the lazaret and the big axe that was lashed to cleats on the storeroom partition. "A hell of a death for a fine ship," he raged, "but better than going down without a fight." Feverishly he felt for the lashings on the axe, and at the same time listened for the sound of boarders clumping across the deck. Nothing! Nothing but distant shouts and orders, and the wonderful sound of fast-running water lapping at tight-caulked seams.

Axe in hand, he got to his knees and crawled into the narrow space between the rope locker and the hawse port. Here in the stern, the anchor cable was coiled, and here too a glimmer of light shone through the hawse hole where the anchor cable went through the hull and down to the anchor on the river bed. He gritted his teeth and swung the axe. There were tortured groans as strand after strand of the cable parted, then a crack like the sound of a fieldpiece as the last strand gave. The flood tide tore the *Sally E* across the surface of the water, scooning her downstream in a splashing arc, with only her forward cable keeping her from piling up on the bank.

Rufus threw his arms up to protect his head as the *Sally E*, almost on her beam, smashed the *Phoenix*'s rudder off its gudgeon pins. The frigate, out of control, started to swing broadside. With a horrible thunderous screeching, the *Sally E*'s stern swept along the frigate's beam and, one after another, tore the open gun port hatches from their battens.

Stunned and dizzy, Rufus picked up the axe and staggered out of the stern. Any minute now the English would get a gun into action, and the *Sally E*, tugging at her forward anchor, was too easy a mark. He had to get to the forepeak and cut the remaining cable. With her stern downstream, she'd tack back and forth enough to make an elusive mark for the frigate guns which were high above the water line, and whose muzzles wouldn't depress far enough to pour shot into the *Sally E*'s sides.

He had greater hazards to face than cannon shot, he thought, as he tore along the tilted deck. If he didn't part the forward cable with the first blow of the axe, a second attempt might be fatal. If the rope should part while he was preparing for a second blow, the parted cable would whip his head off his body before he had time to seek shelter.

Puffs of white, followed by the flat "phut" of musket balls burying themselves in the wood, greeted him when he came to the forward hatch. Six strides along the slanting deck took him into the bow. Bracing his feet against a rib, he swung the axe. The haft was still standing straight out in midair when his fingers left it, and he heard the hollow thump of the head hitting the deck as he leaped back to the shelter of the companionway steps.

With the parting of the cable, the *Sally E* rushed downstream. Without cargo, and well on her beam, her passage was almost as swift as the current itself. Shrieks and yells and hoarsely shouted orders came from every side; Rufus pushed his head up through the hatch in time to see a splintered longboat catapulting navy-blue and gold-braided officers into the Delaware.

Utter confusion had replaced the orderly procession of the last of Admiral Howe's ships. Deck officers on one ship bawled orders that were misinterpreted on another. Canvas came down when it should have gone up. The frigate's gun port hatches dotted the water, and their iron-bound corners jabbed and battered the sloops as the churned water drove the heavy hatches time and again against the sloops' water line.

The next minute was the one Rufus had prayed for. He left the shelter of the companionway hood and pulled himself along the deck toward the flag locker that was held fast by lashings pressed through beckets on the ends of the locker. He felt a moment's admiration for the gun crew of the wallowing *Phoenix*. Despite their unsteady footing on a rudderless ship, the gunners, stripped for action, were hauling a gun forward on its tracks.

It was a race now, to see whether he could bend the swallowtail to the line, hoist it, and break it out, before the *Phoenix* could load and fire. He lifted the locker lid, and drew the pennant toward him. With a speed that surprised him, he hooked the flag line to the eyelet in the pennant. He saw the gunners push a canister down the gun barrel, and as they pulled the ramrod back, he was folding the tails of the flag into its center.

Quickly he repeated the folding, tucking in each corner till the pennant was folded in the complicated ball necessary for a signal break. As he slipped the noosed lanyard about the flag, he could see the gunners hoisting the cannon ball to the yawning black muzzle. They still had to put the wedges behind the gun wheels to keep the gun from recoiling, Rufus saw, and they'd have to put the screw jack under the butt and turn the screw till the butt rose, and the muzzle was lowered.

Mentally he computed the time as he threaded the flag line and the lanyard through his fingers. He could do it, with a second or two to spare, for unless the English wanted to risk losing a gun, the gunners would have to tighten the clamps around the trunnions on which the sea guns were slung. Looking aloft, he pulled on the line. The folded pennant started up and he felt the lanyard slide quickly through his fingers.

A sudden tug on his hands told that the pennant had reached the dead-eye. He gave a sharp whipping pull on the lanyard. The noose slipped, and the pennant broke out, streaming in the breeze. Twisting the line that held the pennant aloft around a deck cleat, Rufus gave one glance over his shoulder at the *Phoenix*. The master gunner was standing, barechested and barefooted, with the fusee hovering over the touchhole.

Rufus threw himself headlong down the companionway. Before he could brace his feet against a rib, the frigate's gun roared. There was a crunching of timbers as the ball bounded along the upper deck and took the *Sally E*'s mainmast at the deck line. Flattening himself against the hull, Rufus listened to the downpour of crosstrees and yards. The shrouds, loosed from their tension, screamed like a gale as they went over the side with the shattered mast.

With her deck awash and her keel almost out of the water, the *Sally E* lost speed and started to circle. The tangled shrouds and spars hanging over the rail and trailing in the water acted as a sea anchor, and the doomed ship turned as though held in a vortex. Water was beginning to spurt between one of the portholes and its hatch. Rufus turned his head and stared at the inrushing water in wonderment.

Till now, he'd given no thought to escape. He'd not dreamed it possible. But if the porthole hatch would still move in its guides—he gripped the rib that was tilted over him like a beam on a ceiling, and worked his way to the porthole. Hanging to the rib with one hand to keep from falling back down the slanting deck, he eased the batten from the hatch.

Water poured in as the hatch slid back. He gripped the lower edge of the port and looked out over the surface of the water. He could just see the wharves of the Jersey waterfront, and not a single English ship lay between him and the shore. Clutching the hatch guide with one hand, he pulled off his boots with the other. A tug on the cord about his waist dropped his canvas pants to his ankles, and he kicked them loose.

Debris covered the Delaware from bank to bank, and if he could get through the port without being seen, he'd wager almost anything that he could make the shore undetected. A pretty picture he was going to make, scrambling ashore naked as a jay in full daylight. With a heave, he launched himself through the porthole, and struck deep into the water. He'd not show himself ashore. He'd swim underwater, as far as he could, and hide under the flooring of one of the wharves till darkness fell.

29   FAREWELL TO VALLEY FORGE

Thence we came forth out of the valley, to see again the stars.——DANTE

"They're gone! The English have left!" Shouting to any who could hear, Private Roberts spurred his horse through the Valley Forge encampment, and down Gulph Road toward the Commander-in-Chief's headquarters.

As he wheeled right around the Ironmaster's Mansion, Roberts could see the effects of his message. Men were pouring down the slopes of Mount Joy. Others, with hands cupped to their lips, were relaying the news across the Grand Parade to the troops at the southeast end of the camp. It had been like this all the way from Barren Hill. Miller, farmer, blacksmith and housewife, had heard the tidings, first with disbelief, then with shouts that rang over the countryside. Shutters and windows that hadn't been used for months were flung open. As though they'd been conjured from the ground, cattle appeared on the farm lands, and horses, long hidden, were led out into the light, and hitched to the ploughs.

Washington was at the headquarters' door before Roberts was out of the saddle. Alex Hamilton ran through the narrow passageway between the dining room and the orderly room, lifted a dispatch case from Washington's desk, and ran on out to the front steps.

"More than half the English must be across the Delaware by now, General." Roberts wiped the mud from his face. "We got word this morning at Barren Hill—from Captain Kimball—that the English were retreating from the city. Captain McLane ordered me to come on here, and said unless you had orders to the contrary, he was taking his sixty horse and going on down to Philadelphia."

"What of General La Fayette?" Washington asked.

"Breaking camp, sir, and awaiting your orders as to where he should march for."

"Get a fresh horse—" Washington pointed to the back of his headquarters—"ride to Barren Hill and tell the Marquis to march out Shippack Pike and join us on the York Road."

"Yes, sir." Roberts saluted, and led his lathered beast to the rear of the headquarters.

"Beat the drums for Breaking Camp." Washington turned to Caleb Gibbs. "And follow it with a roll for the general officers." The Commander-in-Chief stopped and smiled at Gibbs. "Although I doubt that we'll need it—look!"

From every quarter of the camp, officers were converging on the small grass square in front of the headquarters. The order drums started their beat at the end of the line of empty huts that had once housed the Life Guard. The Jersey Line, camped between the inner line of entrenchments and the burned-out forge, picked up the beat. It was followed in quick succession by Wayne's First Pennsylvanians on the outer line of defense, and Henry Knox's artillery in the park that straddled the Gulph Road between Washington's headquarters and the Stone Chimney picket.

The beat for Breaking Camp stopped. For a count of ten, the hum of the men's voices echoed through the Valley. In the tiny hamlet that stretched from the bridge over the creek to the Bull Tavern, the villagers ran out of doors to find out what had happened. Once again the drums throbbed. The pitch was higher, for the slack drums had been braced and the sticks bounded from the tight skins.

"Gentlemen." Washington looked at the general officers crowded about the steps. "There is no need for talk. Colonel Hamilton has the orders. They, as you see, are copies of an order of march I drew up on May the thirtieth. The original order was for General Lee, but it now applies to all of us. Colonel Hamilton, will you be good enough to distribute them?"

Hamilton took the orders from the dispatch case, smiling as he did so. He had laboriously copied them last thing before dropping off to sleep the night before. He wondered, as he passed the orders, what seventh sense Washington possessed to warn him that there would be need for the orders today. There were raised eyebrows, faint smiles, and noiseless chuckles, as one by one the officers realized that regardless of Washington's councils and his seeking of their opinions, his mind had been made up as far back as the last of May.

Head Quarters, 30 May, 1778

Sir:

Poor's, Varnum's, and Huntington's brigades are to march in one division under your command to ——. The quartermaster-general will give you the route, encampment, and halting days, to which you will conform as strictly as possible, to prevent interfering with other troops, and that I may know precisely your situation every day. Leave as few sick and lame on the road as possible. Such as are absolutely incapable of marching with you are to be committed to the care of proper officers, with directions to follow as fast as their condition will allow.

Be strict in your discipline, suffer no rambling, keep the men in their ranks and the officers with their divisions, avoid pressing horses as much as possible, and punish severely every officer or soldier, who shall presume to press without proper authority. Prohibit the burning of fences. In a word you are to protect the persons and property of the inhabitants from every kind of insult and abuse.

Begin your march at four o'clock in the morning at the latest, that it may be over before the heat of the day, and that the soldiers may have time to cook, refresh, and prepare for the ensuing day—I am,

Your obedient servant,

G°. WASHINGTON

Note—The Light Horse is to March in front and upon the Right flank a days and encamp in the Rear of the Troops o Nights.

Black clouds, which had been scudding overhead, opened up, and the continuous drizzle became a downpour as Hamilton handed the last order to General Greene. Washington held up his hand for silence. "General Arnold will occupy Philadelphia with sufficient troops to keep order. The men for that duty have already been detailed. On our march, we will leave no more than the necessary space between divisions. We are going to march a mile and a half for every mile the English cover—and we are going to march on the Pennsylvania bank of the Delaware. We may cross at Coryell's ferry—or Sherrard's—or both. I am determined that no word of our whereabouts shall reach the enemy. For any man attempting to leave the lines, either on the march, or in camp at night, the penalty is death."

Turning to Alex Hamilton, Washington held out his hand for the marching orders. The officers, puzzled at Washington's determination to march on the Pennsylvania bank, looked at each other, seeking the answer. Stirling smiled to himself, thinking of the three plans, Perth Amboy, Monmouth, and Brunswick. If the enemy could be kept unaware of the Rebel Army's crossing place, the element of surprise would play a big part in securing a victory. Silently, he applauded his Chief's decision not to reveal the plans till the last necessary moment.

Again Washington spoke. "These orders are for the march—not commands for the action we shall bring on. The first column: New York—Connecticut—Rhode Island, under the command of General Lee. To be out of camp in two hours."

"I take it, sir," Lee spoke up, "from these orders, that you expect the English to move north—and not south?"

"I do," Washington said abruptly. "And until I see them marching south—these are my orders."

"Yes, sir." Lee saluted and went to his horse.

Washington returned the salute, looked again at his order book. "First and Second Pennsylvania, and the—ah—late Conway division, under the command of General Wayne."

"Yes, sir." Wayne was gone, splashing mud as he ran along the side of the headquarters.

"General Greene will take the Virginians, the Third, Sixth, and Twelfth Pennsylvanians—and the North Carolinians."

"Yes, sir." Greene saluted.

"Meet General La Fayette at Skippack Pike and York Road."

"It will be done, sir." Greene bowed gravely and stepped out across the soggy grass.

"The other officers will command their own brigades. General Stirling will bring up the rear, and I will ride with him. General Cadwalader will accompany General Arnold, and Colonel Tilghman will act as General

Arnold's aide." Washington closed the order book, and looked about quickly. "Wring every minute dry. Press everything to the limit. I want to say farewell to the Valley Forge by sundown."

The dreary afternoon was filled with the splashing of horses high-stepping in the oozing mud. Generals made the rounds of the encampment, and dispatch riders rode off carrying orders to the outposts and pickets. The tents were coming down, company by company. The dark brown marquee that was Washington's orderly room, now that the troops were under canvas, was unpegged and rolled away, leaving for a minute or two a dry oval of earth halfway between Stirling's quarters and the Star Redoubt.

The artillery park, where forty-two of Knox's four-pounders had stood the long winter through, was bare and scarred with the wheel marks of the vanished guns. Sharp-angled redans and wide-armed lunettes, their six-pounders gone, were no more than puny banks of earth and stone piled on the hillsides; and the outer and inner lines of defense were only shallow gutters draining away the rain water that coursed down between the trees on the slope of Mount Joy.

By four-thirty, Lee's column had already disappeared along the road that turned north from the east end of the Valley. There were no waving villagers, no singing voices on the march, and no backward glances of regret or farewell. The Continental Army wasted no kindly thoughts on the slab-roofed and earth-floored huts that stood gaunt and empty and sodden in the rain. Down by Wayne's quarters, Corporal Hayes watched two of his guards on the Stone Chimney picket topple the long sapling they had used for flashing signals along the Swedes Ford Road. The stone fireplace with its rugged square chimney was massive, and more than once, two men at a time had run up the stairlike receding stones to fly a warning of approaching English patrols. The corporal had one pleasant night to remember, and he would tell of it for years to come. The night after he'd recovered the spy map, he had accepted Mad Anthony's invitation and far into the night, over a tankard of ale and cold slabs of beef, the two had discussed the war, freedom, his wife Mary, and Doctor Irvine, the medico of Carlisle, for whom he, Hayes, had worked as barber and bloodletter.

"What about the lanthorn?" one of the pickets called out.

"Leave it in the niche," Hayes said. He watched the picket place the battered tin lamp in the head-high alcove in the back wall of the fireplace, and he shivered as he thought of the snow-filled nights when the hot metal of the lanthorn had been the only warmth in the open fireplace they had called home for six months. "Must ha' been a hell of a big house afore it burnt down," he said to the picket in general. "There's nobody goin' to believe that seven men lived for six months in a fireplace."

He turned away and waved to his men to follow him up the narrow path that led to Wayne's quarters. The First and Second Pennsylvanians were mustering in the fields in front of the long white farmhouse, and the General was running up and down the line checking water flasks and powder horns, and passing out sound flints to replace the flaked and chipped ones in the older muskets.

"Corporal Hayes reporting, sir."

"Oh, yes, Hayes." Wayne wiped the sweat from his face with the back of his hand. "Last picket checked out?"

"Yes, sir. All present and fit, sir."

"Good. Report with the Second—"

"Beg pardon, sir, but could I go with the Seventh?"

"Ah yes, I forgot—with Medico Irvine."

"Yes, sir. To be truthful, sir, he's moving by the most southerly route —and he's most like to be closest to Allentown where my wife—"

"Mary is with her folks. I remember." Wayne laughed. "Request granted, Corporal. I hope you can visit your wife and fight a battle—all on the same journey. Off with you, lad, and fall in with the Seventh.

Mad Anthony climbed into the saddle and, without orders, the column moved off behind him. They swung around onto the Gulph Road and marched past the deserted parade ground, nothing now but a muddy stretch of trampled earth. One or two of the men looked over to the right. They had been part of a funeral firing squad for a Rhode Island lieutenant, and somewhere, on the edge of the parade ground, was a small stone, only five or six inches by seven or so, with the initials J W rudely carved on one face. Of all the thousands in this vast cemetery, Lieutenant John Waterman's was the only marked grave.

Soon it was twilight, and the last troops were over Sullivan's bridge. The Schuylkill and the Valley Creek had the Valley to themselves again. Up at the Old Forge itself, a young farm lad, thinking of the fishing, took a length of wood and forced apart the boards that guided the water to the power wheel. Freed of the sluiceway, the stream spread out over the rocks and joined the water in the natural course of the Valley Creek. Bereft of its power, the wheel slacked its turning and came to a stop. The top board of the bellows chattered slowly down, squeezing the patched leather, and the last wheeze was like a long, tired sigh of something that was glad to die.

Revenge is a kind of wild justice.——BACON

Almost insane with fear and worry over Elizabeth, and tortured by the pain in his shoulder, Jonathan sat on Logan Wharf watching Cults and Poole and a dozen of the river rats diving into the water. Since late morning they had risked being trapped by the submerged rigging, in frantic efforts to trace the *Sally E*'s flag line, and determine whether or not Rufus had flown a signal.

Thank God, Jonathan thought wearily, McLane had come down from Barren Hill. The Delaware Captain had helped him onto a horse and they had ridden from the old ferry to the Ladd house where Mistress Sally and Maggie had bound his shoulder with a fresh bandage. For once, he'd not say a word of criticism about Sally Ladd's incessant talking. While giving him every bit of information she could about Elizabeth, she'd chattered on about Rufus' visit, and how surprised she was to see Rufus and Elizabeth standing by the table in Enoch's room.

The mention of the table had stirred Jonathan to action. Struggling from the chair in the kitchen, where he'd been catching his breath after the ordeal of having the wound bandaged, he'd dashed as quickly as he could through the hall to Enoch's room. Together, McLane and he had opened the hollow table top. There, in Elizabeth's sprawling hand, was a list of possible destinations of the English Fleet and, in a column opposite, the identifying signal flags.

Although every fibre of his being urged him to follow the English, and plans and devices for Elizabeth's rescue rushed through his mind without letup, he knew he could do nothing but what he was doing. If Rufus had flown a signal, then it must be found. Washington's planning might be changed were he to know the Fleet's destination, and Elizabeth's rescue would be effected more rapidly and more easily if the English could be prevented from reaching their port of embarkation.

But hope of finding the pennant tonight was beginning to wane. There were not more than twenty minutes of daylight left, and if they didn't locate the *Sally E*'s flag line before darkness fell, he couldn't ask the river rats to continue the dangerous search after dark. It was a dreadful, hopeless sort of business, diving into the slimy water, grabbing a line and holding on to it trying to follow it till the line ended in a block or a belaying pin or a slack end that trailed free in the mud. And besides all that, he had no way of knowing that Rufus had even flown a signal, for everyone they had questioned had been too engrossed watching the ship itself to pay any attention to a flag.

Pushing his good shoulder against the rope fender which McLane had dragged onto the wharf to serve as a back rest, Jonathan struggled·to his knees. This had been a day neither he nor anyone who had been in the freed city was likely to forget. The last Redcoats hadn't marched aboard the ferry before the city was in a turmoil. Flags that had been stitched in secret and hidden for months were suddenly unfurled. Every combination of white stars and red stripes fluttered from poles or hung from window ledges. Only yesterday, Patriot houses were shuttered and dark, and their owners thought twice before opening a door. Today, the Patriot doors were wide open, and the groups that stood around the taverns and the mouths of the alleys were left unmolested. Yesterday, a grouping of more than two Patriots would have meant seizure and the prison.

"How are you feeling, lad?" Allan McLane, as he slid down the bank onto the wharf, hailed Jonathan.

"Better." Jonathan stood upright to prove it.

"I got word that Rufus was seen—safe and sound—on the Jersey side." McLane pointed across the river. "But nobody knows where he's hiding out."

Jonathan nodded. "He doesn't know that his sister is a prisoner. He thinks that his message is already on the way to Valley Forge."

"Ahoy there, Kimball!" It was Parson Poole's voice. "We've found a pennant."

A moment later, Poole and Cults climbed up the wooden rungs pegged to the wharf piling. Poole spread a muddy, water-soaked swallow tail on the rough planking, and scraped the slime off with the edge of his hand. "'Tis no signal flag after all," he said in disgust, "'tis the house flag."

"It's the signal, Parson. You found it."

"Then we've finished here, Captain?" Aaron Cults bent down and wrung streams of water from the legs of his canvas pants.

"Yes, Aaron." Jonathan looked at the shipmaster curiously, detecting the venom in his voice.

"We have another duty." Aaron waved to the rest of his river rats, and turned back to face Jonathan and McLane.

"Aaron is right." Parson Poole raised his hand. "Vengeance is mine," he chanted, "breach for breach, eye for eye, tooth for tooth."

Jonathan shivered.

Aaron reached out and placed his hand on Jonathan's arm. "Waste no sorrow on Trivers, lad. He betrayed you and Elizabeth. Mistress Darragh says so—and so does Maggie."

At the mention of Elizabeth, Jonathan felt a hot rage sweep over him. Why should he try to spare Trivers? An out-and-out Tory had the courage to wear his label, but Trivers was a traitor and worse, for he'd pretended friendship for Elizabeth. He watched, and said nothing, as Cults and Poole, followed by their crew of river rats, climbed the bank and disappeared on Front Street.

"What port?" McLane asked when the men were out of hearing.

"Sandy Hook." Jonathan held on to McLane's arm. "I'll take one of your horses and ride after Stirling."

"You can do it?" McLane asked anxiously, helping Jonathan up the bank.

"Yes. I'll suffer no more in the saddle than I do standing. The wound isn't bleeding, and I feel stronger now than I did."

"But if you should collapse on the way?"

"I won't. I'd be more like to go mad doing nothing but worrying about Elizabeth."

"In that, I think you're right," McLane said significantly. "You should be able to catch up with the lads at Doyles Town. They'll be camped along the Coryell Ferry Road, about four miles this side of where the Durham Pike crosses York Road. And 'twould be my reckoning that Stirling will use Doyle's old inn, the Fountain House, for his quarters."

"I know the place. I was there when we were camped in the Warwick Hills—before Brandywine."

"Then if you're still of a mind to ride," McLane said briefly, "I have a horse for you in a yard beyond the market. You ride to Doyles Town. After dark, I'll cross the river and follow the English—closely as I dare."

Side by side, the two captains walked along the slippery path that climbed up to Front Street. Reddish glows told that some of the Tory houses on the edge of the city had already felt the weight of Patriot revenge. Loud, raucous singing drifted from the Tun Tavern and the City Tavern, only to be drowned out by angry shouts and the continuous breaking of glass as the aroused Rebels tossed bricks through the Tories' windows, or wrenched the shutters off their hinges and sent them crashing through the frames.

At Spruce and Dock, they saw two bodies hanging from a beam that jutted out from a chandler's shop. Angry howls, and cries of "Tory," followed by the breaking in of doors, could be heard from every corner of the city.

"Of no use trying to stop anything tonight," McLane said. "If you and I had been treated the way these folks have for six months—most like we'd be haulin' on hangman's ropes too."

"I would," Jonathan agreed, "till my hands were burned raw by the ropes. I've heard enough from the river rats to keep me in spleen for years to come. Some of these lads were good prosperous citizens—staunch Rebels —and their names were turned over to André and Cunningham by their Tory business rivals afore the English had been in possession of Philadelphia twenty-four hours."

McLane nodded, and his face was grim as he pointed to the spreading flames in the northern outskirts of the city. By now, the dull, angry murmur of small, roving bands of rioters had swelled to a savage roar. Isolated bands met and merged into mobs, and were joined by drink-sodden looters who were Rebels only for the night, or as long as there was anything left to plunder.

Picking their way along the rubble-strewn streets, Jonathan and McLane pressed on as quickly as they could. Shrugging his shoulder and flexing his arm, Jonathan was surprised to find that his wound didn't give him as much pain as he'd expected. At least, he thought, it promised to be a lot less troublesome than the wound he had received at Brandywine.

They turned a corner. Jonathan stopped, and pulled McLane into a doorway. A dozen men, half of them carrying flaring torches, marched silently down the center of the narrow street. The smoking pine knots, and the unravelled rope ends soaked in fish oil, danced in the mullioned lights of a tôleware shop. Handles of brass and copper threw back little stars of pin-pointed light, and the jet black of trays and tea caddies looked out through the window like gleaming, hateful, black eyes. The marchers stopped in front of the next shop. Back in the hollow behind the window, barely within reach of the probing torches, a flat white face retreated to the rear of the shop. Two of the marchers threw themselves against the door and their followers tramped across it as it fell to the floor.

"Come," Jonathan whispered thickly, "I've no wish to see it."

"Who is—"

McLane's question was drowned in a terrified scream.

"Trivers," Jonathan said. "Come—I'd rather be sick in the saddle— than here in the middle of Arch Street."

31   CAPTAIN KIMBALL AGAIN

The first blow is half the battle.——OLIVER GOLDSMITH

It was after midnight when Jonathan wheeled his horse off the narrow road that ran back of Painswick Hall, and onto the Easton Pike. Due north was Doyles Town, and if McLane had been correct in assuming that Stirling would billet at the Fountain House, the destination of the English Fleet would be in the General's hands within minutes.

The Rebel Army would have to make some forced marches, Jonathan thought, if the English were going to be attacked before they reached Sandy Hook. By moving north on the Pennsylvania side of the Delaware Washington would keep the English in ignorance of the Rebel Army's position, but the Rebels would have to turn and march east after they crossed the river. The English would cut diagonally across the Jerseys, following one side of a triangle, whereas the Rebels would have to cover the greater distance of the other two sides.

Ahead of him, Jonathan saw nothing but blackness. The road climbed a steep hill, and the heavy stand of trees on both sides of the highway hid everything from his view. The horse labored heavily on the muddy road, now rutted and pitted from the gun wheels of Knox's artillery passing over it five hours before. A single light jumped out of the darkness, and Jonathan, leaning forward in the saddle, recognized that it came from the eight-sided fieldstone schoolhouse that sat at the crossroads.

The road flattened out, and the horse picked up speed. As he galloped past the schoolhouse, Jonathan glimpsed Greene and Sullivan bent over maps spread out on the dominie's high, sloping desk. An irregular line of white tents stretched along the highway, and a wide gap in the line showed where Dyers Road cut across the Coryell Ferry Road.

When the lighted windows of the Fountain House came into view, Jonathan slumped in his saddle. The necessity that had driven him over the roads at breakneck speed had also acted as an opiate, but now that his goal was within reach, the pain returned to gnaw at his shoulder.

One of the sentries in the Fountain House yard took his horse as Jonathan lowered himself from the saddle. Pressing his arm against his ribs to keep it from moving, he ran to the tavern door. Stirling, standing with Wayne and Van Steuben at a table by the fireplace, didn't see Jonathan as he came in, but the innkeeper took one look at the Rebel Captain's face, and jumped from his seat.

Before Jonathan had closed the door behind him, the innkeeper was expertly pouring a noggin of rum.

"Gulp it down, man, without stopping." Mine host held out the small mug.

Jonathan's eyes conveyed his thanks as he poured the rum down his throat. Stirling, turning at the sound of the innkeeper's voice, looked at Jonathan in amazement.

"How did you get here?" The General crossed the floor followed by Von Steuben and Wayne.

"Rode, sir. I left Philadelphia just at dark."

"What of Elizabeth?" Stirling asked anxiously. "I've not had a piece of ungarbled information yet."

"She's a prisoner, General." Jonathan leaned against the trestle table that ran down the center of the inn's small common room.

Von Steuben signalled the innkeeper to get another mug of rum.

"Take your time, lad." Wayne placed his arm behind Jonathan's shoulder and steadied him.

Trying to keep his feelings for Elizabeth hidden, Jonathan took his time in drinking down the rum. He handed the mug back to the innkeeper and spoke slowly. "She's under Colonel Monckton's guard—with a court-martial hanging over her—but at least she'll not be mistreated or hanged without a trial as she would be by André."

Stirling nodded. "We understand that the English have taken about forty prisoners with them. They intend using them as hostages I have no doubt. Don't worry, lad, we'll get her free. We have a few prisoners, too, that we can bargain with—and we'll have more."

"I have important intelligence, sir." Jonathan leaned forward and spoke softly. "The English Fleet has sailed for Sandy Hook."

Without a word, Stirling strode to the small door on the left of the huge walk-in fireplace. Wayne and Von Steuben returned to the paper-strewn table that had been pulled onto the wide hearth. Quickly Von Steuben cleared the table and handed the papers to Wayne who put them in a dispatch case.

"No need to study these now," Wayne said over his shoulder to Jonathan. "Not with Perth Amboy and Brunswick out of our planning."

"Alex—Colonel Hamilton!" Stirling called through the open door that led to the back of the inn.

"Yes, sir." Alex Hamilton, a powder and shot tally in his hand, stepped down into the brick-floored common room. "My God!" He ran forward and looked at Jonathan anxiously. "Are you all right?"

"I'm all right, Alex. Or I will be after a rest."

[244]

"He's brought the word that the English Fleet sailed for Sandy Hook," Stirling said excitedly. "Get right over to the Fell house and tell the Chief."

"Yes, sir." Hamilton saluted.

"Ask him if we will put the Monmouth plan into immediate operation."

"Yes, sir." Hamilton handed the tally sheet to Stirling. "If General Washington says yes—shall I order the drums to beat at four?"

Stirling nodded his answer, and thought for a moment. "And send somebody back to the schoolhouse to advise Generals Greene and Sullivan."

As Colonel Hamilton went out to the stable yard, Stirling turned to Wayne and Von Steuben. "I suggest we double the guards—let no one through our lines—and send trustworthy dispatch riders to the ferry to prepare the ferrymaster for our crossing."

"I'll triple the guards if it will keep word of our position from getting across the river," Wayne said.

"Is it worth while to send false information?" Stirling asked. "Let it be noised about that we expect to attack the English at Brunswick?"

"If the Chief agrees, I'd do it." Wayne looked at the Drillmaster for confirmation.

"The smallest measure is worth the while," Von Steuben agreed. "But like General Wayne—I would not, without General Washington's permission, do anything."

"Agreed." Stirling turned to Jonathan. "Are you fit to ride, lad?"

"I'm better riding than lying down."

"Good. Then go to my bedchamber. Rest till four of the clock. I'll have Medico Irvine look at your wound in the morning. If he says you're fit for duty—you'll be my aide when we spring the trap at Monmouth."

32   AT MONMOUTH COURT HOUSE

*If I were an American, as I am an Englishman . . . I never would lay down my arms—never, never, never!——*Pitt

For the people of twelve of the thirteen Colonies, the week ending June 27, 1778, was one of suspense and ignorance. The English had left Philadelphia, and the Continentals had left Valley Forge, but in the streets and markets, the Patriots asked one question: Where are they?

There had been no word of pursuit, no hint of battle, and no daily reports from the Congress in York. The New York papers reported that Gates and his troops had "removed themselves from the vicinity of the Hudson." The Philadelphia news was that "General Benedict Arnold was endeavouring to restore order to the stricken City," and Boston and Charleston admitted that they knew nothing.

But the inhabitants of the Jerseys knew. They were experiencing, for the fourth time, the plunderous march of the King's men. If there were Loyalists left in the Jerseys, they kept to themselves and double-barred the doors at night. Many, who were all for the King a year back, were singing different words to a new tune. The bits and pieces of paper called "Proclamations," and the "Writs of Security" for those who called themselves Loyal, had been no more than bits of paper when the soldiers of George the Third marched toward Sandy Hook.

The English, assisted by their uncouth, pilfering Hessian slaves, had accomplished what Patrick Henry and Thomas Paine had failed to do. They had turned Tories into Rebels, and made prophets of liberty out of scoffing doubters. The newspapers and the Congress might not know the retreat route followed by the British Army, but the trail of the twelve-mile-long column was easy to follow. A succession of still-smouldering barns, gutted houses, and heat-swelled corpses, signposted the pike from Mount Holly to Mansfield, and on to Crosswicks. A wrecked ironworks, standing alongside a demolished fulling mill, was their monument at Allentown, and broken benches, smashed chairs and empty wine tuns told that Sir Henry Clinton and staff had been overnight guests at the Rising Sun Tavern, six miles to the southwest of Monmouth Court House.

Rain poured incessantly. Creeks and ravines overflowed and the Royal Regiment of Artillery sweated and swore and bent their backs digging the eight-pounders out of the mire. Baggage wagons sank into the oozy clay and Von Knyphausen's mitre-helmeted Hessians cursed the weather, the Rebels and the English. General Clinton grew more morose by the day and drank more by the hour. His officers hated him and took little trouble to hide their contempt. Every report he received was obviously false, and the very territory over which he marched seemed to exude a frightening hatred.

Like other hamlets before it, Freehold's thirty-odd houses, surrounding Monmouth Court House, were paying the price of English occupation. The two Covenhoven houses were in flames, John Benham's house and barn were wantonly torn down, and even while Clinton was signing an order decreeing "execution on the spot for any man caught marauding," the houses of Nathaniel Scudder and Benjamin Covenhoven were being put to the torch in full view of the British General's headquarters.

There was scarcely a scrap of food to be found anywhere. Everything of value that had been missed in previous lootings was spirited away. Everyone who could, had stored a supply of fresh water in some secret place, then knocked away the stone copings of their wells, boarded them over and hid them with brush; and forced the invaders to drink the marsh-tainted water in the muddy streams.

Most of the English officers had been on their best behavior in Philadelphia, but, day by day on the march, their veneer of polish had worn through, and they treated the prisoners, including Elizabeth, like criminals instead of prisoners of war awaiting court-martial. Morgan's Rebels, following Washington's orders, kept up a constant harassment on the rear of Von Knyphausen's baggage train. As soon as dusk fell, Dickinson's New Jersey Militia poured round after round of musket fire into the English flanks, until the Redcoat officers, wearied with never-ending alerts, were screaming at one another and barely respectful to their commanders.

In contrast, the Rebels strained every nerve to push the guns through the mud. They were eager to add five miles more to their daily march, and they needed no orderly drum to ready them at four of the morning. They were silent on the march, and their faces were grim and set. The look in their eyes told that they understood what lay before them. This was not just another battle. This was a battle they had to win. General Washington said so.

And now the march was over. Within sight of the Plains of Monmouth, they lay down to sleep. They stuck their bayonets in the soft dirt, and wrapped their clothes about their muskets to keep the pans and muzzles dry.

In the houses clustered about the court house, the English officers made themselves at home. Secure behind their ring of sentries, they drank and gambled in confident ignorance of the nearness of the Rebel Army. The one Tory who slipped through the lines and reported to Grant that the ditches were full of Rebel soldiers was whipped and placed under guard to prevent his lying story from alarming the camp.

To the north of the squat little Monmouth court house with its hip roof and cupola, was the Kidd house where Monckton had his quarters. Double-posted sentries paced it on all four sides, and lanthorns lighted the yard so that no one could leave or enter the house without being seen. These had been André's orders, and he made his own inspection to make certain they had been carried out.

Since leaving Philadelphia, André had taken every precaution to see that Elizabeth was securely guarded. At the end of the first day he'd given orders that she could no longer ride a horse. Afraid that she'd risk musket shots and ride off into the woods that lined the road, André had ordered her into a carriage with four other prisoners. All had been threatened with additional charges if they spoke a single word, and in enforced silence they had stared at each other while a Redcoat with a fixed bayonet rode beside the driver.

It was a journey Elizabeth had thought would never end. The slow passage in the jolting carriage, and the brutal behavior of the Redcoats on the march, were things she was going to remember for the rest of her life. There was nothing the English wouldn't stoop to, she thought, as she stood at the window of an upper bedchamber in the Kidd house. It seemed to her, as she looked back over the ghastly march, that the English had delighted in forcing the prisoners to witness every act of violence on the route. She shuddered. On Tuesday, she'd even been forced to sit in the carriage and watch the execution of Drummer John Fisher of the Twenty-eighth British Foot, for desertion.

Considering the position she was in now, locked in an upstairs room of this massive stone house, there were times she could remember on the journey when escape would have been easier. This Kidd house was like a fortress with its thick stone walls and its upstairs windows twenty feet from the ground. Besides the sentries pacing around the yard, Bygrove or Smythe would be stationed at the foot of the broad staircase that went down to the enormous parlor, and one or the other had the key to her room.

She looked down on the court house, and listened to the drunken singing of the Redcoats who were using it as a barracks. Doubling her fists, she hammered them on the stone window ledge. "Where—where in God's name are Washington's men?"

And where was Jonathan? Her anger fell away, and hot tears started to her eyes. Was he still alive, or lying, dead and unrecognized, in some waterfront house? Or had the English succeeded in capturing him, too? She turned, walked from the window, and threw herself face down on the bed. Her adventure in romance had been tempestuous and short lived. Forced to sit silently in the carriage, she had re-created in her mind every minute she had spent with Jonathan. In memory, even the angry words they had exchanged were something to cherish. There was no bitterness left in them now that she understood. Most of her fighting with Jonathan had been a fight against herself; a futile, angry resistance against falling in love.

Down below, she heard the officers tramping across the floor, and she raised her head and listened. It was time for the evening meal, and Bygrove or Smythe would be coming to fetch her. She jumped from the bed and rubbed her eyes with her knuckles. They'll not find me showing any trace of tears, she swore under her breath, and went to the washstand.

Her one hope of escape lay with Broadmoor now, she realized. Only once, on the whole journey from Philadelphia, had he been able to talk to her alone. Two nights before, Bygrove and Smythe had both been ordered on guard duty, and while the mistake was being corrected, she had been alone with Broadmoor. Again he'd told her of his intention to desert. He had told her, too, that the charge against her was more serious than he'd thought. André wasn't relying on the Mischianza invitation and the Highland Colonel's identification of her as Mary of Scotland. André had written proof, from someone at Valley Forge, that Jonathan was a Rebel officer, and this was a charge to which she couldn't plead ignorance, since she'd said that Jonathan was from her uncle's plantation—an obvious lie.

Broadmoor had warned her to keep on the alert when they reached the Kidd house. He had been in the midst of explaining to her that the house had been his quarters a year ago, and that he had persuaded Monckton to use it, when Smythe returned and put an end to their private talk.

From what she had seen of the house, in the one day they had been quartered there, escape was almost impossible. Three roads struck off to the right in front of the place, and one behind that ran to Colt's Neck. The English baggage train was drawn up along the two middle roads, effectively blocking any escape on either of those. Supposing she could get away from the house, she couldn't use the Colt's Neck Road, for that would lead her right into the English again as they made for Sandy Hook.

Directly west of her prison lay the only escape route, and it was in clear view of five thousand British. Before darkness had fallen, she had seen the gleaming white steeple of Pastor Tennant's church only three short miles away. Closer by half a mile, to the south, was the parsonage with its three chimneys, but long before she could reach the apple orchards that surrounded it, she'd be caught, or shot down by any one of the hundred sentries who were posted within arm's reach of each other.

Her mental planning came to an end with a knock on the door. "Idiots," she murmured to herself, "knocking when they have the key to the door."

"I'm here," she called sarcastically.

The key turned and the door swung open. Lieutenant Bygrove stood bowing. "Colonel Monckton's compliments, and will you join us at dinner?"

Without a word, she walked to the door. Bygrove's next words sent a chill down her back, and she had to bite her lips to keep from showing her despair.

"Major Broadmoor will not join us. Unfortunately, he has been detailed to twenty-four-hour guard duty on the baggage train."

33 BATTLE LINES

To a good general luck is unimportant.——Livy

Lying full length on the soggy ground, Jonathan looked between a gap in the stones of a crumbling wall that followed the sharp curve of a farm road running back of Newell's acres. It was unbelievable, he thought, the way the English sentries walked their posts without the slightest sign of being on the alert. There were plenty of them, on the roadway, and around every house, but they were unaware of any need to be on their guard.

So far, General Washington's precautions had been worth while. If the English could be kept in ignorance of the closeness of the Rebel Army till marching time tomorrow, the Rebels would fall on the Redcoats' backs with devastating results. He gave one last look at the village before he started to crawl backward from the gap in the wall. Elizabeth must be in one of those houses, but his hour's watching had given him no indication as to which it might be.

Since he had first recovered consciousness, Elizabeth, and plans for her escape, had occupied most of his waking hours. In spite of Stirling's assurances that they would exchange a ranking English officer for her, Jonathan clung to the belief that if they did not effect her rescue before she was taken aboard one of the English ships, they never would. No, he felt deep down inside himself, Elizabeth's best chance for escape would be when the English were too busily engaged in battle to watch their prisoners.

Squirming his way back through the tangled brier patches that lay between Tennant's Church and Monmouth Court House, he felt his shoulder starting to throb again. He had crawled most of the three miles between the church and the court house, and except for the roadway running to Freehold township itself, the area was one mass of tree thicket and bramble, with apple orchards and small patches of farmed lands on the edges of the woods. Three ravines, so overgrown as to be almost invisible, scoured the plain from north to south. The middle and easterly ravines were not deep, but the westerly gash was deep enough that a stone causeway had been thrown across it to continue the road. In turn, a small stream cut the ravine in two, almost at right angles, and then meandered on to make the lands marshy and impassable for horses or cannon. In places the briers were twisted and tangled masses of vine and bush that defied penetration, and it was around one of these matted clumps that Jonathan crawled, forearm held before his face, before he dared to stand upright.

Although it was dark, and his face was smeared with mud and soot from the kitchen fireplace of the Village Inn back in Englishtown, he could afford to take no chances. He had wormed his way to within hearing distance of the English sentries, and there was always the danger that the enemy might send out some of their own men on a like errand. He could see the white steeple of the church about a quarter of a mile to the west of him, and down below to the South, a single light showed in the parsonage, where The Pastor was doubtless readying his sermon for the morrow.

A stout hedge ran parallel with the west ravine, and close to the parsonage and barns. It had an opening in it at the causeway, and Jonathan followed it south till he came to the piled stones that formed the only level crossing to the ravine. There he turned right, and tramped along the road that led to Englishtown. He had to keep watch on the right side of the road for the small path that climbed the slight rise to the church where his horse was teddered to the rail fence that enclosed the churchyard.

Reaching the side road, he turned up the hill. Ahead of him, the quaint church loomed white and ghostly. Except for the gilded weathercock, the staring whiteness of the building was unrelieved by any color, and the flat-nailed shingles gave it an ethereal look of standing on air. He wondered what McLane and Von Steuben had learned on their survey of the field. They had followed the southern boundary of what was to be tomorrow's battlefield, and more than likely had been able to get closer to the court house than he had. He came to the fence, and against the luminous white of the church, saw his horse was there, still teddered to the rail. Patting the beast's neck, he took the reins, climbed into the saddle, and took the south slope of the hill that would lead him back to the main road.

In contrast to the noisy drunken Redcoats in Freehold, there was neither sight nor sound to tell that the Rebels were lying on their arms. He knew as he rode along that the fields and the underbrush, even the ditches, hid close to twenty thousand Rebels who had slowly and silently bedded down for the night within paces of where their commanders had halted them just on dark. Never before had he seen such eagerness to get into action, or such confidence that the Colonial troops would win the day.

Tomorrow's battle was going to be different from any he had been in before; different in more ways than one, he thought, as he galloped through the splattering mud. Never before, in any one battle, had the Rebels faced the pick of the British Army officered by their most famous generals. Howe was missing, it was true, but names like Grey, Erskine, Cornwallis, Grant and Clinton were enough to instil fear in the hearts of men who were farmers and merchants, and who never intended to be soldiers.

He was getting close to the Village Inn. A long row of sod-roofed single-story stone houses loomed up on his left. In each a light twinkled, and from each came the same clicking noise. They were the houses of Scots weavers, built exactly as their ancestors had built them in the Highlands, and in each parlor, the clicking sound was the snap of the picker striking the fly-shuttle and sending it flying through the shed from one side of the loom to the other.

Jonathan dropped from the stirrup before his horse stopped. He gave the reins to a military groom who disappeared round the back of the inn quickly and without a word. The tenseness in the Village Inn was something that could be felt, and Jonathan thought of the remark Stirling had made just before the General had sent him out to survey the plains. "Tomorrow," Stirling had said softly, "we must prove that we are equal—or abandon all thoughts of being free."

In the common room, Hamilton and Knox, poring over contour maps, and marking down gun elevation, didn't even look up as Jonathan passed the serving bar and made his way up the stairs. A night lamp on a table at the end of the upper hall dipped and spluttered as he opened Stirling's door and stepped into the General's bedchamber.

A bed quilt was stretched over the window to keep the light from showing. The bed itself was littered with dispatches, reports and roughly drawn maps. Stripped to his breeches, sweating in every pore with the insufferable heat, Stirling was kneeling on the floor fitting sections of maps into a completed plan of the morrow's battlefield.

"No misfortunes, lad?" Stirling sat back on his haunches, making a wry face as his rheumatics stabbed him in a dozen different joints.

"No, sir." Jonathan pulled off his torn and ragged coat and dropped it in a corner of the room. "But it's a hell of a battlefield we've picked." He took a cloth, wrung it out in the water in the basin, and wiped some of the muck from his face. "There's no space to fight in—we'll have to move out well beyond the parsonage."

"We'll do that," Stirling agreed.

"The steeple of the old church is not much use as a lookout post." Jonathan pulled off his boots. "A lookout might be able to see something when there are men moving out on the plain, but 'tis nothing but trees and brier looking down on top of it. You can't even see the outline of the ravine."

"We have to fight beyond that western ravine anyway." Stirling pointed to the maps on the floor. "Cannon would be useless, and I think muskets would be, too."

The door opened, and Von Steuben entered. He was followed by McLane, covered from head to foot with mud.

"Well?" Stirling waited till the door closed.

"Before the English get three miles on that Middletown Road—by us they must be engaged." The Baron took a drink of water from the jug on the small pine commode. "The advantage of us they will have, if we allow them to get so far. They, on the hills will be, with—" he snapped his fingers —"what you call it in English—?"

"Cover?" Jonathan suggested.

"Cover." The Drillmaster was all smiles. "The English have made a change in their alignment. General von Knyphausen's Hessians are camped in—what I would say?—in position of first moving in the morning."

"I hope you're right, Baron." Stirling looked at the map, his eyes tracing the road from Freehold out to Middletown.

"But I am right, of course." Von Steuben smiled broadly. "I know the way in which they are encamped. Through their camp I went without a challenge."

"You—you went through their camp?" McLane asked, aghast.

"Ja." The Drillmaster grinned with delight. "Me—they do not know. I speak to the Hessians in their own speech—I ask questions—they answer. They think I am fine man to speak to common Hessian. They will move— at head of march—tomorrow." He finished with conviction.

"I'll be damned," McLane spluttered. "And I crawled all around there on my belly, all but naked, to catch a word here and there."

"What did you find out, Allan?" Stirling asked between laughs.

"That their cannon are well placed. Several batteries command the main road into Freehold itself. Two or three batteries are placed at the court house. There are at least six guns on Briar Hill." McLane dropped to his knees and pointed to the northeast corner of the map. "Right here is Briar Hill. But!" He swept his finger east. "This is marshland behind the hill—so if we force them out of there, they must come down the south side of the hill, right on top of their own flank."

"You do not say their right or left flank?"

"No." McLane looked up. "Because what is their left flank now will be their right flank when they face about—after we attack."

"So!" The Baron snapped his fingers as he loved to do. "We should call the enemy—north flank and south flank—then always we will be right, ja?"

"No word of prisoners?" Jonathan blurted out at last.

"They have some, yes." McLane got to his feet. "A group, specially

[253]

guarded by Hessians, and with the baggage train. But your Beth is not among them."

"No," Jonathan said grimly. "From what Mistress Darragh said, Beth is with Monckton's Guards—and there she's most like to stay."

"Till tomorrow, Jonathan, till tomorrow." Stirling creaked to his feet. "I must report to General Washington. Let me see if we are in agreement on the terrain." He spread his arms out full length in front of him. "Imagine, please, we stand on the main road—just behind the parsonage. On the left, we have a hill, it has no name. On the right we have Combs Hill, slightly higher. Between the hills we have a distance of three miles."

"Correct," Jonathan said, while the others nodded agreement.

"From our viewpoint, we look toward Monmouth Court House—also three miles away. So we have a square of three miles and on three of the corners we have three hills—Briar on the northeast."

"With marshes in front of all three," McLane spoke up.

"Yes—" Stirling held up his right hand—"and in place of a hill on the fourth corner, we have rolling ground with an apple orchard and a small house surrounded by apple sheds." He stretched his arms out by his sides. "Now, along the back of our square, in line with the parsonage, is the hedge. In front of that is the western ravine, and beyond that, until we get one mile from the court house, is dense forest, filled with brier. From then on, to the sea, stretch the Plains of Monmouth."

"One thing, General," Jonathan interrupted. "The only road that will carry guns is the main road. To get off the main road is to land in swamp—until you get on the far side of the ravine by at least half a mile."

Stirling inclined his head, understanding. "Therefore, we must advance quickly over the causeway, and place our guns. Before dawn, General Greene will have three batteries on Combs Hill, and we will have sharpshooters on the hill without a name which we will call 'Left Hill.'"

"But not too much before dawn, General," McLane said. "From the British camp—you can see these hills clearly. If our guns are in place before our main body is well beyond the causeway—we'll betray the fact that we intend engaging them."

Stirling glanced down quickly at the map on the floor. "You're right, Captain. You've saved us from what might have been a serious blunder." He turned to Jonathan. "Get your horse, lad. You spend tonight on Left Hill. Take a guard of six men and a dispatch rider, and let no one on that hill till you hear from me."

"Yes, sir." Jonathan reached out for his uniform.

"You, Captain McLane, get to Generals Greene and Knox as quickly as possible. Delay their movement of cannon up Combs Hill."

"Yes, sir."

"General Lee should be notified, sir," Jonathan reminded Stirling.

[254]

"General Lee has already retired." Stirling lifted his coat from the bed and slung it over his shoulder. "General Lee left orders to the effect that he was not to be disturbed." He walked to the door. "I will report to General Washington now, and I will inspect both your posts—on Left Hill and Combs Hill, before dawn. Baron," he saluted Von Steuben, "I'll see you at Drum Roll."

34   PROPHECY

"Lookout!"—"Sharp and Keen."——SIGN AND COUNTERSIGN
BEFORE MONMOUTH

At the foot of a gentle incline, hidden by trees and the rise of the land, General Washington had pitched his small tent. The sentry held up his hand as Stirling approached, and the General saw the Commander-in-Chief's silhouette thrown on the canvas by the light from a lanthorn.

No one who knew the Commander-in-Chief could mistake the sharp outline on the tent flap. The erect head, set on the wide level shoulders, and the strong jaw that bespoke unswerving determination, were known to every soldier in the Rebel Army. Washington's arms rested on the edge of a table, and his hands were clasped in silent prayer.

Stirling closed his own eyes, and remembered it had been a longish spell since he'd done any praying. He stood under the trees, the sweat trickling down his ribs, until he heard the Commander-in-Chief shuffling the papers on the table, then he pushed aside the tent flap and bent low to enter.

"Good evening, William. Seat yourself." Washington waved to an upturned box.

"You look worried, sir." Stirling wiped the sweat from the point of his chin with the back of his hand.

"Not worried. But I am still annoyed at General Lee for forcing me into an awkward position."

"General La Fayette understands your position. The Marquis is fully aware that General Lee importuned you for the command of the advance column—after you had given it to the Marquis."

"In truth, William, I am more disturbed at being forced to give the command to a general who has consistently opposed the action we are ready to engage in."

"The Marquis," Stirling said significantly, "is interested only in winning battles—not self-glory."

"I rely on that, in my dealings with him." Washington ran his hand over his face in irritation. "My passions are hot and, in some affairs, quickly aroused. I control them—and endeavor not to speak till I have controlled them—but I think I spoke more sharply to General Lee than he is accustomed to expect."

"It may do him good, sir. Since he asked for the command—I do not see what you could do about the matter. If by any chance things should not go exactly as we like tomorrow, the first question from the Congress would be—where was Charles Lee in the command."

"That was my assessment of the situation, William. I was placed in a most singular predicament. At every council we have held, before leaving the Valley Forge and on the march, General Lee has been outspoken in his opposition to an attack on the English. Militarily speaking, no general should be given a command when he is not wholeheartedly in favor of the expected engagement."

"Exactly, sir. And your position would have been an embarrassing one indeed had you designated General Lee to lead the attack—and he had declined."

"Precisely. Therefore, it never occurred to me to place him in command of the advance. It was quite shocking to me when he came to my tent Thursday night at Kingston and actually demanded to be placed at the head of the advance column."

"You pointed out his previous opposition?"

"I did, William. But he took the view, with some justice I admit, that I had requested his opinion on an attack, and therefore he should not be deprived of the command because he had spoken his mind. Also that it was an indignity to him and to you—to have General La Fayette lead a wing while he was placed in a subordinate position."

"Justice he might have, sir, but little right." Stirling looked at the small tent, the rush chair in which Washington was seated. He tapped the box he was sitting on with the tips of his fingers. "La Fayette is studying the field as of this moment. The Baron has already done so. Wayne has visited every company and post in his reserves and told the men what he expects of them tomorrow. We sit here—and where is Lee? Abed."

"I had another visitor—who upset me somewhat." The Chief waved his hand at the sombre dark of the woods outside, and then at the guttering candle in the folding lanthorn. "For a moment or two—I felt as Macbeth may have felt after the visitation of the prophesying witches—for my visitor made a prophecy."

"Who was it?"

"Doctor Griffith, Surgeon of the Third Regiment Virginia Line. He refused to tell me who had warned him—but he in turn warned me—"

"Of what?"

"To beware of Lee—who would play me false tomorrow."

Stirling tried to lighten his voice as he replied. "Lee will be under observation and in no position—as I foresee tomorrow—to do anything but carry out your orders." He folded his arms and leaned forward, resting his elbows on his knees. "A somewhat disturbing thing to hear about a general —on the eve of an engagement."

"Especially so, since it conforms to your belief, William."

"It will make me no more alert than I am now."

"To the rest of the business then, but 'tis some relief to talk of it." Washington spread a map on his knees, and oriented it to follow the north. "General Lee has orders to march on the first sign of movement by the British."

"That is provided for, sir." Stirling pointed to Briar Hill on the map. "General Dickinson and his Jersey lads are on the heights—a mile north of Briar Hill. They will signal when the British begin their march. Here—" Stirling moved his finger to Left Hill—"Captain Kimball is waiting. When he receives the signal, he will dispatch a rider to inform General Lee."

"Excellent." Washington nodded his approval.

"One thing about this engagement haunts me every minute." Stirling folded his arms. "We have no choice but to break up our columns into separate commands of little more than regimental strength."

"The enemy must do the same thing—when we engage him. He is at present an extended flank and in the manoeuvre of changing to a defensive front he must pass through the stage of being disconnected units with his baggage train at his back. That baggage train will give Clinton greater hindrance than our causeway for all that we are somewhat in the position of passing through the narrow neck of a funnel—and must halt to regroup each unit as it emerges at the mouth."

"Aye—that I know, sir. But the enemy has sixteen miles to retreat over before he reaches the sea. Once our advance troops pass the west ravine—they cannot retreat—not a foot, sir, else they trample over our own remaining forces and reserves coming up to cross on the causeway."

"Meaning, William, that the English would never attack from such a disadvantageous position?"

"Meaning exactly that, sir. And I know it upsets Von Steuben—though he says nothing. The God's truth is it upsets all the officers who know the English—that we should attempt something against the pick of the English Army that they would not attempt against us."

"But that is why I am attempting it!" Washington laid the map

[257]

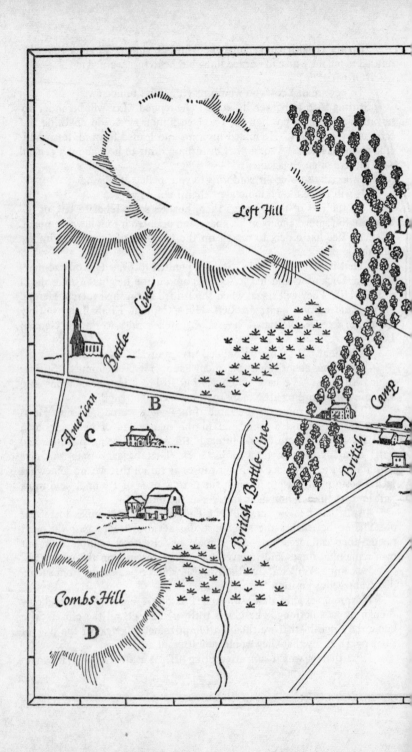

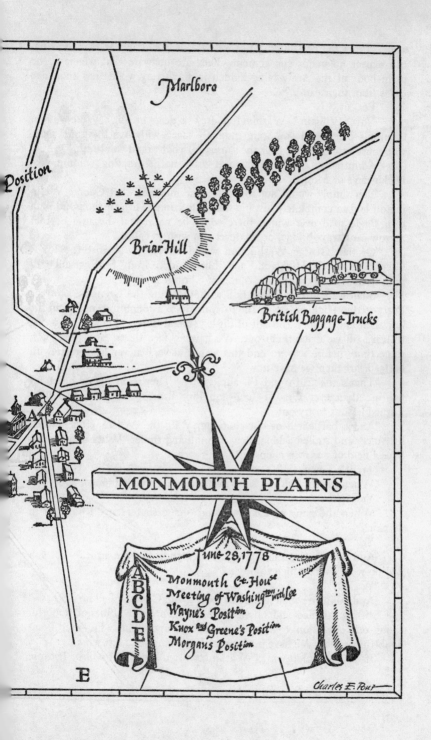

Marlboro

Position

Briar Hill

British Baggage Trucks

MONMOUTH PLAINS

June 28, 1778
A Monmouth C.t House
B Meeting of Washington with Lee
C Wayne's Position
D Knox and Greene's Position
E Morgans Position

A

E

Charles E. Pout

aside. "From the best intelligence we have, it would appear that the English expect no major engagement. They are unaware that we have the main body of the Army lying hidden in these very woods less than five miles from their camp."

"Yes, sir."

"Now, William." Washington drew a deep breath. "Were you in Clinton's place—and you were suddenly faced with five thousand men, who must have marched over the causeway, what would you think?"

"Admittedly, sir, I'd assume it was another raiding column—like Dickinson's or Morgan's."

"You simply would not think, for one moment, that George Washington had so completely lost his wits as to commit fifteen thousand men to a single road over which there could be no retreat—because of that narrow causeway—bridge, or whatever you wish to call it."

"Or that George Washington would pit Rebels against the Royal Grenadiers and the Highland Foot—if he could avoid it," Stirling said with grim irony. "They occupy the center of Clinton's line."

"Shall we win this Revolution without facing the Grenadiers, or the Forty-second Highlanders, or the Fifty-first?" Washington leaned from the low chair and slapped the calf of his leg several times. "They're not going to leave till we drive them out. We have to face them, England's best, some time, before we can end this war—and we'll never have men with better heart than we have now."

"That's the truth and I'll admit to it. They're in better heart for fighting than ever I saw before—and they have the Drillmaster's new-learned lessons to try out."

"And a battlefield of our choosing, William." Washington lowered his voice, and smiled a long, slow, reminiscing smile. "When did we last have a field of our own choosing?"

"Trent's Town, sir."

"When the English and Hessians thought an attack impossible?"

"Yes, sir."

"When the guns were in such sore shape that Henry Knox was in despair?"

"Yes, sir."

"And you were so shocked at my suggestion that we attack—that you had no words with which to protest?"

"Yes, sir."

"And Sullivan's men had no bayonets—and Greene's had no clothes—"

Stirling laughed and raised his hand in protest. "I'm not doubtful about our condition tomorrow, sir, except upon one issue—and I am doubtful on that. We have made no real provision for a left wing."

"If we need a left wing," Washington said slowly, "it will be because disaster has overtaken us. As the matter stands, the English cannot get a right wing into action—we can only require a left wing if the English have a right—and that would mean that my plan had failed."

"Do we have use of the Jersey troops, and the Second New York and the Fourth New York—if disaster falls?" Stirling asked doggedly.

"Yes. They will remain with us—and you and me, William—if, as you say, disaster falls."

"'Tis all I wish to know." Stirling scrambled to his feet, grinning. "I am a cautious man, General, a somewhat timid man—I am a man who latches windows and bolts doors and believes that every letter bears ill news till I have read otherwise—but I am not a man who fears the worst— because I prepare for the worst."

Washington stood up. "By every rule, Lee's command of better than five thousand men should demoralize the English, spread out as they will be on the march. Within two hours we should move in with the reserves, and Greene should close in—like the jaws of a blacksmith's tongs—on the right. Any additional plans we make will be because things have gone amiss—and we will make them on the field."

"Yes, sir." Stirling saluted. "I'm going now to inspect my posts on Combs Hill, and the one we call Left Hill."

"I'll ride part way with you then." Washington picked up his tricorne. "I am going to walk over that causeway. I want to know every stone in it."

35   CRY HAVOC

Cunning and treachery are the offspring of
incapacity.——La Rochefoucauld

Sunday's dawn broke with the promise of a brazen sun pouring scorching heat on the Plains of Monmouth. No ocean breeze stirred the stagnant heat that had enveloped the rain-sodden countryside all night long, and the heat waves were shimmering on the roadways wherever the dawn light shone between the hills and hillocks that surrounded the flat- lands of Freehold.

At half after three in the morning, Dickinson's Jersey outposts had seen the Redcoats erupt from the white, cone-shaped tents that stretched in row after row from Briar Hill on the north of the court house, through the village itself, across the Englishtown-Freehold Road, and down to the apple orchards that bordered the pike they had marched over on their retreat from Philadelphia. Almost at once, Clinton's twelve-mile baggage train started its ponderous move from the fields onto the Middletown Road.

Carts and carriages, wagons and two-wheeled drags, creaked and lumbered over the shallow ditches and lined up on the already rutted and mired road. Officers' batmen led out saddled horses and rode them to the court house, then teddered them to the stake fence that ran along the side of the building where the orderlies took charge of the mounts till the officers had finished breakfast. The white tents came down, were rolled up and loaded on the wagons, and Von Knyphausen's black-clad Hessians along with the green-uniformed Yagers took up the duty of guarding the baggage train.

By four of the clock, Lee was in the saddle and the Continental advance column rose from their hiding places, shook the brush and bracken from their uniforms, and filed from the woods out to the road. Because of the heat, they left their knapsacks along the stone fences, and ate their breakfast of dry bread and cooked ration as they marched. In silence they swung through Englishtown, around the corner of the Village Inn, past a row of weavers' houses—all quiet now in the manner of the Scot Sabbath —and on toward the white steeple of Tennant's Church.

On their right, hidden by the undergrowth of brier, Greene and the men of Marblehead moved with Knox and the cannon, while New Hampshire and Virginia Volunteers brought up the rear. They marched kneedeep on an old road submerged by the swamp that had crept beyond its boundaries because of the week's rains, and the Massachusetts fishermen showed artillerymen how to get guns over water without wetting the touchholes. Their weather-bronzed arms were as steady as the rocks on their native coast as they slipped the cannon draglines under barrel and butt, and lifted the pieces free of the marsh where the road dipped dangerously low.

With sudden brilliance, the sun leaped out of the ocean and drenched the plain with eye-blinding stabs of light. Drops of rain still clinging to the leaves, blazed like falling stars for a moment, and then, evaporated. Like lightning flashes, the reflected rays recoiled from the gilded weathercock on the church steeple, and the many-paned windows of the parsonage shone with the harsh brilliance of molten metal.

Jonathan, lying full length on top of Left Hill, shaded his eyes from the low rays of the sun, rising behind the enemy forces. As far as he could see, north and south of the court house, the plain was alive with red-coated British, and blue, green and black Hessian uniforms. The brass-fronted helmets of the Hess flashed as they moved behind the screen of trees along the Middletown Road, and the high fur busbies of the Grenadiers made them look like faceless monsters as they mustered on the roadway in front of the court house.

Curling spirals of smoke still rose from burning homes and barns, and momentary fear struck at Jonathan as he thought of the possibility that his Elizabeth might have been in one of them. A sharp roll on a drum struck his ear faintly. It was followed by the breaking out of company and regimental colors which hung lifeless in the motionless air. The British Line was beginning its march. At the head of the column, almost disappearing behind Briar Hill, was the Regiment Knyphausen trudging along with the baggage train. Two miles closer to Freehold Village, the kilted Highlanders, acting as escort to the officers' wives and camp wenches, came into view from behind the houses that lined the west side of the Middletown Road.

Jonathan chuckled to himself. Most likely this was Grant's punishment for his failure against La Fayette at Barren Hill. There was another roll on an order drum, and the Seventeenth Light Dragoons wheeled about in sections of four and cantered from the camping ground to the jog in the Middletown Road. Behind the Dragoons, the Second Light Infantry and the Queen's Rangers covered the withdrawal of the Royal Regiment of Artillery from the artillery park; almost a natural redan because of the V-shaped angle made by the jog in the road.

The next regiment of the line was easily identified. There might be no wind, but the flag of the Royal Grenadiers must not be allowed to droop, and a drummer boy marched behind the color sergeant, holding a tasselled cord that kept the golden oblong with its English Jack in the corner, spread for all the world to see. South of the court house, standing at attention, stiff as posts in the ground, and just as proud of their flag, Colonel Cosmo Gordon's Coldstream Guards watched with admiration as their Cosmo rode the line on a magnificent white charger.

From behind Briar Hill on the north side, Jonathan saw a flutter of blue and white. In a moment it was repeated, and then only a patch of blue cloth remained, held steady by two of Dickinson's pickets. Cautiously, Jonathan crawled backward down the slope from his position, and ran to the mounted dispatch rider hidden in the clump of trees.

"Tell General Lee that General Dickinson's Jersey State troops are preparing to attack the head of the baggage train. General Washington's orders are that they keep up the attack till ordered to stop."

"Yes, sir." The trooper saluted.

"And then tell General Stirling," Jonathan added. "You'll meet him on the road—or at the Village Inn."

"Yes, sir."

The dispatch rider shot off through the trees, and Jonathan crawled back up to his lookout post. When he lay down, the ground felt like the

brick floor of a baker's oven, and the marsh vapor stank like a newly
opened crypt as the hot air drew it up from the rushes that skirted the
hill. Puffs of white shot from beyond Briar Hill, and then came the crack
of muskets. An answer from the Regiment Knyphausen was instantaneous
and Briar Hill was wreathed about in a smoke-white curtain that hid
everything but the gaping holes in the Hessian ranks.

The drivers of the baggage-train wagons tried to whip their frightened
horses to greater speed along the escape route. Stolidly standing their
ground, the Hessians never glanced at their fallen comrades. The Jersey
Rebels appeared for a second from behind their sheltering trees, then
vanished again. But in that second, triggers were pressed, flints fell, powder flashed and the well-aimed Rebel lead tore into the exposed Hessians.

Above the crackle of muskets a cannon boomed, and the ball sailed
over the dip in the hill. For more than three hundred yards the black shot
trailed smoke through the air. Jonathan watched it hit the road, bounce
once, and carry away a wagon with its screaming horses still caught in the
harness. Yells and shouts almost drowned the crash of the second cannon.
Lower than the first, it struck the roadway farther north, skittered between
two of the wagons, and tore out the rear wheels of the third and the front
wheels of the fourth.

Hessians and Highlanders ran up from the rear. Wading in amongst
the supplies piled in the road they tried to drag the disabled wagons to
one side. A shattering burst of Rebel musket fire stretched half of them
on the ground, and the others took shelter on the east side of the wagon
train. There was a thunderous roar as the Rebels loosed four of their cannon in one broadside. Without exposing himself, Jonathan could not see
the shot, for this time the gun muzzles had been depressed almost to the
point of hitting the ground a hundred yards in front of the Rebel position,
and the balls gouged the brier and underbrush as they whistled through
the hot air. Round shot struck the stone fence along the western side of the
roadway, separated the wall from its footing, and lifted it almost intact to a
height of a man's head. Wavering grotesquely in the air, the wall was like
some living thing till it fell apart of its own weight and showered the
wagon train with sharp-edged stones and clumps of mud and dust.

Now the Middletown Road was nigh to impassable. Redcoat officers
were running from all directions toward the disabled lead wagons. General
Grant, pudgy and red-faced, rode along the train on his overburdened
mount and shouted orders to the Highlanders to cut the traces and free
the horses. On Briar Hill the trees were alive with flashes as the Jersey
Rebels poured lead down on the roadway. Firing and reloading with a
speed the English had never known, Dickinson's men spat on their blistering hands and rammed charge upon charge down their musket barrels with
ramrods that were as hot as the iron of a fireplace crane.

There was dismay on Grant's face as he wheeled his horse. No chance firing of muskets and cannon had produced this chaotic clogging of the road. This was planned. The gross Scots General waved an order to his drummer. An upward jerk of his thumb sent the wives and camp wenches spilling from the wagons. The order drum's staccato warning brought Colonel Gordon, standing in his stirrups, charging along the road.

"Why in hell don't the bloody R.R. turn their guns about on that hill?" Gordon shaded his eyes as he looked across the plain. "Point the guns at the bastardly Rebels," he screamed, "instead of sitting on your broad backsides."

"The guns are mired, Cosmo," Monckton's voice answered from the smoke.

"Hell and damnation! Haven't we other guns? Scatter a few musket shots at the R.R.'s feet—that'll make 'em dance and free their guns bloody quick."

On the south side of Briar Hill, the gunners of the Royal Regiment, resplendent in their blue uniforms with gold facings, were tugging and pulling at artillery wheels sunk deep in the mud. The muzzles pointed in every direction but at the Rebels. An unidentified voice bellowed from somewhere, "Get the Dragoons to pull 'em out."

But the advice came too late. Dickinson's rebel cannon had been rolled down behind the crown of Briar Hill. An ear-shattering blast was followed by the brow of the hill toppling over the bogged-down British guns. Freed from the clinging mud by the concussion, and shaken loose from the hillside, the Royal Artillery pieces slithered and rolled to the bottom of the incline. Riding in to haul the guns out, the Dragoons galloped head-on into a curtain of lead from the Jersey muskets, and the gun smoke provided a sombre backdrop for the tangled mass of guns, horses and men scattered over the face of the plain.

From down by the court house Jonathan heard fresh shouts of alarm and the frenzied beating of a drum. He crawled as far as he dared toward the top of the hill. A Highland colonel was running toward Cosmo Gordon. He was waving, and pointing toward the church. Cosmo Gordon swung about in his saddle in time to see the strong outpost of Light Foot that had been on duty at the mouth of the causeway break and run. The sound of musket fire was distorted into a weird effect of echo by the sides of the ravine, and the deadly puffs of white smoke were broken up by the mass of brier, but the retreating Light Foot, stumbling, falling, and lying still, with pools of red spreading about them, showed that the unseen Rebel advance was close to the eastern end of the causeway. Convinced now that this was no mere repetition of the harassing attacks that had plagued them since leaving Philadelphia, Gordon flung an order to his orderly drummer. A sharp drum roll brought officers riding up, and seconds later General Clinton and General Cornwallis cantered alongside.

Excitedly, Clinton pointed to Briar Hill where for the moment the Rebels were quiet. Jonathan could see Cornwallis nodding vigorous agreement, and his swinging arm indicating that they should take the lower road to Colt's Neck, and then cut north again to rejoin the Middletown Road once they were beyond the range of the Rebel guns.

After another round of nodding heads, Clinton raised his hand, and the officers galloped off to their commands. Orders flew thick and fast, loud enough to be heard over the broiling plain.

The Second Battalion of Grenadiers marched across the fields, beyond the road and the court house, and east to the Colt's Neck Road.

As the Coldstream Guards went through the same manoeuvre, Jonathan, dripping with perspiration, dropped back behind the cover of the hill. There could be only one reason for the change of direction of the English. They had sighted the Rebel Army. Squirming on his stomach, Jonathan moved to the right, and peering between two rocks, saw Lee's advance column debouch from the ravine.

Turning in his saddle, Lee looked from the baggage train on his left to the retreating Coldstreamers with the Forty-fourth British Foot marching close on their heels. Pulling his horse to the side of the road, he raised his hands above his head, palms of the hands together, then slowly separated them in a signal to deploy. Virginians pulled off to the left. Pennsylvania Continentals took to the right, and the Rhode Islanders doubled their step to close the gap and keep the front intact. Rebel artillerymen, stripped to the waist, hauled on the draglines, and the four- and six-pounders, already loaded, groaned on their axletrees as they rumbled over the rough stone causeway.

Mad Anthony's men pressed close on the guns, and Wayne himself, with the Marquis by his side, rode over to join Lee at the north side of the road. Through the gray veil of smoke, the three officers could see the Redcoats marching beyond the court house. Jolting its way across the fields to reach the Colt's Neck Road, the baggage train was out of range of Dickinson's guns, and an eerie quiet hung over the plain.

"A certain-sure retreat," Mad Anthony said, after scanning the field.

"And therefore the moment to press an attack—is it not, mon Général?" La Fayette wheeled his horse.

"You do not know the English as I do." Lee looked superciliously over the Frenchman's head.

"The English? They have been beaten before—and will be again —that is most certain." Ignoring his rudeness, La Fayette spurred his horse, and moved off to rejoin his reserves.

"He is quick—too quick." Lee turned to Wayne. "We must move with caution."

"But with some speed, General Lee." Wayne pointed to the disappearing Redcoats. "Else Clinton will be embarking his men afore we reach the court house. Do you lead, sir?" He finished pointedly.

Without a word General Lee rode forward. The last of the reserves were clear of the causeway and the five thousand Rebels were spread out across a front of three miles. By now, the sun's rays were bearing down mercilessly and the temperature was nearing ninety. A shout rang across the plain from the men of Jersey when they saw the Rebel main division marching toward the court house.

Down the face of Briar Hill rolled the guns, held fast on the draglines by the men who had won the duel with the Royal Regiment of Artillery. Pounding behind them, shouting a welcome, came Dickinson's smoke-grimed and powder-blackened infantry. Holding their muskets over their heads, their bodies gleaming with sweat, they poured down to join Lee's left flank.

All over the village of Freehold, doors and windows were thrown open. Women and children stood on stoops or by the upper windows, and waved the Rebels on. Behind the advancing Continentals, Tennant's Church, open for Sunday worship, had lost its congregation. Those who could climb were on the roof and clinging to the steeple, while others contented themselves with perches atop the stones in the kirkyard.

From the orchards and farms, men and women ran out to the roadway carrying wooden cider buckets filled with well water. Eagerly, the thirsty Rebels passed the dippers along the line, splashing water in their faces and slaking their thirst without missing a step on the march. A broad belt of trees, running north and south, and coming quite close to the road on either side, afforded a few minutes' shelter from the sun.

General Lee drew rein sharply as a mud-splattered figure on horseback moved out from the shadow of the trees.

"Good morning, General."

"Who the hell are you?" Lee asked in rude surprise.

"Philemon Dickinson, your obedient servant, sir." Dickinson laughed. "Not that I blame you for not recognizing me." The Jersey General raised a hand in greeting to Mad Anthony and the Marquis as they rode up.

"You made them run, eh, General?" Wayne leaned from the saddle.

"But not far." Dickinson pointed through the trees. "They're retreating—but only because they want to. They're making for the shore, and 'tis apparent that they'll not fight—'less we force them to."

"Nonsense, General."

"I beg your pardon, sir?" Dickinson looked at Lee askance.

"I give you the same advice that I gave our impetuous young friend here." Lee pointed loftily at La Fayette. "You, sir, do not know the English as I do—we cannot stand against them. We shall be drawn on at the first—then driven back. We must be cautious."

"It may be so, General Lee." La Fayette's face was red with annoyance. "But I say again what I did say before. British soldiers have been beaten—one may presume they may be again—"

"My dear Marquis—"

"I am not conclude, mon Général Lee." La Fayette sat very straight in his saddle. "The English I say, may be beaten again—and I, sir, would ask permission to make the try."

"We can cut off the baggage, the Seventeenth Dragoons, the Queen's Rangers, and the Second Infantry—all of whom are separated from their main body," Dickinson said hastily, in an attempt to prevent an open breach between Lee and La Fayette.

"Do not tell me, General, what you will do." Lee looked disdainfully over the bridge of his enormous nose. "Come and tell me about it when it is done."

"At your orders, sir!" Dickinson's face was expressionless, but there was angry bitterness in his voice when he asked, "What—are your orders—sir?"

"Follow my movements, sir, and you will find that everything will come out right."

Dickinson saluted, wheeled his horse, and galloped off to take the lead of his troops.

"You, Marquis, will you do me the honor to take the right of the line?"

"Yes, Général." La Fayette saluted precisely, and rode off into the trees.

Almost apologetically, Lee turned to Wayne. "Extreme caution is the watchword when we are dealing with a wily foe—is it not, General? Will you take the center—we shall push on—but be careful in not engaging the enemy too fully."

"One question, General Lee." Wayne lowered his voice.

"Most certainly, sir," Lee said grandly.

"If you did not intend to fight, why did you accept the command?"

Lee's face flushed. He opened his mouth, shut it with a snap, and pointed toward the court house. "I shall fight—at the proper moment. Assume your command, sir."

Remembering that late afternoon by the covered bridge at Stirling's headquarters, Mad Anthony drove his horse along the road between the trees. In front of him, the Monmouth Court House rose up to block the view of the road beyond. A dozen different thoughts hammered at his mind.

Was this timidity on Lee's part? Was Stirling right—were these delaying tactics of Lee's, treachery in its most subtle form?

Riding on through his troops, with a wave of the hand here and a fixed smile there, Wayne thought of how often his own impetuosity had earned him criticism, and how often Lee had been pointed to as a paragon of military excellence. But so far as he could tell, both Dickinson and La Fayette were of the same mind as himself. He reached the front rank, and slowed his pace to suit the step of the infantry. All he could do, beyond voicing his suspicions to Washington, was to watch Lee carefully, and try by his own leadership to keep the center of the line well forward, thereby forcing the wings to keep up with him.

A curious stillness overhung the village as the troops opened up to pass around the court house. The cheers and shouting of the townsfolk died away, almost as though the passing of the ugly old building was the final cast of the die, and the two armies were fatefully committed beyond change. Not given to sentiment, Wayne nevertheless felt the touch of history on his shoulders for a moment. This court house, this monstrosity of a building, might well be the hinge on which the future of the Colonies turned. The English were leaving Jersey soil, of their own will it was true, but if their exit were hastened, or assisted by a severe drubbing, who could say but what the British invaders would never set foot in Jersey again.

A small fieldpiece spoke with its characteristic "snap," and the whirl of the ball ended all speculation. Spent before it reached the Rebel line the two-and-a-half-pound English round shot rolled harmlessly along the roadway. But it was enough of an order for the Rebel guns to move forward. Dickinson's cannon on the left rumbled out in front of the infantry, and Lee's batteries on center and right were trundled across the Middletown Road. Cannon spades tore great gouges in the earth as the tailpieces skidded across the soft field. Battery commanders shouted and waved the guns forward to more level ground where the shot would have a greater trajectory. His reins hanging free, Wayne waved his center up with both arms, then dropped them quickly, and the infantry fell on their faces, their muskets trained on the backs of the retreating Redcoats.

Wayne looked over at Lee, saw nothing but indecision in the mocking face, and with an outburst of angry breath, the Pennsylvanian roared his order.

"Shoot! Damn it, shoot!"

A sheet of flame passed from one end of the line to the other. Two thousand muskets spoke at once, and while the first rank reloaded, the second sent a blasting hail of lead across the fields. The English answer was swift, but it was drowned in the noise of the Rebel batteries. Four-pound balls sailed high, then came crashing down, well spaced on the English column.

"Forward, mes enfants." La Fayette's voice drifted over from the right.

"Press on, lads." Wayne waved his sword and jumped his horse over a pigpen fence.

"Blow the wagons to Hell!" Dickinson was off his horse, hovering behind his battery.

The British Forty-fourth Foot about-turned in their tracks and put up a rear-guard defensive action. Through the clinging white cloud of musket smoke, their four hundred muskets splattered the dirt along the edge of the road. Cornwallis ripped out orders, and the other regiments increased their march, widening the gap between themselves and the Rebels. Pan flashes were dull and yellow in the smoke as the Continentals poured another two thousand rounds on the Forty-fourth. Two four-pounders, fired simultaneously by Dickinson's battery, sent their round shot screaming and whistling through the rear of the baggage train. Wagon beds, shafts, spokes and axles spurted up like a fountain of wood splinters, and fell, smoking and charred over the Highlanders.

"Press forward again, lads, another ten feet!" Wayne shouted his order, and turned to Lee. "I'm going to keep the Marquis from advancing too fast." He galloped off to the right of the line where La Fayette was pushing forward a mite too quickly. The Marquis was likely to find himself under Dickinson's fire, or else compel Dickinson to ease up for fear of hitting the right wing. Riding along, Wayne cursed roundly under his breath. It was Lee's duty to have seen that, and corrected it. Dickinson's men couldn't press forward as quickly as the center or right of the line. They were already closer to the enemy than La Fayette, which was doubtless why the Marquis was pressing.

Over the roar of the cannonading, a woman's scream sent a shiver down Wayne's back. It came from a small house standing by itself on the edge of a tiny, well-kept apple orchard. A second scream followed, and the door burst open. A woman with a child in her arms leaped clear of the steps and ran toward La Fayette's advance. Behind her, the house collapsed. The roof slithered to the ground, the walls fell apart, and amidst a shower of glass and timber, an English cannon ball fell hissing into the dug well at the edge of the garden.

Mistlike smoke, drifting lazily in the hot sticky air, made sharpshooting all but impossible. Only when a burst of cannon fire with its belching black smoke drove the gray into the air could the Redcoats within range be seen. Beyond the range of musket fire, the great mass of the British troops were still plodding steadily along the road to the sea, their dead left behind, their wounded dragged along by the rear guard.

The havoc wrought on the English by the Rebels had been heavy. Still relying on mass quick firing, and shooting from the hip without deliberate aim, the English had inflicted few wounds on the Continentals. But the Americans, always short of bullets, and accustomed to shooting for their food, drew blood for almost every ounce of lead.

La Fayette had left his horse and was on the ground with his men when Wayne reached him. Sliding out of the saddle, the Pennsylvanian threw himself beside the Frenchman.

"I cannot move farther forward, mon ami?" The Marquis grinned at the figure beside him. "You were coming to warn me?"

"I was." Wayne laughed. "I should have known better."

"Between us—" La Fayette reached out and touched Wayne's shoulder—"there are no hurt feelings on exchanges of advice—as there are with some."

There was an ear-splitting roar, and the unmistakable high-pitch whine of grapeshot. Fifty feet in front of La Fayette's position, the ground rose in the air, showering clouds of dirt, stones and part of the roadway over the Rebel heads. In the lull after the salvo, an order drum rattled. It was still rolling when a cheer went up from the English ranks. And into the open rode Cornwallis, and on his right, Colonel Monckton. Behind them, blowing on their pipes to fill the tartan bags, came the Highland band. The color sergeant, mounted now, held the gold grenadier flag, staff against the saddle, as he galloped to Monckton's right.

"God A'mighty," Wayne gasped. "They're going to parade." He raised himself on one elbow and yelled, "Keep firing at them—break them up."

Muskets cracked, and the flanking artillery sent continuous charges screeching over the fields. But the Redcoats stepped over their dead and with bayonets lowered for the charge, turned their eyes smartly to the right and dressed on the flag. A hollow wail came from the pipe band as the first pump of air wheezed through the drone pipes. The drum major's sticks fell, and the band struck up the Grenadiers' March Past.

On the sixth beat of the drum, Cornwallis raised his sword, and the Second Battalion Royal Grenadiers stepped off on the left foot. On the fourth step forward, their voices joined the skirling pipes.

At first the voices were indistinct and the pipes flat. The ground was rough, and the high Grenadier step was ragged, but the lowered bayonets never wavered. As Rebel lead knocked down the men in the front rank, rear-rank Grenadiers moved up to take their place. It was a ghastly sacrifice to pride and discipline, but not a Grenadier missed step or looked anywhere but at his bayonet tip. Horrified, the Rebels listened to the drone of the pipes and the hoarse-throated singing of the fur heads.

"Oh! The girl I left behind me
Was rosy cheeked and small.
She bade me come safe home again,
And not in battle fall.
Oh the days are long
And the nights are lone
And the weeks are more like years
But as long as we must
We will do our fighting first!
For the pride of the British Grenadiers."

"Mon Dieu!" La Fayette gripped Wayne's arm. "Lee—he gives the order for retreat."

Startled, Wayne looked along the line. Lee was standing in his stirrups, waving the palm of his hand backward over his head. Already the center of the line was moving back.

"We must stop them—we must!" La Fayette was crying with sheer rage.

"We can't." Wayne took hold of La Fayette's wrist. "Lee is in command—he said to follow his moves—he may have a plan—though I don't believe it."

"But, Monsieur Mad Anthony," La Fayette was choking, "we cannot abandon the field like this."

"Send one of your men to Washington—ahorse, tell the Chief he is needed on the field. I'll ride back to Lee and see what the hell is afoot." Wayne swung back into the saddle, and La Fayette signalled his men to pull back.

Like some slow-moving dragon, aroused at last, the long English column turned about. The Royal Regiment of Artillery was getting the range, firing one salvo after another of demoralizing grapeshot. Coldstream Guardsmen were forming behind the advancing Grenadiers, and the Seventeenth Dragoons had already gained the Middletown Road.

Setting their pace by General Lee's, the Continentals fell steadily backward. Wayne rode up to Lee as the Dragoons thundered down on the court house. The Rebel line broke under the furious charge, and wheeling about, the Dragoons divided into double columns and hurled themselves at the two broken ends of the American front.

"What orders now, sir?" Wayne yelled above the noise, looking at Lee's expressionless face.

"I will see you later, General."

Biting his lips to keep back a scathing retort, Wayne pulled his horse away and rode down the south side of the court house. Had he been more certain of Washington's orders to Lee, he'd have called on the men to seize Lee, and take the command himself. There was nothing for it now, except to do what the English had been doing, all morning; try to keep out of range. He rode the back of the line, between the Rebels and the English, trying to hold the retreat to an orderly retreat instead of a rout.

"Thank God, the English aren't pressing too hard." There was little consolation in the thought, however, because the English wouldn't press forward too quickly until they had all their men in line. He looked west across the plain, realizing that about the time the English were set for a determined charge the Rebels would be at the narrow causeway. The thought scared him. If the Rebels were caught in that narrow gut, the slaughter would be incredible. Lee's division must have a stand before reaching the causeway. They had to, or be wiped out.

His mind in a whirl, Wayne watched Lee at the far left of the sweat-smeared line of straggling Rebels. Lee was hunched forward in his saddle; his tricorne, low on his forehead, hid most of his face. Was Lee, in spite of all the praises heaped on him for his military skill, completely incompetent, utterly incapable of holding a command together? Or was this a display of unprovable treason?

Since they'd entered the plain, Lee had given but two orders. To follow his lead and—to retreat. Wayne summarized things quickly in his mind. He himself had started out in command of a reserve force. Lee had absorbed the reserve into the main body. Lee had sent La Fayette to command the right, when Washington had placed the Frenchman as a link between Lee's advance troops and the reserve. Lee, without consultation, and with a completeness that was alarming, had reduced La Fayette and Anthony Wayne to positions of no more authority than corporals.

Glancing back over his shoulder, Wayne judged the distance and disposition of the enemy. He urged his men to faster retreat. If retreat they must, then he would do it quickly, rejoin Washington's main body of Continentals, and tell the Chief, whether he liked it or not, that Lee was not fit to command an outpost picket.

Corporal Hayes, a hissing fusee in his hand, stood stock-still. He held the fusee a foot away from the touchhole of the number three piece of the six-gun battery, and pointed across the road to the court house. Less than a minute ago, when he'd stood watching his matross swab and load the gun, the Rebels were pushing forward. Now, as he held back on firing the piece, the whole Continental line was in retreat. As he stood, hesitant, the English Dragoons swept across the field, sliced through the infantry front leaving the Rebel line like the two ends of a frayed rope.

"Retreat! Retreat!"

The shouts rose over the din of musket fire as another wave of white smoke blotted out American and English alike. Hayes rubbed the gummy sweat from his eyes, and looked along the road for the battery commander. It was a vain search, and Hayes knew it, for the battery commander had gone to a council with La Fayette, and he was completely cut off from the battery.

"They're yellin' at us to retreat!" Number Six Gun, hands cupped to his mouth, shouted.

"But they don't say where to," Hayes yelled back. "There's not a bloody one of us would get across that road—even did we leave the guns—an' I'm not for leavin' mine 'cause some infantry lads say so."

"What's the damn use of settin' here to get us heads blowed off?" Number One Gun came over as the corporal stuck the fusee in the ground.

"Don't aim that we should," Hayes said, looking up. "I got me an idee." He waved to the gunners and matrosses to join him. "Gather round, lads."

The gunners leaned over the hot barrel of number three, and the matrosses, black with gun-fouling from swabbing and loading, lay on the ground. At cooking heat now, the sun was burning its way through the leaves, making ramrods and canisters and shot as hot as the guns themselves. Looking north, they could see the British advancing more rapidly with every step. Charge upon charge was made by the Dragoons, but none penetrated the Rebel line as the first slashing onslaught had done.

Corporal Hayes pointed behind him, south, to the apple orchards. "Back in there a-ways is two small ravines. The first one is somewhat of a stinkin' swamp—but we can get the guns through it. The second one has a mess of thick trees. We could set the guns up and hit what we could—and I doubt me if the English could tell where the shots come from."

"They kin tell," Two Gun spoke up. "They kin see our smoke as well as we kin see theirn."

"Not there they can't," Hayes insisted. "We'll be behind two ridges. Them bastardly English might hit a tree or two—but 'twould take better shootin' than I've seen for them to send a ball a-tween the trees—a ball that would hit us."

"What the hell we waitin' for then?" Number One slid his arms off the gun butt. "Lessen we move fast like, we're more like to get surrounded than to plant a ball or two in the tail end o' these Redcoats."

No order was needed. The gunners made quick work of hauling the pieces backward through the brush, and the matrosses kept abreast of them with the swab sponges, ramrods, powder bags and shot. The continuing exchange between the Continentals and pursuing English furnished a smoke screen behind which the abandoned battery was scarcely visible, and Dickinson's guns, despite the retreat, halted every few yards to give the English front line a buffeting that dissuaded the Redcoats from attempting a bayonet charge.

Shedding most of their clothes as they went, Hayes and the gun crews hauled the guns back from the field that edged the Englishtown Road. The ground dipped quickly into the small ravine and, holding the rims of the wheels, the gunners lowered the cannon, one by one, into the swampy morass. Six inches below the surface of the muck, the ground was solid, and the wheels turned slowly as the four-pounders were trundled over the small stones that had been gathering for centuries in the natural catch basin.

Once across the boggy depression, gunners and matrosses laid on the draglines and inched the guns up the ten-foot slope. The heavy stand of trees hid them completely, but the hot smell of decayed undergrowth and stagnant water steamed upward in a noxious mist.

"Damn!" Number One Gun held his nose. "Jest about as soon be shot as stay long in this invisible outhouse."

"You'll recover," Hayes said grimly. "Some shots you don't never recover from." He wiped himself down with his rumpled breeches and threw them on top of a brier patch. "No inbetweens in this bloody war. Live for months in a fireplace—with fingers so cold you couldn't load a musket. Now it's so hellish hot you can't lift a ramrod." He pointed through the trees at the stretch of road. "See what I mean?"

Looking toward the field, the gunners nodded as they saw clear spaces between the trunks. A well-aimed cannon could lob a round shot without hitting a branch, and they set about lining up the four-pounders. From their vantage point, they looked northeast to the Middletown Road. Almost north of them lay the court house, and to the northwest, the Englishtown Road was theirs for as far as cannon shot would carry.

Hayes squinted along the barrel of number three, estimated that the charge he'd been ready to fire before they withdrew would throw a ball just beyond the last house on the opposite side of the Englishtown Road. His matross, a short rotund little coffinmaker from Maine, with a perpetual air of sorrow about him, handed up a lighted fusee.

"Good timing." Hayes grinned. "I see some Redcoats sneakin' along behind them houses. Rest o' you ready—I'm a-going to let her go in a count o' twenty."

"I'm on this side of the road," Number One Gun said. "'Bout a hundred feet this side of the last house."

"Can you fire now?" Hayes waved his matross to take the fusee to number one.

"Hell, yes."

"Then count five—let her go—and bring the fusee back to me."

Number one roared. They heard the ball "woosh" through the trees, then watched it as it plummeted to the roadway and bounded toward the houses. Startled Redcoats jumped from behind the buildings and searched the plain to see where the shot came from. Hayes' cannon belched and the second ball rose in the air. The Redcoats, looking into the sun, couldn't see it till too late, and the round shot careening and spiralling along the edge of the road carried them off in a bloody mass of arms and legs.

Behind their screen of trees, the battery watched the English officers riding back and forth trying to locate the hidden guns. Grimacing through their grime, gunner and matross alike swabbed the barrels, threw in the powder bags, rammed home the wadding, and rolled in the shot. The smoke, dissipated in the treetops, gave no clear hint of the battery position, and the gunners waited for the next wave of English to come into range.

"How did ye know of this place, Corporal?" Number One spat on his hands and tested the heat of the gun butt. "You're from t'other side of the river."

Hayes closed one eye, and pointed behind him. "Small house back in that apple orchard. My wife Mary is there—with friends. Mary is a Jersey lass, born in Allentown."

"She followed you?" Number Six asked admiringly.

"She followed the English," Hayes corrected. "Knowed we'd be along soon, so she stays here and waits. Doubtless she's watching from one of the upstairs windows—you can see—" he stopped abruptly. "Get ready to fire the whole bloody battery—look!"

Out in the open poured a company of Highlanders with Dragoons flanking them left and right. Behind came the Coldstream Guards with close to a hundred Hussars bringing up the rear.

"Are the guns well enough spread?"

"I'm to your right," Number Six answered.

"And I'm way on the left of your last one." Three held his fusee aloft.

"Let 'em go!" Hayes brought the fusee down on the touchhole.

Earth-shaking, the blast threw the slime from the morass up into the trees. Nothing could be seen for the black pall of smoke that shot out in rings and then drifted over the trees like louring storm clouds. Sulphurous fumes mixed with the marsh vapor to make a rasping, choking poison that seared the eyes and burned the throat. Coughing and spluttering, the battery wiped the tears from their eyes, and looked at the devastation they had wrought.

"Like—like a—a bloody slaughterhouse." Number Six turned aside and spewed over the barrel of his gun.

"Great God!" Number One stood transfixed.

"Best we load again." Hayes' voice was quiet. "They'll take their revenge for that one—and they must ha' seen the smoke."

In silence the matrosses pushed the swabbing sponges down the barrels. Each knew that what he had seen lay in store for him, should the English find their range. Musket balls splattered in the morass in front of them; spent balls that had lost their sting and were short by a hundred feet. But the Royal Regiment of Artillery was moving into place. The sun sparkled on the brass bands around the barrels and on the polished caps of the trunnion bearings.

"Sixes and eights." Number One grunted.

"You're just as daid from a four—iffen it hits you," Number Six said sagely.

"But they can outshoot us," Number Five spoke up.

"In distance—but not in hitting." Hayes ground a hollow in the soft dirt with his heel, six inches to the right of the tail spade of number three. A quick thrust with a ramrod, and he levered the tail into the depression. Running to the other guns he bent down and took a quick sight along the barrels, held his fingers up so there would be no mistakes. "Six—two—three—five—one and four." He took a second quick look along number six, stepped aside and brought his hand down.

Number six spoke, and number two following quickly, sent the ball through number six's smoke rings. In rapid succession the remaining four threw their round shot, and the crews, without waiting to see the damage done, set about reloading. Smoke still curled from the muzzles as the swabs went in, and the gunners stood cautiously to one side as they threw in the powder sacks. Drawing deep breaths of relief as the fresh shot settled against the wadding without blowing off, the crew paid little heed to the two charges of enemy grape that shrieked overhead and fell crashing among the apple trees behind them.

"Only two?" Hayes looked across the plain, and saw men, horses and guns scattered over the front yards of the houses on the Englishtown Road. English officers, dashing about, were trying to bring more guns into position but the roadway itself was blocked with dead and dying.

"Would you be liking a drink o' cold spring water, Corporal Hayes?"

Hayes spun about at the sound of his wife's voice. "Mary, my darling." He leaped toward her. "What are you doing here?"

"Careful with the pitcher, John, 'tis Annie's best." Mary bent her head toward the orchard. "She'd not let me have it till I promised I'd not get it broke." She put her hands on her hips and watched John Hayes drink a mouthful. "Drink long and deep, lad, there's a spring right behind you and there's plenty more where that came from."

"They're getting ready again, Corporal."

Hayes took one long gulp, handed the pitcher to his wife, and turned back to the cannon. "Same firing order, lads, but take time for a drink, and shake hands with my wife, Mary Hayes."

Passing the pitcher from hand to hand, the men's eyes lighted as they thanked the buxom lass in her blue homespun dress with its white apron.

"You'll soon be getting help—I saw the rest of the Rebels marching from Englishtown—"

"Guns, lads." Hayes dropped his hand.

Again the screaming shots tore through the trees. There was a moment's silence as the gunners stared through the thickening pall, and then a white flash, tearing the smoke cloud apart, told that some of the loaded guns had been hit. Chips of iron and brass fell down through the leaves all about them, and a shower of stinking mud rose from the morass where the grapeshot ploughed in. But all the gunners could see on the road was that the pile of dead was bigger, and stretched farther in both directions.

"Will you fetch us some more water, Mistress Hayes, whilst we reload?" Number One Gun, faint from the sight as much as from the heat, was white and shaking.

"I'll fetch more water." Mary raised the pitcher in her hand. "As long as the fight goes on—Molly Hayes and her pitcher will go to the spring." Turning away with a laugh on her face, she disappeared over the edge of the ravine.

"We've blowed up ten of their guns I know of," Hayes said matter of factly. "And I'll not guess at how many Lobsterbacks we've maimed or killed."

"'Tis something more important than that I'm thinking of." Number Two spat on his gun butt and watched the steam rise. "We've give General George an extra fifteen minutes to get his reserves up. He should by rights make us all corporals."

Riding on Washington's left, Stirling looked up the short road that led to the Old Church. Parishioners still crowded the shake roof, and from their gestures, they were waving the Rebels on with more eagerness than either he or the Chief had seen in many a long march. What had sounded like summer thunder was easily recognizable as gunfire now that they were drawing close to the field, and the continuous crackle of musketry was proof enough that for once Lee had obeyed the Chief's orders and had really engaged the enemy's rear.

By now the English rear guards should have been forced off the Middletown Road. Dickinson's men to the north, with a good crossfire, would keep the tail of the enemy column from re-forming. Most important of all, the causeway and open plain beyond it would be out of musket and cannon range, allowing Washington to march through and deploy for action in a clear space, and with ample time to align the troops to the greatest advantage.

Looking at the Commander-in-Chief's serene face, Stirling knew that for once he felt exactly as Washington did. For the first time in the war, he was entering a battle with the conviction that they couldn't lose. For the first time, they were attacking a retreating enemy; a situation much in contrast with other battles, and one which accounted for the raised spirits of the troops. There was no mistaking the tense eagerness of the Rebels, and only Washington's strict orders kept them from singing and shouting on the march.

Ahead, just beyond the hedge that ran past the parsonage, lay the causeway, hidden by the slight bend in the road and the tall stand of trees. With incredible swiftness the road, which had been empty a moment before, filled with Rebels pushing and scrambling through the narrow bottleneck. A single horseman, laying about him with the flat of his sabre, forced his way through the press. With one look at Washington, Stirling spurred his horse and flew down the road.

"God A'mighty, what's the meaning of this?" Stirling shouted as he wheeled his mount across the path of the horseman.

"General La Fayette sent me to tell General Washington his presence is needed on the field."

"Report by all means—" Stirling pointed to Washington—"but it would seem your request is somewhat tardy." Stirling watched the horseman ride off toward the Chief, then turned to the men who had gained the open space.

"What's the tale—the cause of the retreat?"

"Go on, in there, General, and you'll see reason enough for the retreat," a six-foot sergeant with a bloody rag about his head spoke up. "The enemy is in there!" He spoke fiercely and labored the word "there" with a jerk of his thumb. "Columns of the enemy horse and foot—and gunfire like the mouth of hell."

"Damn it!" Stirling roared. "What did you aim to find in there—a kirk session?"

"We was ordered to retreat, sir," a little Carolinian said wearily. "We didn't do it on our own."

"You're right, lad, of course." Stirling nodded to him. "My apology to you all—you obeyed orders—but orders by whom?"

"No one can rightly say, sir." There was more respect in the sergeant's voice. "I'd thought myself, I had, that we was doing right well— when all of a sudden—the whole bloody line starts to pull back—just on account the English turned and snarled at us."

"Lie down and rest—off the road." Stirling rode on as Washington came up behind him. "Make way! Make way!" he roared as he spurred his horse along the side of the retreating troops. One glance at Washington's face had been enough to convince Stirling that for once the Chief had lost both his calm and his temper. Utter confusion greeted the two generals as they rode through the break in the hedge. Officers and men alike converged on Washington as though they expected that by some magic or cabalistic sign he could transmute defeat into victory.

"Where is General Lee?" Washington waved the clamor to silence and repeated his question in a voice that carried half across the field. "Where is General Lee?"

From out the press, General Lee, sullen and dark faced, rode forward.

"I desire to know, sir, what is the reason—whence arises this disorder and confusion?" Washington barked.

"Sir—sir!" Lee's face was red and his cruel lips stammered.

"I repeat, sir!" Washington rose in his stirrups and his voice was bitter with passionate denunciation. "What is all this confusion for—and at once, sir, the cause of this shameful retreat?"

"It was my intent, sir, to occupy that hill." Lee pointed to Combs Hill. "And, sir, had—"

"That hill, General Lee, Combs Hill, is already occupied by our troops—whom you have deprived, sir, of a flanking movement that would have proved beneficial to our arms."

"It was my belief, General Washington, my studied opinion, sir, that it was unwise to continue the attack and bring on a general action with the whole British Army." Lee's voice rose and some of his customary arrogance crept into his manner.

"Whatever your opinion, sir, I expect my orders to be obeyed. I am sorry, sir, that you saw fit to assume a command merely with the intent of doing as you pleased: in this case, turning your back on the enemy."

So intense was Washington's anger that Lee made no reply. The troops fell back and made room for the officers who came galloping up. Washington's raised voice and restrained fury were so unlike the Chief's usual calm that there was awed silence even in the midst of the disastrous spectacle.

"Get those men off the road and into the woods." Washington's enraged gesture sent the men scurrying. "Serve them a ration of rum and let them rest." The Commander-in-Chief turned in his saddle and looked at Lee with eyes that flashed his contempt.

"You damned poltroon! Retire to the churchyard and await my future pleasure!"

36 ESCAPE

*But as the flounder doth—leap out of the frying pan into the
fire.*——HEYWOOD

White and sick at the sight of the slaughter, Elizabeth stood to
one side of the bedchamber window. Stray shots had pitted the walls of the
Kidd house, and two of the downstairs windows had been smashed. One
Rebel cannon ball had ploughed its way across the front yard and scattered the springhouse over the roadway.

Down below her, she could hear the officers shouting and swearing.
Bygrove and Smythe were furious at being held from the field, and
strangely enough, despite Broadmoor's talk of deserting, he had looked
as if he wanted to get into the thick of it when the firing first started.

All morning she had watched for an opportunity to escape, but instead of the battle making it easier, it had made it impossible. The house
was completely surrounded by Redcoats. A company of Highlanders had
taken position behind the wall at the front, and a troop of Dragoons were
stationed at the back of the house.

Not only was she sick, she was furious. She burned with an anger
she hadn't believed could be raised in her, at the cowardly retreat of the
Rebel Army. Small wonder, she thought, that the Rebels couldn't win
battles. They didn't stay long enough to try. They'd turned tail at the
first sign of English resistance. And now the Redcoats had them on the
run.

She turned from the window in disgust. Even the despicable Grant
had brought some sort of order to the baggage train, and General Grey
was sitting out there with several thousand men Clinton hadn't yet ordered into the battle. And from the shape of things, the British Commander wouldn't need them. Her whole body was afire with anger, for
she'd had to stand and listen to the jibes and jeers the officers downstairs
had made certain she would hear.

Only once had the officers shown any real concern, and that was
when the Rebels first poured out onto the plain. But their worry had been
short lived. André had come galloping up to the house. Seeing the looks
on the officers' faces, he'd told them not to worry. With a knowing, superior look, he'd predicted that the Rebels would withdraw, and he was willing to wager ten guineas on his belief.

A roll on the drums brought shouts from the parlor below. Orders that she didn't understand were mingled with the sound of running feet. Stepping back to the window, she saw the Highlanders leaving the front yard and forming into a column, ready to march. Up at the head of the baggage train a trumpet sounded. Grant raised his hand, the Highlanders turned left, lowered their bayonets, and stepped out toward the battlefield.

She heard a sharp crack behind her, and whirling about, saw the gleam of a bayonet between the edge of the door and the jamb. Her hand flew to her throat, and she stood, unable to move her feet, watching the blade work its way down to the lock. There was another crack, louder than before, and she bit on her knuckles to keep from crying out as the door flew open and Broadmoor entered.

"There's not a moment to lose." He pulled the splinters from the edge of the door. "I've been ordered to join Monckton. I came back to get my pistols." He threw the bayonet under the bed, looked out into the hallway, and turned to her. "There's a hidden room in the house—I learned of it when I was quartered here before—that was why I told you to keep on the alert when we got here."

"Where is it?" Elizabeth's voice was low and her throat was dry.

"It's behind the stones of the big fireplace but the entrance is in the closet in Monckton's room." He stopped, held his finger to his lips, and closed the door quickly.

Elizabeth could scarcely hear the footsteps in the hall outside for the thumping of her own heart. She watched Broadmoor's face as he listened to the footsteps pass the door and go on to one of the other rooms.

"We have to wait," Broadmoor's lips moved silently. "That was Bygrove. He pleaded to be sent to the field."

In agony, Elizabeth waited for the returning Bygrove. She saw Broadmoor's lips tighten, and watched his hand move to the silver-mounted cavalry pistol in the top of his jack boot. Then she heard the footsteps, accompanied by a clanking, dragging sound. Bygrove was buckling on his sword, and the scabbard tip was scraping along the plank floor. The steps hesitated for a moment. Elizabeth could almost see the young Englishman standing there wondering if he should bid her goodbye.

At last the steps moved away. Broadmoor opened the door noiselessly. At his signal, she joined him and together they ran down the hallway to Monckton's bedchamber. Once inside, Broadmoor closed the door. Crossing to the big clothes press that filled the space between the chimney and the wall, he opened the door.

As Elizabeth came to his side, he threw his arms about her. His lips were pressed on hers before she knew it, and he kissed her with all the passion he had displayed that day in his Philadelphia quarters. Just as suddenly, as if remembering their danger, he stopped and let her go. "I'll wait till dark. Then I'll hide out till they're aboard ship. When I know it's safe—I'll come back and let you out."

He stepped down on the baseboard on the inside of the press, and the plank floor rose slowly. There was scarcely a glimmer of light, Elizabeth noted, as she stepped to the edge of the oblong opening.

"Is there a ladder?" she whispered.

"No. I'll have to lower you."

She sat down on the floor and slid her legs into the opening. Another roll on the drums came faintly from outside, and there was the sound of running feet from downstairs again. Broadmoor gripped her wrists, and she felt herself lifted clear of the trap door. Reaching with her toes, she tried to feel for the floor as the Major lowered her. Suddenly she was free. The drop was more than she had counted on and she lost her balance as she landed on the flagstoned flooring of the room. She heard Broadmoor's whispered, "Goodbye, Elizabeth," and watched the slit of light narrow quickly as he closed the trap.

37   HIC JACET

The battle is not to the strong alone; it is to the vigilant, the active, the brave.——PATRICK HENRY

There was shock and dismay in the officers' faces as they watched General Charles Lee ride from the field. The traitor's tricorne was pulled well down over his forehead, but it could not hide the cruel lips with their mocking smile. Ignoring the discredited General as he guided his horse along the churchyard wall, Washington saw that Lee's troops had lost their morale. Their support would have to be discounted till a change for the better took place in the tide of battle. As Washington made his decision, he turned and looked for his aide.

"Colonel Hamilton."

"Yes, sir." Hamilton, who had just ridden in from the outskirts of Englishtown, was shocked at the scene.

"Ride to Combs Hill and ask General Greene to open up on the enemy the moment our lads are clear of his guns. And tell General Knox to make every shot count—even at the risk of losing a cannon or two."

"Yes, sir." Hamilton saluted. "I have information for you, sir. General Cadwalader and Colonel Tilghman have come up from Philadelphia with six hundred volunteers and several wagons of ammunition."

"Thank you, Alex. Tell them to move behind us and be ready to become a left wing."

Hamilton rode off and Washington signalled the officers to draw about him. All traces of the Chief's flash of temper had disappeared. His voice was steady and calm and loud enough to be heard by all. "Generals Wayne and La Fayette—you have been out in front—how much time have we?"

"Not over fifteen minutes, sir." Wayne answered promptly while the Marquis nodded affirmation. "The Guards are not over three hundred yards away from this point," Wayne said after a second's thought.

"Then we must hit fast and hard to open up space in which to give ourselves elbowroom. Listen carefully—do exactly as I say, since we have not time to change our minds."

The officers answered in a chorus, "Yes, sir," and leaned forward in their saddles. This was the Chief they knew, the Commander who was at his best when the odds were the worst; the man who would be found where the musket fire was the thickest.

"General Dickinson—you use your cannon to throw round shot as far into the enemy ranks as you can, sir—leave the front ranks for the muskets. Post your batteries, sir, on the causeway—our lads will open up when they see their own cannon facing them."

Dickinson's artillery heard the order. With shouts, and yells, they turned their guns about and pushed them muzzle first into the fleeing Rebels.

"General Wayne—you, sir, draw your men off as quickly as you can and force your way to the woods at the foot of Left Hill. Use the bayonet—but dig your way through to those woods."

"On my way, sir." Wayne backed off from the group, his horse's flashing hooves clearing a space through the crush. His men were after him, squeezing into the narrow path before the gap had time to close.

"Marquis!"

"Yes, mon Général?"

"Stay with me and we shall force our way with the main body—across the ravine by the causeway."

"Yes, sir." La Fayette's face betrayed his pleasure at being on Washington's command.

"William!"

"Yes, sir?"

"You know what we have to do—I rely on you, William, to make it possible for us to get through."

"I'll get it done, sir."

"You'll have to suit your action to the others—we have neither men nor time for duplication of effort."

"I'll watch it, sir. Give me the Baron—and I'll get you elbowroom!"

"Yes, William." Washington pointed to his right. "You know Henry Knox's pattern—anticipate him if you can, and I'll know how to plan—without messengers running back and forth."

"Yes, sir." Saluting and turning away, Stirling rode down to the rear of the main division. His mind worked furiously on the plan he had formed. Von Steuben rode by his side, but seeing the look of concentration on Stirling's face, the Drillmaster asked no questions. At best, Stirling had ten or twelve minutes to put his move into effect; and at least five of them would be required to get his men to the north side of Left Hill. He drew rein in front of the Third New Hampshires.

"Third and First New Hampshires. First Virginians and First Continental Artillery—fall out and follow me."

Out from the column the men came on the double. They lined up beside their officers with speed and in a quiet that made the Drillmaster smile with approving pride.

"How fast could you lads run if the English were chasing you—even on a blistering day like this?"

There was a laugh from the men, and Stirling silenced it with one wave of his hand. "Will you run faster to meet them?"

Affirmative shouts rang up and down the battalions, and again Stirling waved them quiet. "Listen, lads. The one place the English do not expect an attack—is from the north side of Left Hill. 'Tis a dangerous spot. We may hit our own lads—and they may hit us, but either-which-way we'll pour hell on the English." He stopped and tapped his chest. "I don't know how you lads feel, but for me, if I'm to be hit, I'd as lief get it from one of my own. I'm going up on that hill—" he pointed to Left Hill—"with the guns. You lads follow the Drillmaster around the bottom of it—and be ready to fire when we let loose our first salvo." He held his hand up and prevented an answer. "I know you can."

"Of some pattern of General Knox—the Commander made mention —it is what?" Von Steuben watched the men assemble as he asked the question.

"On a battery of six guns, Knox lays down the shot in the shape of a cross—with the sixth shot beyond the other five—"

"Like a star—with a tail—a—a comet?"

"Yes, Baron. I will try to lay my shots so that there is a clear space between Knox's tailshot and my farthest shot—"

"Thereby leaving a place into which the General Washington can safely moved with his men." The Baron beamed at the idea.

"It may not be safe, Baron, but leastwise he'll not get shot in the back by his own guns. Shall we go?"

"It delights me, Lord Stirling, to enter battle with you." Von Steuben wrung Stirling's hand and was on his way. His sword flashed up and the Rebels speeded their pace as the red-faced General spurred his horse along their right flank.

Never before were guns trundled up the side of a hill with such speed. Draglines tugged and whipped, and gun crews manhandled the pieces as though they'd been made of wood. Wheels slithered and stopped and spun as the crews lifted the four-pounders over the rough stones, and the matrosses ran ahead, laid down their ramrods and swabs, and ran back down the hill to help the gunners.

Stirling slid from the saddle just before he reached the crown of the hill. Keeping out of sight, he crawled to the top and saw Jonathan. "What's the position, lad?"

"Grenadiers and Coldstreamers are within a hundred yards of the causeway. Royal Highlanders are marching on the south side of them. Dragoons are held in reserve to cut down any of our lads who try to make a stand—and a battery of Rebel Artillery is hidden in the woods south of the court house. They've played hell with the English—and what the hell happened and where the hell has everybody been? I've been lying here on my belly till it's cooked raw."

"And now you can cook your feet and blister your hands and face, Kimball, for here come the guns." Stirling jumped to his feet, grunted as a stab in the back reminded him of his rheumatics, and ran to the first gun. "Leave her nose high in the air—give her a full sack of powder and send me a ball as far as you can into the fourth rank of the English. Don't aim for the front ranks at all—leave them for the lads with the muskets."

"What's for this one, sir?" a gunner called out.

"As level a barrel as you can—aim to get the fourth rank of the bastards with the fur hats." He spoke to Jonathan. "Keep an eye out for Von Steuben and his men. When they're within a hundred feet of rounding the hill—let me know."

"Yes, sir." Jonathan ran to the eastern tip of the hill and looked over the edge.

"Number three over here." Stirling pointed to a flat spot. "Send me one about a thousand feet out. Have it light well back in the fur-headed Grenadiers' ranks."

"Number four ready, sir."

"Where do you look like hitting, lad?"

"A good thousand feet out—fourth or fifth rank of the Grenadiers."

"Leave her then." Stirling ran to number five. "All the elevation she'll take without throwing herself back on you. Drop them on the right flank—north flank of the Coldstreamers."

"Yes, sir." The gunner grinned and plopped the ball down the barrel.

"Number six!" Stirling walked over to the gun on the far right. "Think you can land one a fifty-feet this side of the causeway?"

"Fifty or sixty, sir."

"Good lad—do it at sixty and we'll be safer."

"The Baron's lads are two hundred feet away, General."

"Give me the call when they're a hundred, Captain, and then help me put the pieces in alignment—get the other cannon lined up to duplicate the pattern I've laid out."

"Yes, sir," Jonathan answered.

"Stand by, lads, for quick loading and re-aiming—we've got to keep the guns firing." Looking down on the English, Stirling noted that their rate of advance was about what he had counted on. He glanced around at the gunners and saw them tense, gripping their fusees. "Loosen up, lads. The English don't even know we're here yet."

"A hundred yards."

"To the guns then, Captain—be ready to roll the second battery into position. Fire, lads, fire!"

With full powder charges behind them, the shot streaked out over the open. Given added elevation by the slope of Left Hill, the screaming cannon balls went far beyond their normal range. They were still whining when they were over the English, and the peak of the trajectory was reached. Abruptly the whine stopped, to be replaced by the frightening vibrating roll of an accelerating ball rushing straight down to the earth.

Before the dust had cleared enough for Stirling to see the results, Jonathan had the second battery ready. Stirling's arm swept down and the second salvo burst through the smoke with crashing flashes like lightning splitting a jet-black cloud.

"First battery ready to fire, sir," Jonathan sang out.

"Hold fire!" Stirling called, peering into the plain below. "Let me see how we are doing."

Von Steuben's men, in a wedge-shaped mass, were moving along the west edge of the ravine. Their musket fire was steady but careful. Less than thirty yards separated the Rebels from the English, and the English held the advantage in more ways than one. Any English fire, so long as it was to the west, ploughed into the Rebels, but Von Steuben and Washington could find themselves shooting at each other at any sudden twist of the other.

Almost as if the Drillmaster had heard Stirling's thought, he looked up to the hill. Stirling swung his right arm in a circle and then shot it straight out from the shoulder, hoping that the smoke wouldn't hide the signal. "He saw it! He saw it!" Stirling rocked on his feet as he watched the Drillmaster repeat the signal and the wedge veered away from the edge of the ravine. "Now! Fire, now!"

Down came the fusees of the first battery and the four-pound rounds shrilled as they bored through the hot turbulent air.

"Second battery—fire!"

Hideous cries rising from the choked causeway were drowned in the thunder of the guns. Before the barrage from the first battery had found its mark, the second load of death-dealing iron was on its way. A third deafening booming rolled over the field. Knox's batteries were in action from Combs Hill. Canister shot, falling like red hot rain, streamed down on the British Forty-fourth Foot and the left flank of the Royal Highlanders.

Stirling searched the thickening smoke for Knox's pattern. Jonathan leaped to his side and scanned the less than mile-square area bounded by the church, the parsonage and the ravine.

"He dropped them all between the parsonage barn and the ravine," Jonathan said.

"And all well clear of the main road," Stirling added, "with his tail-shot toward his own battery."

"Which means?"

"That his next salvo will be still farther south—away from the causeway." Stirling whipped about. "Change the gun position, lads. Take the second battery, Jonathan, give every gun all the angle you can—and a full charge—ram the shot home tight. I want to come within hitting the causeway."

With shouts of understanding the matrosses fell to with the picks and short-handled shovels tied to axletrees. They hacked and dug away the stones under the tail spades and the gun muzzles inched up as the barrels tilted on the axles and the tail spades sank into the holes.

"We're raising hell with them, General, but they keep on coming—they've not slacked a damned bit."

"They will, Captain." Stirling clapped Jonathan on the shoulder. "After this round, we change our pattern—and I'll wager you a good dinner at the Village Inn that friend Knox does likewise."

"Ready, sir," the gunners shouted with one voice.

"Stand to, then." Raising his hand, Stirling watched the English fill in their torn ranks. Dimly, he could see a Grenadier colonel with uplifted sword waiting to give the order for another surge forward. A glittering circle of light danced in the air. A second flash started at one end of the Grenadier line and rippled along the ranks as the Redcoats lowered their bayonets for the charge.

The Grenadier's order to charge came within a breath of Stirling's down-swinging arm. From the tilted muzzles, the shot streaked high in the air. Stirling could see General von Steuben, head thrown back, watching the flight. Down they crashed, throwing rocks in every direction, and into the debris Von Steuben's muskets poured a devastating fire. Shouting defiance, the Coldstreamers rushed in to plug the new gaps in the English line. Knox's canisters filled the air with their metallic rattle of death, and the relieving Coldstreamers were chopped down halfway to their goal.

"God—what a mess," Jonathan burst out.

"Aye. And now you and I, Captain, go to work to make it worse."

"How so, sir?"

"You take number one gun of number two battery—I'll take number one of one. Get the gunners here." Walking to the edge of the hill, Stirling waited till the gunners gathered around, then he pointed down to where the causeway breached the ravine. "Somewhat like an hourglass is it not—wide on the church side of the ravine—wide on the court house side and a narrow neck about sixty feet long joining the two. We're going to get shot at from now on—we'll be in clear view of the English—and the sooner we do our sweeping job—the sooner we get back out of sight."

"Sweeping job, sir?" Jonathan was asking for the gunners as well as himself.

"Yes—best name I know for it. We have to do three things for the lads down there—before General Washington can rout the English."

"You think he can, sir—the odds are agin it," a gunner asked quietly.

"He can—if we do our part."

"You said three things, sir?" Jonathan asked, eyeing the Dragoons movings out from the causeway toward their hill.

"One! We must cut off the English from getting across that causeway to help their mates. Two! We must separate the British regiments already on General Washington's side of the causeway—so that Wayne, Washington and Cadwalader can get in to close quarters with the English regiments without being fired on by us. Three is most difficult—but we must drive the English back from the opposite end of the causeway—the east end—so that our lads will have room to move once they gain the east of the ravine."

"We can do that on our own—with twelve guns?"

"Yes, lad." Stirling looked at the gunner. "We can—but we won't be doing it on our own. General Greene is behind Combs Hill—waiting the exact moment to take the field. General Knox will use his guns to clear the way for that move. Captain Kimball and I will watch Knox's shots— and we will follow his lead—always taking care to leave room—two hundred yards or so—clear for our lads to break into." He moved his hands from side to side like a swing. "When Knox's shot drives the English this way— we drive them back—till at the precise moment, we both stop—and allow our infantry to complete the job. You understand?"

Heads nodded in agreement, and Stirling went on. "All of you will plant your shots to the left of Captain Kimball's and mine, never—never —to the right. Each man will be his own captain—try and get your shots in rotation—each a little to the left of the other—that's what I mean by sweeping."

"These Dragoons are making ready for something." Jonathan followed the horsemen with his eyes as they circled the south edge of the hill.

"The Delaware Light Horse will take care of them," Stirling said assuringly. "McLane, Aaron Burr and Laurens have their troops hidden by the church. Come on—our work is gunwork."

Down below, some of the disorder had disappeared. Lee's men were no longer choking the road and the two opposing forces were drawn up in some order, a little more than a quarter of a mile apart. As Stirling and Jonathan swung their guns into place, as close to the brow of the hill as they dared, the British Dragoons changed their indefinite riding and charged down on Wayne's men who were formed directly in front of the church. The Pennsylvanian's troops met the Dragoons with a full burst of musket fire, and the well-aimed shots broke up the cavalry formation.

Wheeling about to regroup, the Dragoons failed to see the Delaware Light Horse come from behind the church like an arrow loosed from the bowstring. Sabres flashing and horse pistols spitting lead, McLane and Burr with Laurens bringing up the rear led their Light Horse down on the English troopers. Oblivious of everything but the pawing hooves and weight of the Delaware sabres, the Dragoons rode right into the fire of their own Queen's Rangers. McLane yelled a warning to Burr but it was too late, and Aaron Burr, following too close behind them, felt his horse go limp and fall dead beneath him.

Standing swinging his sabre, Burr faced the Dragoons who wheeled about and rode toward him. Another blast of Rebel musket fire stopped them in their tracks and in that instant the Delaware Horse thundered in a circle around Burr and carried him back to the churchyard, leaving the area covered with the English dead.

Stirling and Jonathan, perched precariously on the edge of the hill, grinned at each other as they saw the Delaware Light Horse move off victorious. Their two guns were pushed as far beyond the brow as gravity would permit, and both men were squatted on the carriage spades sighting along the under side of the barrel to protect themselves from the hail of lead that splattered the hilltop. There was no need for orders now. The gunners knew what to do, and Stirling and Jonathan were waiting Knox's next salvo. It came with brilliant flashes and belching black smoke that bespoke full bags of powder. Heaped-up rubble and showers of mud marked the star formation just to the south of the causeway and in the foremost ranks of the Grenadiers.

"Lower the spade a hand's width," Stirling shouted, and crouched under the butt.

"I can land one," Jonathan said.

"Then you fire first!"

One after another the guns of the battery barked, and the howling shot tore along the English line. Knox loosed round shot now and the star-shaped bursts drove the Coldstreamers against the Grenadiers' left. Stirling's batteries whipped the ground from west to east, cutting like a huge scythe through the depth of the front. Knox speeded up his fire when he saw the sizable gaps in the English line. With all twelve pieces going, there was no letup in Stirling's firing.

Now the English were pinned down; trapped like a fox surrounded by coursers. A move south brought them under Knox's terrifying stars. To escape to the north brought them under Stirling's scythe. Standing still they bore the full brunt of the Rebel muskets. The gap between the regiments grew wider and wider, and encouraged by what they saw, the Rebel gunners reloaded and fired with such speed that the gun butts scorched the gunners' hands.

Slowly the English began to fall back. Their Highlander reserves, pressing in through the causeway, pushed them back into the Rebel fire, and the hill batteries tore their flanks to shreds.

"Time to change our fire, Jonathan." On his hands and knees Stirling crawled from his gun. A musket ball caught his sleeve and tore it from his shoulder, and he threw himself flat on the ground.

"The fire is coming from the west side of the ravine, General." Jonathan swung his gun around as he saw the puffs of smoke from the hidden sharpshooters.

"Give them a round, lad, while I set the guns to rake the east end of that bloody causeway."

Jonathan's gun fired, and the ball rattled and twisted along the top edge of the ravine. Screams rose momentarily above the hubbub, and the sharpshooters were silent. Again Knox's batteries boomed from Combs Hill but this time the shots fell on the eastern end of the causeway, and the impetuous Highlanders eased their pressure on the causeway.

"Come, lads. Come!" Stirling was on his feet. "We can fire as wildly as we like now. Pour everything we have on the Highland reserves and anything that moves on that east side."

Exhausted as they were, gunners and matrosses needed no urging. Their backs ached from swabbing and ramming, and their arms were sore from rolling shot into hot muzzles, but the four-pounders were rolled back and ready for firing by the time Stirling had cut the shreds of his sleeve free from his coat.

"Cut them loose, boys! Cut them loose—anywhere and everywhere."

Knox was following suit. Gone was the precise star pattern, and a mixture of canisters and round shot cascaded down on the British reserves. One of Knox's chance shots hit the ground, spun in the air and carried off the muskets of one whole rank of the Forty-fourth British Foot leaving them helpless in the center of Monmouth Plains.

Indecision, the first sign of panic, showed in the British ranks. Piercing Rebel yells came from the north side of Stirling's hill as the Eleventh Pennsylvanians followed by Dickinson and his Jersey troops came charging round the base of the hill and back into the battle. Their circling charge was followed by Greene and his men who debouched from the ravine at the foot of Combs Hill.

No longer was the struggle one of isolated units fighting over separated stretches of a three-mile plain. Freed at last of the restraint brought about by Lee's confused retreat, the tide was turned and battle joined on a major scale. The Royal Regiment of Artillery pulled their batteries back and tried to throw their six- and eight-pound charges over the heads of their own reserves. They were hampered at every turn by the fluid movement of their infantry, and the high-thrown cannon shot landed noisily but harmlessly in the impassable stretch of the ravine between Left Hill and Combs Hill.

It was impossible now to operate the guns from the hill, and Stirling's gunners stared at the systematic destruction being carried out below them. Stirling gave one quick glance at the field and turned to Jonathan.

"Your horse is in the woods?"

"Yes, sir."

"Then you'll ride with me. We'll go fetch Lee's men—they're rested by now and we'll need them afore this is over."

"You think so, sir?" Jonathan was surprised.

"I do. The English still have the Hessians and a division of Highlanders they've not thrown in as yet. They'll make another effort to stave off complete retreat—you'll see." He beckoned the gunners to him. "You lads take the guns down the hill. Report to Colonel Carrington who is handling the guns for General Wayne."

"Yes, sir." They faced about and went to the guns.

"Come, Captain, every minute counts or darkness will be on us before we've cleared the field."

Down on the plain, by the side of the parsonage, Washington watched for the puffs of musket smoke that would tell him Greene's right wing had rounded Combs Hill. He could see Mad Anthony, on foot, going from man to man in his command giving them a word of encouragement before they faced the English bayonets. There was no need to wait for the musket smoke. The shouting of Greene's and Dickinson's men rose above the uproar, and Washington, his sword held straight in front of him, spurred his horse forward.

Wayne's men, with the Pennsylvanian General at their head, charged. Monckton, standing at the center of his Grenadiers, gave the order for the bayonet charge, and the Redcoats ran out into the field. At the right of the Grenadier line, drummers kept up an incessant roll on the drums, and at Monckton's right, the color sergeant waved the gold banner.

With frightening speed, the distance between the charging lines lessened. Wayne and Monckton were no more than a hundred feet apart when Wayne roared at the top of his voice:

"Pick the King birds, lads. Pick the King birds."

"Guards up! Guards up!"

Monckton, with Broadmoor at his left, shouted the rallying cry of the Guards, and the two British officers, swords swinging at every step, crashed into the Rebel line. Wayne's second line of muskets fired over the shoulders of their front-rank men. The range was close, and the results, bloody. Guardsmen went down in mangled heaps on the sodden plain.

A wild wailing cry rose from the Grenadiers, and a protective circle of bristling bayonets was thrown up around two figures lying on the ground. Wayne's men lunged forward. Their hours of drilling on Valley Forge's parade ground stood them in good stead, and with muskets carried at high post, they thrust the Guards' bayonets aside and broke into the circle. Broadmoor was dead, riddled with shot. Monckton still breathed, his glassy eyes fixed on the golden banner with its twin crosses of St. George and St. Andrew, bloodstained now. Touching the tip of his tricorne in salute, Wayne signalled two of his men to carry the dying Colonel from the field.

Fearing the loss of their flag the stricken Guardsmen formed a solid square about the color sergeant, but nothing could halt the Rebels now. They'd not only stood up to the famed Grenadiers, they'd given Britain's best, three for one, and bayonets held no fear for them any more. One company of the First Pennsylvanians with Captain Wilson at their head threw themselves bodily on the British square. Swaying from side to side, moving back a pace at a time, the Guards went down one after another, till Wilson with a shout of triumph reached out and tore the golden banner from its staff.

English efforts to rally were futile. Cosmo Gordon, his spick-and-span uniform torn and bloody, was helpless to stop the flight of his Cold-streamers. Cornwallis and André pleaded uselessly with the stony-faced Clinton to abandon the baggage train and call Grant and Von Knyphausen to the field. No-Flint Grey stood with Clinton and argued that their duty was to retreat and save the Army—not lose it.

Seated on the churchyard wall, Lee, incredulous, listened to Washington's order drum beat the command to charge. With insane hatred, he watched the Rebel Army he had ridiculed execute a relentless crushing movement that was like an embrace. Washington in the center, moved forward. His left arm, with Wayne for an elbow and Von Steuben for a left hand, scooped up the English and pulled them toward the causeway. The Chief's right arm, with La Fayette as the elbow and Cadwalader for the hand, squeezed the Royal Highlanders and the whipped Guards in from the south.

Wherever the English turned they faced Rebel bayonets. Where the ravine had been impassable before, it now became the only escape route, and the thick mass of thorned briers that tore the uniforms from their backs, and the skin from their faces, was easier to face than these grim-faced men who had learned the Drillmaster's lessons so well.

With all the suddenness of a dam breaking, the causeway was clear. Washington, using his sword to point, threw orders right and left; orders as crisp and clear cut as flashes of lightning.

"Wayne—center! Steuben left! La Fayette right and join with General Greene! Cadwalader—flying division—last and on my left!"

Like exploding canister shot, Wayne's men burst through the gap in the ravine. Von Steuben's division, knowing they were under the eye of a master, executed a perfect fours-right, followed by a left-wheel, and quick marched over the causeway as though they were passing in review. La Fayette's lads, not to be outdone, executed the manoeuvre in reverse and made a right-wheel that was as sharp as the corner on a building.

Washington twisted in his saddle as he heard the thunder of hooves behind him. Stirling, coatless and waving his tricorne in his hand, was leading Lee's reorganized division. Jonathan had gathered up all the mounts he could find, and was leading a troop of irregular Horse along Stirling's left.

"Go on through, William." Washington pointed with his sword. "Take the left and I'll follow on the right."

The causeway that for over six hours had been a bottleneck, debouched ten thousand Rebels in half an hour. As quickly as they moved onto the open plain, they took their battle positions and waited for their flanks to move up. Greene ordered his command to close to the left, and Dickinson's Jersey troops obliqued to the right.

Retreating over the bodies of the men they had lost earlier in the day, the broken English Army couldn't pause long enough to mount a battery. And the day-long battle had taught them that their musket fire was no match for the Rebels. Chagrined, and bitterly critical of Howe for giving the Rebels six months in which to build an army, Clinton had but one idea: to get away from this field where his losses were ten to the Rebels' one. Already Sir Henry was debating in his mind what he would write to Lord George Germaine, the Colonial Secretary.

"Bad show!"

Clinton turned and saw General Cornwallis. "Yes, Charles, very bad show."

"Want to try another go at it—we could—at the court house?" Cornwallis wasn't insistent.

"Look behind you, man, and ask that again."

Though he knew what he would see, Cornwallis obeyed Clinton's suggestion. On either side of him were defeated regiments, some without an officer below the rank of major. He'd venture a guess that the men couldn't average ten rounds apiece, and that neither the Guards nor the Highlanders could be driven to a bayonet charge. There was anger, tinged with disloyalty to Clinton, in his heart. He, Charles Cornwallis, would not have led the Army into this trap, he had too much respect for Washington and Greene and Stirling.

Sir Henry Clinton pursed his lips. Two things had led to his defeat. About the surprising superiority of the Rebel Army, he could do nothing. But why had he committed the troops to an attack because André had said that Lee would retreat? Why had he allowed himself to be swayed by André's disclosure that Lee was a traitor? Why had he been such a fool as not to realize that Lee might be removed from command? Clinton shook his head at his own stupidity. He should have let well alone, and marched for the sea when Lee made his retreat.

Cornwallis turned and looked behind him again. Contrasted with the broken English line, the Rebels were spread out solidly, and in good depth, over a front of five miles. No, there would be no sense in making a stand, at the court house, or anywhere else. Besides his anger and his disloyal feeling for his commander, there was intense grief at the loss of Monckton, Broadmoor, and the other twenty or more officers he had known for so long.

"What about the wounded, sir?" Cornwallis tried to keep his voice level.

"How many do you think?" Clinton kept his face to the front.

"Well over five hundred, sir."

"Saint Peter's in Freehold won't hold them?"

"No, General." Cornwallis' voice rose a little. "Saint Peter's and the court house together won't suffice."

"I'll leave a letter to Washington—at Saint Peter's—asking him to succor our wounded." Clinton looked at Cornwallis for the first time, and his voice was petulant. "Great God, Cornwallis, can't you grasp it—our only hope of escaping annihilation is to keep moving till darkness falls."

"And leave the Rebels to bury our dead—as well as nurse our wounded." He sucked in his lips. "Another bad show it will be—explaining that to the House of Commons."

"I shall answer it when the time comes." Clinton dropped his voice. "How many—would you say?"

"I don't know, sir. But I'd not wager against a man in Burke's gaming chambers who'd say—"

"What, man—out with it?"

"If there are less than a thousand, sir, I don't know how to count dead men—and I think I do."

Over to the right of the court house a battery roared, and the round shot sent Clinton's horse rearing. Cornwallis lifted his mount over a spent ball that kicked from one stone to another as it rolled to a stop less than ten feet away. A cheer went up from the advancing Rebels, and musket shots splattered the ground at the generals' feet.

"That damned battery that plagued us all morning—I'd like five minutes with the Royal Regiment—"

"Don't behave like a fool, Charles." Clinton wheeled his horse flank to flank with Cornwallis, and he gripped the bridle. "Do you think I want to add you to the day's toll of dead?"

In a small ravine at the foot of the apple orchard, Corporal Hayes and his gunners wearily drew the sponges from their guns. Burned black with gun-fouling and streaked with sweat, they could scarcely drag themselves from gun muzzle to touchhole. Just as black, her clothes in shreds and her hair tangled and snarled from countless trips through the briers to the spring, Mary Hayes could still manage a smile when one of the gunners whispered through black, cracked lips, "Molly! Pitcher please!"

Jonathan, riding the left flank of the Rebel line, could scarcely see the retreating Redcoats. The English fire had fallen off, and now the infantry were fighting a desperate rear-guard action to save the Royal Regiment's cannon. By contrast, the Rebel line was solid, and musket fire blazed steadily as Washington, leading the center of the line, pressed on relentlessly, driving the English back against their baggage train.

Suddenly, so suddenly that Jonathan could scarcely credit it, the English broke and ran. It was as if Clinton had said, "Every man for himself." In the space of a breath, not a Redcoat was left within musket range. Grenadiers and Coldstreamers, heedless of screamed orders, leaped the low walls and were lost to view on the Colt's Neck Road. Grant's Highlanders brushed the doltish Hessians aside and seized the wagons. Cornwallis, brandishing a horse pistol, threatened to shoot in the back the first Light Infantryman who left the line.

Twilight was blacked out by the sky of smoke. Washington's right and left flanks were invisible to the center of the front. The day was gone—and it had been won. The Commander-in-Chief raised himself in his stirrups, waved his sabre over his head, and brought it down, point to the ground. The orderly drummer beat the Cease Fire. Up and down the line went the shouted words: "Cease Fire!"

"Cease fire!" Corporal Hayes and his battery heard the cry faintly.

"Cease fire!" The traitor-general, Lee, in the graveyard heard it, but muttered, "They are only resting—they cannot be defeated."

"Cease fire!" Elizabeth, choked with the smoke fumes that had filled the Kidd house, couldn't guess which side had won.

Shouts and cheers rang from one end of the line to the other. Men from Marblehead threw their arms about the shoulders of Virginians, laughing, crying and shouting at one and the same time. There was no need for any man to tell another what the victory meant. They, the despised Rebels of Valley Forge, had driven England's pride from the field. They had stood up to the dreaded Highland bayonets, had turned them back, and had seen the rear of the swaggering kilts for the first time in their lives.

Fifes and drums, striking up "Yankee Doodle," led the general officers, along the front, to Washington. The Grenadiers' flag, tied now to a staff, was paraded past the Rebels, and planted in the ground in front of the Commander-in-Chief. In moments, it was flanked by captured cannon from the Royal Regiment. Washington's efforts to speak were useless; his voice was drowned in the cheers that wouldn't die down. Greene came running up, Corporal Hayes and his gunners close on his heels. Shouts of "Corporal Molly" swept along the line as Greene, waving his tricorne, urged the smoke-grimed Mary Hayes forward to meet the Commander-in-Chief.

Wayne, Stirling and Von Steuben, uniforms in tatters and grimed almost beyond recognition, rode slowly along the front. Each was thinking the same thoughts. Never again would the Rebel Army be called ragtag and bobtail. Never again would "Yankee Doodle" be played in derision by any band—English or Hessian. Von Steuben grinned broadly through the muck on his face. This—his eyes ranged the shadowy line—was an army. Together, he and the other officers had brought it to birth at the Valley of the Forge. And here on the Plains of Monmouth, he had seen it christened.

Gradually, exhaustion took its toll and the cheering died away. The officers who had been at the distant corners of the field closed in to pay their compliments to Washington. Knox, black and ragged as any of his gunners, could be heard all over the battleground as he rode up. "A fine party, sir. From this time forth—less of Brandywine and Germantown—let us talk of Monmouth."

Cadwalader, far from looking like a "Silk Stocking" in his dishevelled brier-snagged uniform, raised the hilt of his sabre to his chin in salute. "An action for the drill books, sir."

"Thank you, General." Washington's smile was as broad as a grin.

"The every order—the every movement made by you, General Washington, since the command you took—was perfection exactly." Drillmaster Steuben bowed from the saddle.

"The worth of your drilling, General von Steuben, was proved in this day's engagement." Washington returned the bow.

"Never would I have believed that drill could produce such an effective army." Hamilton was at no pains to hide his admiration.

"Since credits are being passed out at this party—" Knox, his thunderous voice soft for once, raised his hand—"I now put in my bid for a gunner at the next party we attend. I want William Stirling."

"Pay that compliment to Colonel Carrington, Henry. He trained these lads—I only gave orders."

"Gentlemen." The laughter fell away and the general officers faced Washington. "We will rest on the field, and the men will sleep on their arms. I desire all the officers to remain on the field with the exception of General Stirling who—unfortunately—still has much work to do. William!"

"Yes, sir?"

"You will return to the Village Inn at your convenience, and I will send Colonel Hamilton to you later."

"Yes, sir."

"I think—" Washington looked about—"I will choose the shade of that tree for my quarters tonight. Any who wish to join me are welcome to share the accommodations. They are more spacious than any I have enjoyed for some time."

Stirling wheeled his horse from the group and saw Jonathan riding toward him from the village.

"What were our losses—" Washington continued to look about. "Does anyone have an estimate?"

"More men suffering from sun and heat exhaustion than anything else, sir," Wayne spoke up. "But Colonel Bunner, Major Dickinson, Captains Ellis, Fauntleroy and Munro are all killed."

"But a number of the heat exhaustion cases are dead, too," General Dickinson said sadly. "I have had thirty deaths from heat alone, about twenty by musket fire and some unknown losses from cannon fire."

"Will the officers try—without parading the men for a muster roll call—to obtain accurate figures. Give your findings to Colonel Hamilton and he will convey them to General Stirling."

"I'll await them at the inn, sir," Stirling answered as he rode off to meet Jonathan. The General could see, although the dusk was settling fast, that Jonathan had word of some sort. "What is it, lad?" he asked as the Captain reined his horse.

"I've located André's quarters in Freehold, sir."

"You think that is important?"

"In a way, sir." Jonathan pointed to the court house. "I rode around the side of the court house and damn near ran over André. I could have shot him, but for a dozen Guards who were facing the other way and would have turned at the shot."

"Did he see you?"

"No, sir. He was running and I saw him go up the steps of a house— third one from the court house. As he reached the door, someone drew aside a curtain in the window—our old friend."

"Our old friend—!" Stirling was puzzled. "Who?"

"The man who had the spy map—the man responsible for Elizabeth's capture—the man with the odd hair—Quimby."

"And you want permission to—follow him—hunt him up—kill him— or what?"

"I don't know, sir. But I'd like to watch the place and see if I can learn anything."

"You'll get yourself hanged for a spy—that's what you'll get."

"I didn't in Philadelphia—when I did it for you, sir, and the Army. I'd like to try it, sir, for just one night for myself."

"That appeal I cannot refuse, Jonathan. You have my permission— mainly since I know you'll do it anyway—and I'd not like to have you escape hanging at the hands of the English—only to end up hanged for leaving the battlefield."

"Thank you, sir."

"Don't thank me till you're back at the Village Inn—all in one piece."

At the opposite end of the battleground, the roof of the church was deserted. The parishioners, tight-lipped and silent, went about the business of caring for the wounded lying on the narrow seats of the boxed-in pews, or stretched out on the flat stones in the kirkyard. English cannon ball littered the graveyard, and the white-shake east wall of the kirk was pockmarked by musket shot.

There was no discriminating between friend or foe, and the congregation strove to stanch bleeding, bind wounds, and revive the exhausted, among English and Rebel alike. Volunteer gravediggers, under the guidance of the sexton, worked without ceasing to get the dead buried before morning, and at the northwest corner of the church, two men, each called

Henry by his friends, lay side by side. On the left was twenty-two-year-old Henry Fauntleroy, Captain in the Fifth Virginia Continental Line, killed by a cannon ball; and on his left, Henry Monckton, Colonel of His Majesty's Forty-fifth Regiment of Foot.

The dour Scots parishioners paid no attention to the cheering down the hill. They were still shaking their heads and asking forgiveness for this breaking of the Sabbath. They paid even less attention to the little officer who carried a crushed tricorne with a general's rosette under his arm; when Lee mounted his horse and rode off toward Englishtown, no one saw him go.

38   QUIMBY

He [André] was by nature mean, he slandered dead
men.——CAPTAIN BYGROVE

They were grim, weary, and disillusioned British who saw darkness fall over the Plains of Monmouth on Sunday, June 28, 1778. Rank and file were openly critical of their General Clinton, and while officers said little, there was agreement that Sir William Howe, or Charles Cornwallis, would never have been led into such a disastrous trap.

Clinton, unable for the moment to frame a report to his superiors that would tell a semblance of truth and at the same time absolve himself of blame, drank himself into a stupor. Uttering excuses of exhaustion, and the necessity of seeing to the men, the officers left their commander to himself, while they returned to their quarters of the previous night, and in subdued voices refought the battle, as it should have been fought, to bring them victory.

Not only were they disillusioned and weary; they were hungry. Clinton in his anxiety to save the baggage train had ordered it on to Middletown, and the soldiers had not eaten since breakfast. Before they could get another meal, they faced a twelve-mile march. By the time they had covered that, the baggage would be aboard the ships at Sandy Hook, and the most optimistic reckoning was that they'd go hungry till Tuesday morning.

All this, and more of the same, Jonathan had heard as he made his cautious way from the Rebel outposts on the west side of the court house, to the side street where André had his quarters. Whatever Clinton's orders might have been, the officers were making no effort to maintain discipline, or mount a secure guard. From some of the groups he had worked his way past, Jonathan had heard plain talk of outright desertion. According to the knowing ones, the Hessians had deserted by the hundreds, and were being made more than welcome by the Colonists who cannily argued that besides depleting the enemy army, the Colonies gained good farmers to replace those who had donned the uniform.

But Jonathan was unprepared for the scene he came on as he crept cautiously to the back window of the house he had seen André enter. A fat oil lamp smoked and spluttered in the center of a table off to one side of the room. A four-poster bed, its quilt rumpled and soiled with mud from the pair of jack boots and splattered uniform lying on it, stood against the back wall. Between the commode on one wall and the highboy on the other, a livid, blustering, cursing André strode back and forth.

André's whiplike voice lashed at Lieutenant Bygrove one instant, then turned on the black-clad Quimby the next. Bygrove stood at stiff attention, his lips pressed into a tight, bloodless line. Quimby, silently furious, twisted his broad-brimmed hat in his hands, and his mouth was half open, ready to speak if ever André's tirade ended.

"Someone—or more than one," André spluttered, "told that God-damned Rebel commander that we were marching for Sandy Hook. Washington never would have guessed that! He kept his Army hidden, and these bastardly Colonists helped him keep it hidden—till the moment when we were most vulnerable. It was no chance attack that caught us here. He must have known—and he couldn't have known unless someone told him." He flung out an arm and pointed at Bygrove. "The Fleet hasn't even been sighted—it won't drop anchor till tomorrow at sundown. Tell me, Lieutenant, how could anyone possibly guess that we were making for Sandy Hook—in the stead of Amboy—or New York?"

"I don't know, sir. And I don't know how anyone could betray what they did not know. I did not know we were to embark at Sandy Hook till you said so."

"Monckton knew!"

"Are you, sir, accusing a dead officer of being a traitor?" For all his fear of André, Bygrove bristled.

"Broadmoor knew." André spat. "And dead or not, I didn't trust him. He helped the Ladd wench escape, and you'll not convince me differently."

Jonathan held in his breath and pressed closer to the window. Elizabeth had escaped. He felt his heart jump. A choking feeling, as if invisible fingers had gripped him by the throat, made his eyes water, and he swallowed quickly, trying to catch his breath again. Somehow, by any means at all, he must find out where Elizabeth was. He could tell from André's manner that the spiteful little fiend wouldn't waste time with charges and court-martial now—not with Monckton and Broadmoor dead. Pressing against the house to steady himself, he moved as close as he could to the window. In the excitement of the battle he'd forgotten his wound, but the drain on his strength was beginning to tell. Nerves tight, he watched the Lieutenant turn to Quimby, shrug his shoulders and spread his hands helplessly. Then he faced André again.

"I told you, sir, as did Lieutenant Smythe. Major Broadmoor did not speak to her when he returned, and the Ladd girl never left the house. Before anyone could have helped her escape, she would have to pass Smythe or myself to get outside—and she would have to pass two of eight sentries. Are you suggesting, sir, that either Smythe or myself—or both of us—as well as the sentries, were all engaged in a plot at the request of Major Broadmoor?"

"Then she is still in the house."

"We searched it, sir."

"I searched, too." Quimby clapped his hat angrily on his head.

"Then search it one time more." André's voice dropped to a venomous quiet. "Bring Monckton's effects—and Broadmoor's—here to me. I'll go through their papers. You, Mister Quimby, search that house again. If you don't find her, set the bloody place afire, that may smoke her out—or burn her for what she is—a Rebel witch."

Jonathan slipped back from the window, and sidled along the wall to the corner of the house where he could watch the two men as they went down the front steps. At least Elizabeth wasn't in their hands, and that was some relief. But if Bygrove spoke the truth, then she hadn't left the house —whichever house it was. She'd not have had much of a chance to escape during the battle if the house was in the village, for Freehold had never been completely empty of English.

Quimby and Bygrove walked down the steps and out onto the Middletown Road. "Thank God," Jonathan murmured inwardly, when he saw that they passed the horses teddered to the post at the small swing gate.

Hugging the stone fence that bordered the bend in the road, Jonathan saw his quarry turn to the right and follow a wide carriage road that led to a big block of a house without lights. The place stood by itself, so he bent down, rolled over the wall, and, darting from tree to tree, came to a hedge where he would be hidden, before Quimby and Bygrove reached the front door.

Quimby followed Bygrove through the doorway and a moment later, a lamp lighted the big hallway and the wide staircase. A second lamp spurted alight, and Jonathan saw Lieutenant Bygrove tramp upstairs carrying a twin-burner lamp with a tôle draft shade polished on one side to act as a reflector. The weak beam of light jerked from side to side as the

Englishman climbed the stairway, and after a momentary disappearance, Jonathan saw the light again through the upstairs windows.

"You're wasting your time searching down there, Mister Quimby." Bygrove's voice sounded hollow in the empty house.

"How so?" Quimby appeared at the foot of the stairs.

"Mistress Ladd came up here—I saw her—and she never came down."

"That's what you say, Lieutenant."

"Listen to me, mister. Whatever Major André cares to think is of no concern to me. What he says is my concern. I am no traitor to assist in a spy's escape—if a spy she was or is."

"I tell you she is." Quimby stamped his foot on the bottom step. "And I'll report your insolence to Major André."

Bygrove appeared on the stairs, his arms loaded with Monckton's and Broadmoor's uniforms. He ran down quickly and placed them on the long settle standing against the staircase wall. "These uniforms, Mister Quimby, belonged to two honorable officers whom Major André has accused of treachery. They are dead and cannot defend themselves. But I will defend them—when I get back to England. The Honorable, the Prime Minister and the Privy Council will be told of Major André's accusations, and Major André will publicly apologize for them. Would you care to tell that to Major André?"

"I will, sir. The moment I finish my search." The fringe of red hair on Quimby's head quivered with hate and anger.

"Then, mister, do you know what I will do?"

"No—and I do not care."

"You will!" Bygrove tapped his sword hilt. "I will call you a liar, mister, and challenge you, and run you through like the slimy, stinking swine you are."

Bygrove leaned over the settle, picked up the uniforms, and walked past Quimby without a glance. Jonathan watched the young Lieutenant till he was well clear of the house. Despite his attitude, Quimby had evidently believed the officer, for when Jonathan looked back to the front door, Quimby was disappearing up the stairs.

Running across the few feet that separated the hedge from the door, Jonathan went into the hall, closed the door softly, and silently pushed the bolt into its socket. He took the steps two at a time and paused at the landing. The light Bygrove had left in Monckton's room burned steadily. A flicker, and the nose-biting smell of fish oil, came from one of the chambers to the right. Sounds like the opening and closing of press and closet doors echoed along the upper hall, and the heavy tramping of Quimby's boots, pounding across the floor, indicated that he was making a thorough search.

Crouching in the shadow at the head of the stairs, Jonathan tried to think out a plan of action. The house had been searched before and no trace of Elizabeth found. Quimby was everything the young officer had called him, and more, Jonathan agreed, and it was more than likely that the lickspittle was as adept at searching a building as he was in his other nefarious exploits. That being so, how could Elizabeth escape being found if she were still in the building?

All of these big houses had secret closets of some sort, just as did the bigger places in Virginia, but a diligent hunt by the English officers, especially under the orders of André and with the guidance of Quimby, should certainly have disclosed any such hiding place in this house. Besides, Jonathan thought, there was the possibility that Elizabeth had slipped out of the place during the battle and hidden herself somewhere else.

He moved back down the stairs a couple of steps. His guessing would have to wait, for the vertical streak of light between the door and the frame was widening, and Quimby was coming into the hall. The Tory swine stood uncertainly with the smoking lamp in his hand. Frustration and anger and indecision were all marked by the lines in his face as he looked along the hall, baffled at his inability to learn anything. Suddenly he moved forward and opened the chamber door at the head of the stairs.

Inside, the room was a wreck. Evidently, Jonathan surmised, the English must have thought this room was Elizabeth's hiding place. The feather bed was tumbled to the floor and the highboy had been pulled back from the wall. Even the window curtains had been stripped from the windows, and the clothes-press door had been wrenched from its hinges.

There was no indecision now in Quimby's face as he pulled an empty drawer from the highboy and tossed it on top of the feather bed. He placed the lamp on the floor and dragged the splintered clothes-press door across the room and dropped it on the empty drawer. Going to the wall, he took the bayberry candles from their glittering claret and blue Chelsea sconces, broke them to leave their wicks exposed, and folded them like fuses into the bedding.

So intent was Mister Quimby on destruction and the firing of the house, that Jonathan was able to gain the landing and reach the door of the chamber, unseen and unheard. Jonathan stood, just inside the door, as Quimby bent down to lift the lamp.

"No, Quimby—don't." Jonathan stood over the bent figure and watched the look on the man's face change from plain surprise to astonishment. At the same instant, Jonathan caught sight of himself for the first time since the battle commenced. There was reason enough for Quimby's stare, for Jonathan found himself looking into the gilt mirror on the far wall, at a figure he could not recognize as his own. His hands and arms, where they showed through his tattered shirt, were like black leather. One side of his face was pocked with gunpowder, while the left side was a crust of dried blood from a musket graze he'd not even felt. But worst of all, and the thing that gave him a wild appearance, was that his eyelashes were gone, and his hair was crisped and burned back from his forehead, from pressing against the gun butts.

Slowly, never taking his eyes from Jonathan's face, Quimby withdrew his hand from the lamp. Almost imperceptibly he straightened his back and drew himself erect. "You—you know me?" he asked at last.

"I know you for a bastardly English spy—a bootlicking Tory rogue who'll hang—as Trivers hanged—if I don't kill you with my own bare hands."

"Trivers—hanged?" Quimby licked his lips, and a trace of fear tinged the surprise in his eyes.

With the speed of a striking snake Quimby lunged past Jonathan and tore along the hallway. His hand shot round the doorway and flashed out again holding a horse pistol. "Didn't know I had this on the table—did you, Mister Rebel?" His sardonic grin was triumphant as he pointed the pistol at Jonathan's head, and pressed the trigger.

There was a metallic click, and nothing more. The grin switched back quickly to the look of astonished fear and Quimby's trembling fingers fumbled with the serpentine as he tried to force it back to a cocked position. Jonathan measured the distance and leaped, his arms swinging. Less than six feet separated them when Quimby threw the horse pistol. The heavy metal butt caught Jonathan on the temple and he went down on one knee. Through blurred eyes he saw Quimby jump over him and run to the stairs.

Jonathan tried to reach for Quimby's legs, but his own arms wouldn't move quickly enough. He heard rather than saw the Tory clump down the steps and the sound jolted him back into action. Quimby had reached the front door when Jonathan was halfway down the staircase. Quimby's hand reached out. He turned the iron door handle and pulled. In his hurry Quimby failed to see that the door was bolted, and so powerful was his wrench on the handle, that his fingers slipped and he staggered back into the hall.

Jonathan jumped the last steps and was waiting with legs braced as Quimby turned. Quimby tried to pull his head aside when he saw Jonathan's clenched fist swing. The crack was louder than the fall of the serpentine on the useless pistol, and Jonathan felt his knuckles sink through the beefy jaw and strike hard on solid bone. With an odd gurgling sound, his eyes rolling wildly, the two-hundred-pound Tory was lifted clear of the floor and he crashed down with a dead weight that shook the house.

Rubbing his bruised knuckles on his thigh, Jonathan went to the table, tore strips from the cloth, and bound Quimby hand and foot. On his way back to the table to fetch a strip for a gag, he stopped, one foot in the air, and listened intently. Everything was quiet as before, but he knew he'd not been mistaken. There was someone in the house besides himself. Someone, upstairs, had slammed a door.

Frightened lest the sound of the trap door falling back into place had been heard, Elizabeth stood shaking in the corner of her hiding place. After hours of effort, effort which had left her aching in every bone, she had succeeded in pushing the trap open a few inches, only to have it fall back again with that betraying slam.

Earlier in the afternoon, she'd come to the decision that if she expected to get out of her trap, she'd best set about doing it herself. The strict watch André had placed on the English Major would make it more difficult than ever for Broadmoor to desert, and if he didn't come back for her, all the shouting in the world would never be heard through the narrow slits that let air into the stone room.

In the dim light that filtered into her stone-walled hiding place, she'd sat down on the floor and eyed the trap door ten feet above her. "Ten feet is no different from a hundred when it's beyond reach," she said aloud with the uncomfortable realization that she was talking to herself more and more as the day wore on. Panic and clear-headed reasoning in alternate surges had torn her apart, and the fear of being buried alive took possession of her more often and stayed with her longer.

No matter how often she tried to reassure herself, one thought hammered at her brain with frightening logic. No one would have the slightest reason to look for her here; if they did, they'd have no more chance of finding her than the English who'd ransacked the house in the afternoon. Hunger had come and gone, and even thirst was pushed into the background by the strangling lack of air. Every unnecessary move used up the fresh air faster than it drifted in through the small slots, and standing on tiptoe with her mouth to the opening brought no relief, since the outside air was smoke laden and rasped her lungs like a burr.

It was some considerable time since she'd made up her mind that discovery by the English was preferable to the slow death she faced in this stone box. Hanging or shooting, either was a pleasanter exit than the one she saw looming before her. Somehow, she had to attract attention, and that meant reaching the trap door above her, and banging it. First, she had tried to gain a foothold on the rough mortar squeezed out between the stones of the wall, but that had crumbled at her touch, and the lime and ground oyster shells had filled the cell and her eyes with dust.

Finding the mortar so crumbly had given her a better idea. If the mortar gave way so easily, then she could scrape it out from between the courses of stones, and use the stones themselves as toeholds to reach the trap door. "But if I can do that—" she talked to herself again, "I can get out!"

Taking off one shoe, she had gone to work in a frenzy of excitement. Coughing and choking as the dust flew about her, she gouged at the spaces between the stones with the toe and and heel of her right shoe. It hadn't lasted long, and the left shoe had fallen in pieces from her hand before she'd scraped a ledge big enough for her toes. But now she was frantic and wouldn't stop. Her comb was next and the horn teeth pulled the mortar out in a steady stream.

Intent on scraping out her third toehold, she'd not noticed the tramping feet above her. It was only after she wedged herself in the corner, her bleeding toes clinging to the third course of stone, and her hands pressed against the wall, that she'd heard the sound of someone running down the staircase. She put one hand over her head, thrust the trap up a palm's width, and listened to the running feet. But the plank flooring was too heavy for her and, in spite of everything she could do to hold it back, the trap door fell into place with a noise like a banging door.

Furious at her stupidity, she bent down and pressed her hands against her trembling knees. Two hours ago she'd have given anything to have made a noise like that. Now, when she was trying to be quiet, she had to act like some witless wench and let the trap all but take her fingers off her hand. And there was no sense in trying to cozen herself into thinking the noise had not been heard, for feet, slow cautious feet, were climbing the stairs again.

With her ears she followed the steps along the upper hall as they came closer to Monckton's bedchamber. Whoever it was hadn't been misled as to where the noise came from, and she shrank farther into the corner when the searching feet crossed the room. Looking up, she could almost see a hand come out and open the clothes-press door. A moment later, the door closed with a slam, and after a breath, it slammed again.

Once more the footsteps crossed the room and the bedchamber door slammed. The feet continued their way along the hall and one after another the chamber doors were closed with a bang. Mister Footsteps, whoever he was—she thought grimly—was methodically trying every door to see which had caused the noise. Back along the hall came the steps. Again the bedchamber door opened, and the steps continued across the floor.

Almost breathless, she listened for the next sound. Not a footstep this time, but a distinct knock on the floor. It was a dead-sounding knock, close to the hearthstone, she figured, and waited for another. They came, in a quick series, as though the searcher were tapping the floor in successive spots radiating from the fireplace.

As anxiously as she had followed the footsteps, she listened to the thumping. It sounded like the butt of a heavy pistol, or one of the andirons, but whatever it was, the wielder was a far shrewder searcher than his predecessor had been. For one brief flash she thought it might be Jonathan, and just as quickly she discarded the possibility. Even if Jonathan were with the Rebels he had no way of knowing she was in this house, and no way of knowing she was hidden. Jonathan had no way of knowing she was even with the English. Suddenly the skin on her neck tightened, and a drawn feeling worked up the back of her hands and her wrists. The blood sang in her ears and the thudding of her heart was like the beating of a drum. The sound of the hammering on the floor had changed. It was directly over her head and it was hollow, so hollow that the difference was unmistakable.

The searcher had noted it, too. She knew that he had. Thump followed thump; first on the floor, then on the trap door, and back to the floor again. She had the wild idea of clambering back up and holding the trap shut by main force, but there was nothing to cling to. Tears spurted to her eyes, and she clenched her fists till her knuckles creaked as she saw a thin streak of light glide slowly down the stone wall. Above, the streak widened to a wedge-shaped glare. After the darkness of her cell, the feeble light of the oil lamp was excruciating in its brightness.

At the side of the lamp, a horrible face peered down at her. Distorted and black, and hideous with its glaring, bloodshot eyes searching the darkness for her, it was like one of the hobgoblins with which Maggie used to frighten obedience into her as a child. She could hold her breath no longer, and she knew that when the air rushed from her lungs it would be in a scream. Her mouth opened, her hand flew to her throat when the face spoke. "Is that you, Elizabeth?"

He knew it was, and before she had time to answer, he was lying on the floor, his long arms reaching down into her hiding place. She jumped, and he caught her wrists. Pulling her up to the floor beside him, he dragged her back from the opening and let the trap door fall. Together they stood up, and she fell into his arms weeping.

"Don't let down now, lass," he said, trying to calm her. "We still have to get out of this place. André will be looking for the flames—and he's like to come searching if he doesn't see them."

"Oh, Jonathan, you don't know what it was like, I—I thought I was going to die down there—and I found out I was afraid to die."

"Nobody wants to die, Elizabeth." He kissed her on the lips and she clung to him, shaking with the sobs that she couldn't hold back.

"Come, sweetheart, it's all past now." He led her to the commode, and, dampening a towel with water, wiped the mortar dust from her face.

"I thought I would never see you again, Jonathan. I reckon I'm not as brave as I thought I was." She clung to his hand.

"You're brave enough to suit me, Elizabeth." He put his arm around her and held her tightly to him. "None of us is as brave as we think— 'tis hard being brave when you're all alone." His lips touched her cheek, her tangled hair and again her lips. "I love you, lass, like I never loved anything else," he whispered, "and I can't stand the thought of being separated from you again—but if we don't make haste away from here we'll both end up prisoners of the English."

She nodded, understanding, and gave her face one more wipe with the towel. "I'll make out now—if we don't have to go too far on foot." She pulled back her dress and showed her blood-soaked toes.

"We'll get horses at the first Rebel outpost. We have a prisoner to take with us, too." Jonathan led the way to the stairs.

"A prisoner?" Trying to push her hair back from her face, Elizabeth looked at Jonathan. "Who?"

"The man who betrayed you to André—with the help of Trivers. Tracy Quimby—the odd-haired man." He pointed, as he reached the stairs, at Quimby lying where he had left him, still bound, and still unconscious.

"What—what will happen to him?" She clutched Jonathan's arm and held him as they went down the staircase.

"They'll try him—but they'll hang him—of that I'm certain-sure."

She shivered, then kissed Jonathan's cheek. "I hope not. I know what it's like—to be afraid of hanging—"

"But, lass—" Jonathan squeezed her hand—"he's a traitor. He got Jarrett hanged—and God knows how many more besides."

"I know." She loosed his arm as they reached the hall. "Ever since I was captured, I hoped he'd hang some day. But I've had my fill of killings today, watching the battle—and now I'm free—I—I wish there could be no more."

"Elizabeth." Jonathan bent down and took Quimby's shoulders, signing her to take his feet. "You have no more distaste for killing than I have. But today's battle won't end this war—and traitors must die—as a warning to other traitors."

"You're right Jonathan, I know you are. 'Tis just that I'm being womanish—as women get when they're left alone too long." She pointed. "But even so—we're practical at times—the door is bolted."

Grinning through his mask of black soot, Jonathan loosed Quimby's shoulders, went to the door, and drew the bolt. He opened the heavy oak door and for the first time since dawn, the air was fresh and cool. There was no singing in the English camp tonight and only the far-off challenge of a British sentry up on the Middletown Road broke the quiet.

"Do we aim to carry him—" Elizabeth lifted Quimby's feet— "through the English lines?"

"No, lass." He went to the table and tore another strip from the table cloth. "I was about to do this when I heard the trap door close." He bent and stuffed the piece of linen in Quimby's swollen but open mouth. "We'll leave him down behind the hedge, and send some of the lads after him."

He signalled her again, and they lifted the beefy Quimby from the floor. Once outside, Elizabeth drank in the night air, and stepping sideways they carried Quimby toward the hedge.

"What of my brothers—and my father?" she whispered as they lowered the Tory traitor to the ground.

"Rufus rammed the devil out of the English ships with the *Sally E*, and escaped to the Jersey shore. He flew the Sandy Hook signal that brought us here. Matthew got away with some of the others and joined up with Commodore Barry down Penn's Point way. Your father is home." He put his arm about her and guided her along the back of the hedge. "I hear your mother and father hold me somewhat to blame for your capture."

"How can they?" She looked surprised. "Didn't they know you couldn't dare do anything but hide, with the whole English Army searching for you?"

"I couldn't do anything anyway," Jonathan said ruefully. "I was unconscious for days."

A frightened look came to Elizabeth's eyes. "I didn't know. They told me you were wounded but—"

"It's all but healed."

"As for my mother and father holding you to blame for anything, they'll get over it—once I'm home."

"I think not, Elizabeth," he said seriously. "'Tis my belief they'll oppose our wedding together."

She stopped and faced him. "Opposing, Jonathan, is not preventing."

He swept her into his arms. "When you push your chin out like that, lass, and speak like that, I have no care for what the obstacles are. If I had my way—I'd marry with you tomorrow—"

"And what stands in your way?"

"Why—why—"

"Nothing—but your saying so." She pointed out into the darkness. "Tennant's Church still stands—despite the battle."

He kissed her quickly and pulled her along the hedge. "We'll be wed tomorrow then—and end all debate on it—but we'd best be getting back to Stirling's quarters, else I'll spend tomorrow under guard, instead of being wed."

39 A WISH

To General Washington

Englishtown

. . . our retreat from the Court House was not occasioned by the want of numbers, positions, or wishes of both officers and men to maintain that post. . . . No plan of attack was ever communicated to us, or notice of a retreat, until it had taken place in our rear.

ANTHONY WAYNE

The Village Inn at Englishtown was the busiest spot in the Jerseys that Sunday night. Ever since nightfall, dispatch riders had ridden to and from the flat-roofed shed that sheltered its front door, and the teddering ring on the post by the road had jangled incessantly as horses strained at their halters in an effort to reach the well that instinct told them contained cool water.

Up on the hill, moving lights behind the windows of the church showed tired parishioners re-dressing wounds while barber-surgeons let blood from the soldiers who had failed to recover from the heat. Flares and candles, wedged in cracked tombstones, shed a yellowish glow over a hundred deep graves where Rebel and English dead, each nameless as the other, were laid away with a last word from the pastor and elders, and a single last tap on a draped drum.

On the battlefield itself there was quiet except for the patrolling of the pickets, and the hoofbeats of the cavalry troops that cantered back and forth, four abreast, between the field and the village of Freehold. The Rebel camp was quiet. Stupefaction at Lee's disgrace was deep. Disliked as he was, he had held a place of esteem in military minds, and no one wanted to ask, "Is he a traitor?" and still less did anyone want to give an answer.

To the south of Combs Hill, General Knox and his aides, carrying folding lanthorns, checked and examined, and checked again the guns that had seen a solid day of continuous firing. As quickly as their touch-holes and barrels had passed the General's critical eye, the pieces were trundled down into the swamp. There the shrinkage of spoke, felloe and rim, caused by the fiendish heat of the day, would be counteracted by rolling the wooden wheels in the morass.

In the common room of the Village Inn, Colonel Alexander Hamilton stood at the small serving bar reading and initialling the dispatches and reports spread out on the heavy pine board rubbed satin smooth from the sliding tankards. Clustered about the open door, seated on benches and stools, mine host and his guests were full of opinions on how the day had gone; and on General Lee's part in the affray.

General Lee, it would seem, had taken quarters two doors away from the inn and was holding forth, to all who would listen, on how by a timely retreat he had saved the Rebel Army from disaster, and handed victory to General Washington who had repaid him with insults and a reprimand in front of half the Army. General Lee, it also appeared from what Hamilton overheard, did not relish such treatment, wasn't used to such treatment, and did not intend to accept such treatment without answer. So, the worthy Lee had written General Washington; yes, he had, he said, demanding an apology for the Commander-in-Chief's "remarkable manner of addressing him" on the field.

Hamilton drew a piece of paper toward him, dipped a quill in the ink, and scribbled a note. The potboy, hovering close by, went to Hamilton and on the Colonel's signal of an upthrust thumb, took the dispatches and note and disappeared up the stairs.

Dressed in a clean uniform, Stirling pored over the messages Wayne had brought in from the field. Mad Anthony sat on the edge of the bed, a slice of cold ham in one hand, a glass of wine in the other. He put the wine glass on a table beside the bed when the knock sounded on the door, crossed the room and took the papers from the potboy who goggled at Stirling whom he had last seen looking like a scarecrow.

"What is it, Anthony?"

"The casualty lists." Wayne held them to the light. "We had eight officers killed—fourteen wounded."

"The men?" Stirling's voice was dry.

"Fifty-two killed—one hundred and twenty-six wounded and heat victims."

" 'Tis not as bad as I feared, Anthony."

"No—I had expected worse." Wayne turned to another sheet.

"The English?"

The Pennsylvanian nodded. "Twenty-four officers known killed and eleven wounded prisoners—seven unwounded officer prisoners." He looked up from the paper. "Alex estimates over one thousand dead—six hundred prisoners—and the captured officers believe over four hundred deserted."

"A loss of over two thousand." Stirling shook his head. "Not very encouraging for Sir Henry Clinton in his first engagement. What's the other note?"

Wayne glanced at it. "More on Lee's activities." He placed it among

Stirling's papers. "Alex says that Lee has written the Chief demanding an apology."

"The man must be out of his mind." Holding a paper out to Wayne, Stirling scratched his chin thoughtfully. "It does help, however, in formulating charges for a court-martial—if the Chief decides to hold one."

"I know he'll court-martial Lee!" Wayne was emphatic. "He'd not have spoken of you as President of the Court if his mind had not been fixed on the matter."

"I suppose not," Stirling said reflectively. "A charge of treason will never stand, of that I'm certain, Anthony. Disobedience of orders—conducting a shameful retreat—failure to issue orders to his officers—"

"That I will testify to myself," Wayne cut in. "I'll write a report on it before I sleep."

"Well!" Stirling shuffled the papers in front of him. "A court-martial will have to wait. Our march on to New York is more important."

Wayne again sat on the bed. "When I left the Chief, he had already asked Nat Greene to do double duty as Quartermaster—and Nat will leave tomorrow to make provision for supplies along the line of march."

"He'll have to gather supplies from a wide area." Stirling grunted. "This part of the Jerseys is wrung dry."

"Cadwalader, Hamilton and Tilghman will all return to Philadelphia tomorrow." Wayne leaned forward. "While Washington didn't say so—I'm of the opinion that we as an Army won't stir out of here till Tuesday."

"You think he suspects the English may try a counter-move?"

"I don't think he does, William, but after today's experience with Lee, he's staying on the battlefield—and very, very close to our front line." Wayne looked at Stirling. "Wouldn't you?"

"Yes—I would."

"There is one thing I'm certain of, William." Wayne rose and paced the small bedchamber. "Today's battle should silence those mutterings—in the Congress and out of it—about Lee's superiority as a general."

Stirling's laugh was without humor. "Lying tongues lie."

"But they'll get no support." Wayne slapped his hand on his breeches. "How can they? Lee was utterly routed—Washington took the same forces and thoroughly whipped the same English."

"In a measure, Anthony, you may be right," Stirling acknowledged. "It could well be the end of such cabals as Conway's. But the battle has a significance far beyond that."

At the serious note in Stirling's voice, Wayne stopped his pacing. "Meaning what?"

"Meaning that today—on Monmouth Plains—this ceased to be a revolt of colonies."

"What?"

"I mean it, Anthony. This was not a skirmish between His Majesty's troops and a handful of discontented rebels. This was war. It was a battle between the full might of the English Army—and America's first Army. Instead of revolution as it has been in the past, this was war between America and England. And in the first battle—we won."

"There is no debating that." Wayne laughed.

"It will have a profound effect on the English troops, as well as on the English Parliament. Hitherto, the English have regarded themselves as loyal troops, fighting in their own colonies for the possession of what was theirs. In one day, that is changed. They are on foreign soil—invaders —fighting an enemy army."

"Certainly Clinton must feel that way."

Stirling folded his arms. "I know the English. I know them well. It is a far greater defeat for the English Parliament than it is for Clinton. Sir Henry may be able to explain his defeat to the Department of War, but Parliament will never be able to explain it to the English people. Today—even in English eyes—we became a nation."

Before Wayne could answer, a knock again sounded at the door.

"Come in." Stirling turned in his chair, then jumped to his feet as Jonathan pushed Elizabeth before him into the bedchamber.

"My God!" Wayne was dumfounded.

"So he found you, lass?" Seeing her on the ragged edge, Stirling hid his surprise, and placed his chair for her with as much casualness as he could assume.

"I found her, sir, under the floor of a closet in Monckton's quarters— although how she got there, I haven't had the time to ask."

"Major Broadmoor hid me." She threw back the hair from her face as she sat down. "The Kidd house was his headquarters before and he knew of the room."

"How in hell did he expect you to get out?" Jonathan asked sarcastically.

"He was to return and let me out—after the English left."

"Then he did intend to desert?" Jonathan said softly.

"I'm afraid, lass, you'd have had a long wait for Major Broadmoor." Wayne poured a glass of wine and handed it to her. "Broadmoor was killed—with Colonel Monckton."

"They—the English—didn't mistreat you, Mistress Ladd?" Stirling eyed her dishevelled appearance.

"No, General." She put the wine glass down. "Colonel Monckton and Major Broadmoor protected me from André. I think André would have hanged me afore we left Philadelphia, but for Monckton."

"We ran into Dan—General Morgan and his men on our way back."

Jonathan pointed out the window. "They're reporting to General Washington now—and they have a prisoner."

"Where in God's name were they all day?" Wayne blurted out.

"Waiting beyond the hills—to the south—for orders that never arrived."

Stirling looked at Wayne, and back to Jonathan. "You say they have a prisoner, Jonathan?"

"Yes, sir. I think you'll both be glad to speak with him. Mister Tracy Quimby—the man who called at your quarters, sir, at Valley Forge—in the guise of a visiting Congressman."

"The man who had the spy map?" Wayne asked.

"The same, sir."

"We will be glad to question him." Wayne pointed to the papers on Stirling's table. "We may yet find evidence of a charge of treason, William."

Elizabeth laughed. "I don't think he'll do much talking for a spell. From what I saw—I'd reckon Jonathan broke his jaw."

"He'll be able to write," Wayne said amid the laughter.

They stopped as the door opened and Alex Hamilton came in followed by the innkeeper carrying a huge tray. Wayne pulled out the trundle bed, and mine host placed the tray on it. "Be my guests, Milady and Gentlemen." He shrugged his plump shoulders slightly. "The food is not of the best—but the wine is." His eyes were a little moist as he looked at them. "I'd like to say, Milady and Sirs, God keep you for this day's work— for tonight I breathe free air again. 'Tis a sad thing—is it not?—that some men must do without it before they believe its worth." He turned and went to the bedchamber door, wiping the corner of his eye with the edge of his white apron. At the opening he turned. "I have bedchambers for Milady, and the young Captain." He blew his nose violently, and closed the door behind him.

"I'm going back to report to the Chief," Alex said, but he looked hungrily at the food. "I was so damn busy I forgot to eat—"

"Then now's the time to eat a bite, Alex." Stirling waved at the floor as an invitation to sit down. "General Wayne and I will ride with you— we'll all report to the Chief together."

Wayne raised his glass. "I give you a toast: The death of the Conway Cabal—may it never be resurrected."

"I drink to that with fervor." Stirling sipped the wine appreciatively. "Now I give you: The Chief!"

They drank the toast and attacked the loaded tray. For minutes, the only sound that broke the silence of the tiny bedchamber was the spluttering of the lamp that sat on the paper-littered table. Stirling thought of his beloved Sarah, and wondered if on that march to New York he would have a moment to see her at Baskingridge. He hoped that Mad Anthony was right, and that they had reached the end of the conspiracies against Washington. Suddenly, he caught a glance between Elizabeth and Jonathan, and he grinned from ear to ear.

"Would you like to propose a toast, Mistress Elizabeth?"

Elizabeth held her glass out to be filled. "Since Captain Kimball is somewhat shy—I will, General. Tomorrow, if the Army stays long enough in one place, Captain Kimball and I will be wed in the old church—Tennant's."

Before she'd finished, Wayne and Hamilton were shaking Jonathan's hand. Stirling had bent over Elizabeth and kissed her soundly. He straightened up and held his hand out for silence. "There's but one thing amiss in your toast, Elizabeth. By tomorrow, he will be Major Kimball." He lifted a paper from the table. "All this lacks is General Washington's signature—and that it will have before we go to sleep tonight."

He gathered the papers from the table, turned and reached for his tricorne. "You sent supper to the Chief, Alex?"

"Yes, sir—and the villagers are doing their best to add to the men's cooked rations with milk and bread and cheese—and the Chief ordered a ration of rum in the water."

"Good. Then let's to horse and report to him." He walked to Jonathan and placed his arm about the Captain's shoulder. "Only a few of us know how much we owe you and your lass, Jonathan. But tomorrow, you shall have an arch of swords outside the kirk to walk your bride under—and a salute from Henry's cannon." He crooked his finger and Elizabeth rose and walked to him. "You, lass, I have one great hope for."

"What is that, General?"

"That your first-born will be a free American—never having owed allegiance to His Britannic Majesty George the Third—or his heirs and successors."

POSTSCRIPT

The conspiracy known as the Conway Cabal was one of the meanest pieces of underhanded character assassinations ever attempted. That it was encouraged by men of standing and influence makes it the more sordid.

The plot to destroy Washington's reputation for integrity started with a series of letters published in English newspapers and copied in the American press. These letters, it was said, had been found in Washington's dispatch case when Billy Lee, Washington's personal servant, was captured. Billy Lee never was captured. The letters were diabolically clever, written in imitation of Washington's style, and written by someone who knew a great deal about Washington's private life.

One, addressed to Martha, was as follows: ". . . I love my King, you know I do, a soldier and a good man cannot but love him." Here the forger was unaware that Washington wrote to "Patsy" not Martha. Another, supposedly to Lund Washington: ". . . It is a pity methinks, that Congress had not better information on their subject: if they had, it is to be presumed, they would not have precipitated the Declaration for independence so as to preclude any possibility of negotiation." This letter of course proved that the forger was unaware of the fact that Washington went to Philadelphia in June to urge the Declaration.

In one letter, Washington is supposed to have written: ". . . A thousand considerations determine me to strain every nerve to prevent the army's being under any other control whilst I live. . . ." In this letter the forger gives it an air of truth by having Washington close with a personal note, urging Martha to be vaccinated. But here again the forger slipped, because Martha had already been vaccinated, when she accompanied Washington to New York in December, 1775.

In addition to the dozens of forged letters, anonymous letters quoting what Washington was reported to have said were sent to the Congress. One sent to Governor Patrick Henry contained the following: ". . . No doubt Henry is in many respects, the unfittest man in the State for Governor of Virginia—he has no property, no learning, but little good sense, and still less virtue or public spirit: but he is the idol of the people."

Besides trying to undermine Washington, the members of the Cabal did their utmost to remove or discredit those officers they knew could not be seduced from Washington. Congressman Burke of North Carolina wrote to Sullivan: ". . . I heard officers in the field lamenting in the bitterest terms that they were cursed with such a commander; and I overheard numbers during the retreat [Brandywine] complain of you as an officer whose evil conduct was forever productive of misfortune to the Army. . . ."

Gates, Conway and Mifflin, as members of the Board of War, were given authority over Washington by the Congress, and tried to separate La Fayette from Washington by sending the Frenchman on a futile expedition to Canada. They tried to wean Greene away from Washington by making the Quaker General Quartermaster General. Greene was never misled, and accepted the post on condition that he retain his right to lead a wing, under Washington, in any battle. Greene wrote the Congress that Conway had obtained his rank of Major General by the "most dirty artifice."

Stirling they labelled a drunkard, and said that he could not be trusted out of Washington's sight. But Stirling, during his career, commanded every brigade in the American Army except Georgia and South Carolina, and he was preparing for the second Battle of Saratoga when Washington won at Yorktown. A long way for Washington to keep an eye on a general who loved his toddy so much. Stirling, of course, incurred the undying hatred of the Cabal when he presented General Washington with the first tangible evidence of the disloyal correspondence between Conway and Gates.

From Conway to Gates: ". . . Heaven has determined to save our country, or a weak General and bad councillors would have ruined it." Charles Lee, in December, 1776, had sent a similar letter to Gates in which he called Washington "damnably deficient."

Some apologists have tried to claim that Conway was a tool in the hands of the Cabal, but Conway's letter of apology to Washington asking forgiveness for his part in the Cabal refutes this. It is well to remember that Conway, wounded in a duel by Cadwalader, thought he was dying when he wrote the confession.

Contrary to Stirling's hopes, the Cabal did not die with the victory at Monmouth, for we find the illustrious Doctor Benjamin Rush still disparaging Washington, while continuing to praise the disloyal generals, in a letter to John Adams: ". . . Characters appear in one age, and are known in another. General Conway, who was the nerve; Mifflin, who was the Spirit; C. Lee who was the Soul of our army, have all been banished from Headquarters. The last has been most unjustly condemned by a Court Martial for saving our Army at Monmouth on the 28th of last June."

AUTHORITIES CONSULTED

Glazier, Captain Willard, *Heroes of Three Wars.*
Philadelphia: Hubbard Brothers, 1880.

Headley, Joel Tyler, *Washington and His Generals.*
New York: Baker and Scribner, 1847 (2 Volumes).

Lossing, Benson John, *Pictorial Field Book of the Revolution.*
New York: Harper Brothers, 1860 (2 Volumes).

Pennypacker, Morton, *General Washington's Spies, on Long Island and in New York.*
Brooklyn: Long Island Historical Society, 1939.

Anburey, Thomas. *Travels Through the Interior Parts of America.*
Boston and New York: Houghton, Mifflin and Co., 1923 (2 Volumes).

Willard, Margaret Wheeler, ed., *Letters on the American Revolution, 1774–1776.*
Boston and New York: Houghton, Mifflin and Co., 1925.

Williams, Henry Smith, ed., *The Historian's History of the World.*
London: The History Association, 1904.

Encyclopaedia Britannica (11th Edition).
New York, 1911.

Papers, maps and relics in Museum and Library of Monmouth County Historical Society.

Papers, maps, etc., in Bucks County Historical Society.

Proceedings of a General Court Martial . . . by order of His Excellency General Washington . . . For the trial of Major General Lee . . . Major General Lord Stirling, President.
Philadelphia: John Dunlap, 1778.

Valley Forge Park Commission, access to various headquarters.

Stryker, William Scudder, *The Battle of Monmouth.* Edited by William Starr Myers.
Princeton University Press, 1927.

Collections of New Jersey Historical Society.

History of St. Peter's Lutheran Church, Barren Hill, Pa., 1752–1952.
Philadelphia: United Lutheran Publication House, 1952.

Archives of The Smithonian Institution, Washington, D. C.

NOTE: Old Scots (Tennant's) Church still stands on the edge of the battlefield and Fauntleroy and Monckton have headstones, side by side. The Village Inn, very little changed, retains its hitching post and well. Mary (Molly Pitcher) Hayes's spring gurgles quietly at the foot of the apple orchard, about a mile east of the spot marked as Molly Pitcher's well. To this day at Valley Forge, John Waterman's is the only "marked" grave. The headquarters of Generals Washington, Stirling, Mad Anthony, Huntington and Varnum and others are very much as they were in 1778, and the lines of defense and Forts are clearly defined. Potter's Field, Philadelphia, has lost its grimness and is now a tree-shaded square, overlooked by the windows of the J. B. Lippincott Company. Barren Hill is little changed; the graves of the Indians and the six soldiers are marked. The Grenadiers' flag captured in the Battle of Monmouth is in the Monmouth Historical Association Building. Although the battlefield is much changed, the spot where General Washington stopped Lee's headlong retreat is seen, though not recognized, by the motorists driving, pleasure-bent, toward the Jersey beaches.

Port Chatham is the only fictional town mentioned.

Charles Lee was not related in any way to the illustrious Lees of Virginia. The proofs of his treachery did not come to light until an examination of the Howes' private papers in 1857 disclosed his correspondence and "plan" for the defeat of the Colonies. The two insulting letters Lee wrote to Washington are wrongly dated, but mistakes in dates were quite common during that period. Both Hamilton and La Fayette misdated their reports, and La Fayette was even in error on the date of the Battle of Barren Hill.

A thrilling novel of courage,
love and treachery during the
years of our country's birth

FAREWELL TO VALLEY FORGE

by David Taylor

The desperate year of 1778. Philadelphia
is occupied by the British. Not far away in
Valley Forge the ragged and courageous
army of George Washington is just coming
through its bitter winter stand. Meanwhile
the Continental Congress is being belea-
guered by a number of officers and influential
people to replace Washington as Commander of the patriot armies. At the center
of this cabal is General Charles Lee.

In this setting of intrigue and revolution-
ary passion, David Taylor has woven a san-
guine and stirring narrative of young Captain
Jonathan Kimball of Virginia, assigned to
live as a servant in the house of Enoch Ladd,
an imprisoned Patriot shipowner, and to spy
on the British. With him in this enterprise is
the lovely and daring Elizabeth Ladd, daughter of the household and a spy herself.

Mutually suspicious at first, Jonathan and
Elizabeth only come to trust one another
after each has been through some dangerous
escapades. There is the time Elizabeth over-
hears some vital information at a masquerade ball she attends on a stolen invitation,
and the time when Jonathan helps La Fayette
out of a trap set by the British.

With wonderful insight into this exciting
historical period Taylor tells of the British
Fleet trying to evacuate the Delaware, of the
bravery of Molly Pitcher, and the almost disastrous treachery of Lee. Climaxing the
whole story is a blow-by-blow description of
the illustrious Battle of Monmouth.

Jacket design by William Hankinson